The Art of Clarinetistry

*The Acoustical Mechanics of the Clarinet as a Basis
for the Art of Music Performance*

by

WILLIAM H. STUBBINS, MUS. D.
Professor of Music, The School of Music,
The University of Michigan

Ann Arbor Publishers
610 Forest
Ann Arbor, Michigan 48104

665-9130

DEDICATION

This book is dedicated to my dear friend, Frank L. Kaspar, who, by his consummate craftsmanship, and his sympathetic understanding of the problems of clarinetists, has contributed so very much to the Art of Music Performance.

Library of Congress Catalog Card Number : 65-27731

FOREWORD

This book is an attempt to bring together in one place, information about the clarinet concerning its acoustical nature as a sound producing tool for the raw material of music, and the mechanics of exploiting this sound production by the clarinetist as a means for realizing the philosophy involved in the art of music performance. This book is not a method book, nor an instruction book. It is not intended to replace the functions of a teacher nor the excellent material available for study of the instrument. Rather, it is hoped that this book will provide a depth of perspective and understanding by the clarinetist which will lead to a greater appreciation and enjoyment of his art.

There are certain timeless values in facts and in their relationships which may be applied to the practice of any art, no matter what the specific problem of the moment might be. Therefore, there will be found no lists of literature, no reference to methodology as concerns material for study, nor suggestions for applied study as routine. These are matters which each individual will undertake to formulate for himself or with the help of his instructor.

What should be gained by exposure to the material presented here, is an understanding of the underlying principles on which the actual practice of music depends, with a certain enlargement and development of some areas which demand a certain degree of demonstration.

There are no apologies necessary for the information herewith presented, but there are numerous credits and acknowledgements due to the devoted work and accomplishments of many musicians interested in the why as well as the how of music, and of many scientifically minded persons interested in the substantiation of the art of music by theory and fact.

To Mr. Frank L. Kaspar, I wish to extend my warmest thanks and appreciation for his long and enduring friendship throughout many years, and for the sympathetic sharing of his great knowledge of woodwind craftsmanship. Without him, this book would have been quite impossible to write.

To Mr. Leon Leblanc and to Mr. Vito Pascucci of the Leblanc Corporation goes my thanks and appreciation for their support

i

in generously providing information and assistance with experimental needs as required.

I wish to gratefully acknowledge the assistance of Professor Robert Warner, Curator of the Stearn's Collection of Musical Instruments at the University of Michigan, and Dr. J. H. van der Meer, Director of the Germanisches Nationalmuseum in Nurnberg, Germany for permission to use photographs of clarinets in the respective collections.

To Mr. Walter Vogt of Akron, Ohio goes a special note of thanks for an extensive and interesting correspondence, and an engineer's viewpoint of the mechanics of clarinet playing.

To Mr. Kalmen Opperman of New York, a particular acknowledgement of our friendship and collaboration through discussion and correspondence concerning the art of Reed-making.

And finally, acknowledgement to my many students, who throughout my years of teaching have provided me with the inspiration and constant challenge of their developing talents, and their critical evaluation of the ideas presented to them during the courses of instruction in which we have truly learned together.

It will be obvious that material has been drawn from numerous texts and sources. Since facts belong to no one person, but to a field of endeavor, and therefore to all who have a common interest, the anonymity of contribution is deliberate. A bibliography has been appended which will permit the reader to develop in detail the individual patterns of investigation involved. Inclusion in this bibliography is sufficient recognition of the value of any contribution to this study. The author's own work in the several fields of performance, teaching, and the acoustics of music is offered as at least an equitable balance to any concern which might be felt in this regard.

WM. H. STUBBINS
The University of Michigan
Ann Arbor, Michigan
1965

THE ART OF CLARINETISTRY

*The Acoustical Mechanics of the Clarinet as a Basis
for the Art of Music Performance*

TABLE OF CONTENTS

iii

CHAPTER I

The Art of Performance

The art of playing a musical instrument is admired by many, envied by some, amuses others and frustrates still another group. This elusive art is a developed skill, enhanced by special talents, and in common with other artistic endeavors, is accorded high respect as a value, to which the human hand, heart and mind may aspire. This respect is tempered however, with the considered judgement that the values involved, are such that they cannot be measured by any means other than by their own unique standards of self-expression, and self-satisfaction.

There is a difference between artistic endeavors, which concerns the expressive medium of the art, and this difference may be marked by the relative permanence of the artistic product. In architecture and in sculpture, as in the graphic arts, the artist may leave his art as a record for all to see and enjoy, far beyond his span of endeavor.

In the art of music, the element of permanence is superceded by the flux and flow of the temporal immediacy of sound. It is true that music notation may be preserved, and that modern techniques of recording, enable sound to become a frozen moment, to be reproduced again and again. However, reproducing techniques require the temporal immediacy of the sound ultimately, even though it may be infinitely repetitive. When the music stops, be it the last note to end the echo in a concert hall, or the last groove of a record, or bit of magnetized tape, the air is still again, and the magic of the art is gone into the irreclaimable past, and is no more—until the next time.

This strange art of music is based on nothing which we can grasp, or hold, or examine under microscopes, reduce to chemical ash, or feel between our fingers. It is totally impermanent by nature, evanescent in existence, and sublimated in contemplation. Yet of all the arts, it has a most real and direct effect upon the emotions. No human, few animals, and almost no

1

living thing with auditory responses, can ignore the effect of sound. It is as real as light, and bathes us in ecstacy or incites us to rage, soothes our pounding pulses or fires our imagination.

Music however, does not wait on any man. Sound, which runs the gamut from random noise, to perfectly tuned frequency, depends for its control and production in certain ways, by men who are bent on using its natural phenomena in certain ways. Musical instruments have been devised for this specific purpose. It is not enough to shout, man has found, but it is also necessary to sing. It is not enough to pound or scrape, or simply whistle. It is necessary to strike and pluck, and bow, and blow! And in exactly the same way that man has found that mechanical tools multiply his strength a thousandfold, he has found that musical instruments serve as the tools to give him strength in producing and controlling sound.

And also, in the same way that it is not simply enough to have a giant mechanical crane, but also necessary to operate it, man has found that musical instruments alone are not enough. Skill in using them is required from the hand of man, guided by his mind, and inspired by his soul, to transform the sound into music.

This is indeed a strange art. It is a striving to produce and control that which is doomed by its very nature to the immediate oblivion of the moment, but yet so attractive and compelling in its insistent demand of sheer doing, that the now is all important, and the past and future are of no import, nor even exist for him who plays.

The various kinds of musical instruments have been classified according to the method of their sound producing medium, but whatever they may be by descriptive analysis in this way, they are all designed for the specific purpose of producing and controlling sound for musical purpose. And in addition, they must all be used by the human hand to realize their function. In the hands of a musician, a musical instrument becomes a living thing. Without this hand, the musical instrument is no more than a museum piece to be admired, perhaps for the ingenuity of its design, or the beauty of its craftsmanship, or historical significance, but no more than that.

Musical instruments represent a certain unique development in the inventive life of man. Since the discovery that certain sounds are more pleasing than others, the creative genius has been striving to express itself by means of these sounds which have so fascinated and captured the imagination.

So has music come to be—and the instruments with which to give expression to its voice, have been so wrought from wood and wire, and skin and metal. Musical instruments may, therefore, in this sense claim to be the product of invention. A closer scrutiny of the matter, however, will show that such invention has rather often been a matter of sheer expediency—as a means to an end—instead of a thoughtful and ordered procedure of intentional plan. Because of this, the improvement of musical instruments has waited upon the time when the skills of the art have demanded the cooperation of the artist and the artisan, in accomplishing the things that must come to be, if greater powers of expression are to be realized.

In order to create the pleasant sounds which he so desires as music; man, the artist, has generally been in such a hurry to play his music, that he has not been willing to sacrifice time for the perfection of the tools of his art. His desire has often outstripped his scientific ability, and he has made more music on inadequate instruments, than even his dreams have led him to believe possible. Only the tremendous skill of his hands, guided by the desire in his heart, has enabled him to do what should in most cases have been impossible with the means at hand.

For anyone to observe the truth of this, let him but wander through the past and take up in his hands the musical instruments of his ancestors. Let him tinkle the spinet, tootle one of the first horns, run his fingers over the worn holes of an early five-keyed clarinet and marvel that Anton Stadler could have played young Mozart's concerto on such an instrument.

And so it has been, until some era was marked in musical instrument development, by some musician who became a little less fascinated by the music which he was producing, than by the means with which he was doing it. Thus came about the invention of the piano by Cristofori, the perfecting of the old viol into the Stradivarius violin, the work of Theobald Boehm on the flute, and the invention of the clarinet by Johann Christopher Denner. These men ushered into being a new concept of performance, made possible by a greater measure of perfection of the tools of musical art; and thereby opened for the rest of the musicians, the composers, the players, and the dreaming audiences, new horizons of possibility, limited only by the new concepts which sprang to life in the newly found facility of sound production for music, provided by these "new" instruments.

Touched with sound, man's ear has given expression to his soul; and, placed in his hands, the musical instrument has become the tool of music which has builded for her such a magnificent temple.

Since the days of the handcraftsman have so largely passed away, and the wonderful age of the machine has come to be, man has found not one hand to work with, but has increased his capacity and his skill by the hundredfold. He has found how to do whatever his mind's eye may guide him to create, and the fabrication of all things which he uses for his needs and his pleasures, has become almost commonplace.

Not the least of his accomplishments in this respect has been the making of his musical instruments. Because of his love of the art of music, he has poured out his genius and his skill in this use of his new-found powers. He has turned the best of his knowledge to work for the best of his art; and this is as it should be, for one of the first crafts since he began to use his hands creatively was the making of his musical instruments.

We have come a long way since the day of the first hand that drove a bone drill through a hollow reed, or stretched the membrane of a sheep across an empty gourd. The gifts of our mechanical age have brought wonders which are ever increasing. We deal in ten-thousandth parts of an inch now instead of by "just so long" or "just so wide." And because of our present skill we can retrace our steps a little, and inquire into the possible solutions of certain matters, which have for so long been as dilemnas which were mysterious; to be battled but not to be overcome.

The function of the instrument as the sound producer and controller, must be understood if the most efficient use of it is to be made, as a medium for the most perfect expression of the art. The function of the player must be understood with respect to the instrument chosen as the medium of expression, since music, by its very nature, is a living breathing art.

Therefore, the study of any musical instrument may be

conveniently divided into two main areas. First, the physical aspects of the instrument, with all of the ramifications provided by its constructional necessities, including its acoustical nature and mechanical functions; second, the physical requirements of performance as pertain to the human anatomy for activating the musical instrument, to realize its potential, as an acoustical tool for sound production and control.

The philosophical implications of self-expression and the aesthetics of musical art may therefore be taken leave of for the moment, and reserved for a later discussion, after these more basic requirements are dealt with. Suffice it to be said here, that all too frequently these latter are confused both with and by too many musicians, and those who would hang onto the skirts of the art as critics and dilettantes, as being the only necessities of the art. There is more necessary than that the heart should be in the right place—so must the notes.

The players of instruments will tell a different story, and one of greater truth—that the making and controlling of sound on a musical instrument is a first requisite of the art, and that a pre-occupation with this problem, is the matter which almost completely dominates the situation. What comes of it all, is of course music, and musical expression, but what goes into it is a hard and calculating effort of muscle and nerve, and string and wood, and reed; and it is for this purpose of understanding and knowing about one kind of this effort, that this present discussion is composed.

It is all very well to shrug one's shoulders and say that the bricklayer has but a small part in the architect's dream—but without him no buildings would be built. And if the architect himself knows how to lay bricks, he will be a better architect. And furthermore, if the bricklayer has vision, and imagination, why then he himself is the architect.

The Socratic dictum 'know thyself' was never more pertinently applied than to the practicing artist. For the musician, must be appended the full truth of the situation, by yet another dictum, 'know thy instrument.' Then finally, to make a paraphrase on Shakespeare's famous advice from Polonius to his son, 'Unto the facts of thyself and thine instrument be true, and it shall follow as night the day, thou canst be false to any music thou mayst perform.'

The art of Clarinetistry is composed of two primary requisites, the clarinet and the clarinet-player. A good deal has been written and said about both. Of the two, a discussion of the clarinet itself is first in order; since without the instrument there would be no point in preparing oneself to play it.

Lest this statement should be taken in jest, it should be noted that while much is said each day about music, no music ever says anything in return. There is probably no more argumentative group than the several proponents of musical taste, but there is absolutely no argument among musical compositions themselves . . . nor really among instruments—and rather rarely among the best instrumentalists. The latter know too much about the difficulties not to appreciate the performance of each other.

It is not possible to play a scale either 'for' or 'against' anything. It is not possible to pit Brahms against Shostakovitch or Gershwin against Bach. The argument is always one of words— "afterwords", so-to-speak. There is no conflict among art forms or art works.

The Venus de Milo did not lose her arms defending herself against another sculpture. Conflict between art works is an utter impossibility, since an art work exists as a completely aesthetic moment in time, as does the appreciation of it by the observer. It is only after the aesthetic moment has passed, that contemplation of effect can cause disagreement or agreement by comparative tastes—and by then the experience has past—and certainly the art work is not the subject of its discussion—but rather the ideas about it, which those who discuss it have themselves supplied. Art itself is immediate—and aloof, only men argue.

CHAPTER II

The Phenomenon of Sound
as a Basis for Music

Sound is a natural phenomenon which provides the raw material for the art of music.

Sound provides, for man, a means of communication. Whether sounds or gestures, or a combination of these was first used for the purpose of communication between men, is immaterial. The use of sound has been a means to the sophisticated end of an extensive and complicated communicative structure between human beings.

Sound for musical purposes, probably originated, in the use of calls or cries of the human voice, to indicate warnings, or to give vent to the emotions as in laughter, contentment, pleasure, pain and anger.

Language and verbal communication, in this way has developed for the transmission of what are loosely termed 'ideas', and 'meanings.' Music, on the other hand, can only transmit 'images', or 'feelings.' Musical 'ideas' ,are not ideas in the verbal sense, nor are musical 'meanings.' Unfortunately, the structures of language itself, permits a vast range of ambiguity.

However, it is possible, without going further into the science of semantics, to state that it is obvious, for any ordinary discussion, that words are translated by the mind immediately as a meaning; or as a meaning with a specific image attached. The word 'dog' for example, immediately becomes an 'image', and is not only a word alone.

On the other hand, a musical phrase, or even a tone, is immediately translated by the mind, as a 'feeling.' One may 'feel' sad or happy, but not 'dog.' How then, may we describe the words sad or happy, which themselves are words, and are used to describe what we say we cannot describe—and this to which we refer as being another word again, 'feeling?'

To be perfectly candid, the answer is that we cannot talk about music, anymore than we can express the idea of the square-root of two, by means of a musical tone.

The ear hears words, and the ear hears tones. It is a sensory matter, which provides the final decision. You cannot for example, smell 'red' or 'blue,' but you can see them. You cannot feel, 'sweet' or 'salty' but you can taste. You cannot by the same token, hear 'blue,' 'red,' 'sweet,' or 'salty,' but you can hear 'pitch,' 'quality,' 'intensity,' and 'duration' of sound.

The performing musical artist therefore, no matter how vivid his imagination, is limited by the province of his art. This is essentially an art of the transmission of sounds used for music, as a means for communication between human beings, which evoke 'feelings,' 'images,' 'ideas,' and 'meanings,' but not in the verbal sense.

The recognition of the province of music, and the direction of effort to perfecting the possibilities of its area, will conserve the efficiency of the situation. A performing artist must not try to do *more* than his art, but he must do *all* of his art. He *cannot* play music as a protagonist for social reform, but he *can* perfectly deliniate the *balance,* and *order,* of a perfect musical line.

The performer therefore, has certain responsibilities to himself, and to the art of music. He must as a first order of business, be conversant with the nature of the raw material which he uses for his musical communication, Sound. This will imply some orientation with respect to the science of Acoustics.

He must in addition, be informed and aware of the nature, potentialities and techniques of the sound producer, or musical instrument which he uses to manufacture, and to transmit the raw material of his art. He must therefore, have information concerning the special field of Acoustical Mechanics.

The performer must also be aware of the deliniation of his art, as to the form of its expression, which includes the notation of music. He must therefore, have some knowledge of Musical Theory.

The performer must be prepared to transmit and translate the results of the Theory of Music, into the sound of music, by means of an adequate technique of playing an instrument. He must therefore be a schooled instrumentalist.

The well informed performer will also be aware of, and prepared to define and defend, the limits of musical expression, and communication with which he deals. He must therefore, have a knowledge of Aesthetics and Psychoacoustics.

In short, the performing artist musician must be more than a simple mechanical extension of his chosen instrument, as well as being a master of its potentialities. He must be a cogent and sensitive mind, as well as a well-disciplined body, able to appreciate both the limits, and the scope of his sphere of influence. That so few men are able to meet the demands of performance in music, is not surprising; but that all players of musical instruments should not at least be aware of their specific instrumental problems, and oriented as to their function in their art, is mainly a matter of availability of adequate information, in readily accessible and organized form. Left to his own devices, and suddenly abstracted from all civilization, man would probably soon construct the same type of sophisticated behavior, that we have in our present society. Such a 'tour de force' is expected of no one, and this is probably in the last analysis, what education is all about.

The education of the performing musical artist, must therefore consist of developing criteria for the best exploitation of his field. This will consist of studying the raw material of his art, in order to learn how it may be perfectly controlled; how his instrument may be correctly designed and adjusted; and what skills are needed for manipulating it, and how these are to be attained. In addition, how the sounds of music are intelligibly ordered and prepared as an art form for communication, and how the human sensory system receives such communication both physically, as in hearing, and as a psychological result of such sensory perception.

THE DIMENSIONS OF COMMUNICATION OF MUSIC

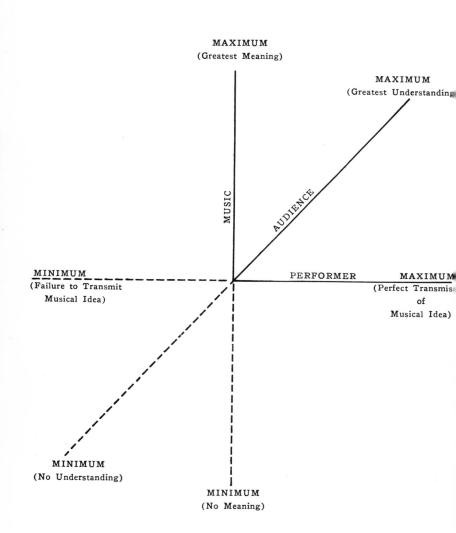

Sound is a natural phenomenon which is initiated by vibration. It is transmitted by some medium such as a gas, a liquid, or a solid, in which vibration may be sustained. No sound is possible therefore in a vacuum. The results of such transmission of vibration are various, due to the nature of the medium involved, and develop as reflection, diffusion, refraction, absorption and resonance.

Sound requires a human ear to recognize and identify it as Sound. The existence of the phenomenon of vibration in nature is exclusive of man. But this fact is totally irrelevant to any examination or discussion of Sound which is the result of a sensory appreciation by the human ear. Any discussion of any natural phenomenon when observed, or 'sensed' by man, immediately taken on meaning necessary to human reason. Its existence then assumes the proportions of man's world, which is the only world of any consequence to the experience of man. Theoretical conclusions can be made, in the form of postulates exclusive of actual experience, but these in turn are based on the actualities of sensory perception. There are really therefore, three levels of discussion which may be developed by man with respect to his environment. First, the discussion of any natural phenomenon exclusive of the existence of man; secondly, the sensory powers of man in direct relationship to the phenomenon 'sensed'; and thirdly, the calculated, and reasoned effect of the whole situation, which may include all past experience, and postulated or predictable results.

The art of music depends on all three levels of discussion for its total effect. The nature of vibration must be studied, as a phenomenon exclusive of man's powers of observation or control. The sensory apparatus with which he is equipped, must be understood, and the impingement of the natural phenomenon on the sensory apparatus, must be appreciated. The control of the natural phenomenon, and its potentialities for presentation to the sensory apparatus of man, must be calculated and developed.

In brief, a musician must know what Sound is, and what to expect from it as a natural phenomenon. He must know what his ears can, and will do, and he must have some ideas concerning what his control and use of Sound will, and can do, for the communication of a 'feeling' to his fellowmen.

Stubbins

The Dimensions of the Sound Potential

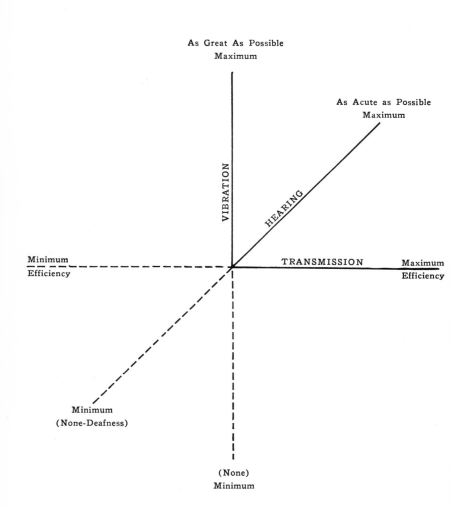

The phenomenon of Sound as a natural phenomenon, includes all vibrational phenomenon which can be transmitted by some sustaining medium, and be thus detected by the human ear. It is necessary to order this vast spectrum of transmitted vibrational phenomena, for recognition and control, if it is to be used as the medium of an art.

The first broad division of Sound, is easily made by recognizing the difference between a periodic, repeatable and recurrent pattern of vibration, as opposed to a sporadic, sudden, and unrepeatable pattern. The sustained vibrational possibility, is usable for communication, since it is possible to predict its repetition, and its recurrence, at a time and place, if its nature and production is understood. The second category of sounds, is also usable for communication, but such use must be recognized immediately as a random event, which will never be repeatable, and cannot be predictable as to time and place. Obviously, the first category will provide a substantial base for calculated usage, while the second will be reserved merely as a miscellaneous reference, to which all sounds not in the first category may be assigned.

The division of Sound into these two broad categories, for the purposes of communication in the art of music, does not however, preclude the observations of all sound as a natural product of vibration; and the nature of sound must first be defined and understood with respect to its basic aspects. In other words, all sound has the same origin, that of vibration, transmission by a medium, and reception by the ear, whether or not the sustaining or repetitive qualification is assigned to it. While this may seem to be obvious to the scientific disciplines, it is this very point that has caused such great concern with the aesthetic measures of the phenomenon. It is particularly necessary to support the 'magical,' and 'feeling' texture of the sound, as an artistic medium, with the web of scientific strength provided by objective analysis. The musician abhors the thought of a reduction of his image of tone-quality to partial frequencies, and the scientist is generally amused, at the painful and exhaustive efforts of the artist, to achieve just the 'balance', and 'color', of the sound image required for his aesthetic need. A chemist probably has in general, the same attitude regarding the mixing of colors by a painter, and perhaps a geologist with like reference to Michelangelo, selecting his block of marble for sculpture.

Generally speaking, sound which may be repeated, sustained, and identified by a stable characteristic, is a musical sound. Random sound, or that which is not sustained, or identified by a stable characteristic, is noise.

Since all sound, whether it is termed as musical or noise, is produced in the same elemental manner, and is perceived by the ear in the same way, it is necessary as a first procedure, to understand the nature of this raw material, which the musician subsequently uses for expressive purposes.

The Nature of Sound

Sound consists of three inseparable and necessary factors. First, an initiation of energy by the movement of some elastic body, in a periodic or back-and-forth movement, which is frequent enough to be termed vibrational. While it is theoretically possible to speak of a back-and-forth movement made once, as a vibration, it is not generally accepted that vibration is accomplished, unless the back-and-forth movement is repeated at least once. Second, the back-and-forth movement, or vibration of the elastic body, must occur at a time and place, which provides a transmission of this vibration pattern to a carrying medium, such as a liquid, a gas or another solid. Third, the carried vibrational pattern, initiated by the vibrator, and transmitted by the medium, must be received by the ear, as an auditory sensation.

If the movement of some elastic body occurs at a time and place where there is no transmission medium, there will be no sound, since there will be no transmission of the energy pattern initiated. Likewise, if a vibration of an elastic body occurs at a time and place where a transmission medium is present, but the transmitted vibrational pattern is not received by some ear as an auditory sensation, there will be no sound.

Sound must be defined as a three-factored situation, vibrational initiation, vibrational pattern transmission, vibrational pattern reception.

The three factors of sound may be considered separately however, as far as function is concerned.

The initiation of vibration, by the expenditure of energy

of elastic bodies, is represented by the various musical instruments, which may be considered basically, as vibration producers.

The transmission of the vibrational patterns initiated by the vibration producers, may be studied as patterns in the usual medium of transmission, air. These patterns, are what are known as sound waves.

The receiver of the transmitted vibrational patterns is, of course, the human ear, which provides the necessary attributes for the auditory sensation.

THE THEORY OF VIBRATION

When the molecules of a body at rest, are acted upon by a force, and displaced from their position, the degree to which they tend to return from the displacement, is known as the elastic modulus. In a situation where the elastic modulus is high, not only do the molecules tend to return to the original position, but due to the reaction to the force applied for displacement, they more than overcome the displacement, and return beyond the original point of rest. The cause of this additional energy in the molecule action, is due to the compressability of their structure, and the tendency for this compressability to respond with a subsequent expansion, to off-set the compression effected by the application of the displacement force.

When this action of compression and subsequent expansion, as a reaction to the compression takes place, the molecules of a body move back and forth, in a pattern which is determined by their elastic modular structure. The pattern so initiated, persists until the effect of the original energy applied for displacement, has been modified by the elastic modular effect, and is exhausted; at which time, the molecules again assume their original rest position. Elastic modulus is inherent in certain structures, and may be imposed on others, by the creation of mechanical tension. A tightly stretched string, a stretched drumhead, or a certain spring-form shape, are all means of achieving potential tension situations in bodies used for vibrational purposes.

The pattern of motion achieved by compression and expansion of a body, by the application of a force, is the vibrational pattern of the body.

A cycle of vibration is measured from the beginning of the initial application of force, and the beginning of the compression of the body, though the motion as it continues to a point of maximum compression, with its subsequent return by elastic modular action to the point of original rest, and continuing beyond this point to the extent of the expansion reaction. Since it is easier to measure displacement values from maximums, a cycle is usually measured from maximum compression point to maximum expansion point; the number of cycles of vibration completed in one second, is termed the frequency of vibration.

Since the energy applied as an initial force, and modified by the elastic modular reaction, expends itself until the point of rest is finally achieved, the measurement between the points of maximum compression and expansion, becomes smaller and smaller after the first cycle has been achieved, if no further force is applied.

If additional energy is applied to the elastic body as the cycle is first completed, the body continues to render a vibrational pattern of maximal motion which is sustained as long as the force applied remains constant.

The amount of force applied, will vary the maximum displacement, and subsequent reaction of the elastic modulus. The measurement of the cycles of vibration as to their comparative differences in size, is termed the amplitude of vibration.

In addition to the primary displacement, and reaction pattern of any elastic body, due to an application of force, numerous additional secondary motions of the various portions of the vibrating body may occur. These secondary vibrations, always occur in a certain definite order, as to relationship with the primary vibrational pattern. Both the primary, and secondary vibational patterns, depend not only on the elastic modulus of the body, but also on its shape, and size, as well as to the manner in which the force to initiate the vibrational pattern is applied.

The shape of musical instruments, and their size as well as the method of applying force to their elastic modular potential, is therefore a determinant of the vibrational pattern to be achieved.

THE TRANSMISSION OF VIBRATIONAL PATTERNS

(PROPOGATION OF SOUND WAVES)

The vibration patterns established in elastic bodies, by the application of force, is transmitted to the medium around them, if this medium also has a vibrational potential. The usual medium for such transmission in the art of music, is air.

The molecules of air, may be displaced in the same manner, in which the molecules of a body may be displaced. Air is an elastic medium, and surrounds the definite elastic bodies, which have been made to vibrate, due to an imposed force.

The molecules of the air, are compressed by the expansion of the elastic bodies as they meet these molecules, and the air molecules return to their position of rest, as a rarefied, or less dense situation between them is provided by the compression of the elastic vibration bodies. An expansion of a vibrating body, therefore compresses the air adjacent to it, and in turn rarefies the air adjacent to it, as the body itself is compressed.

This movement of the air molecules follows the same patterns, of primary and secondary vibration, developed by the vibrating body adjacent to it.

The movement of the air particles directly adjacent to the vibrating body, transmit their motion to similarly adjacent air molecules, and an expanding action of alternate compression and rarefication of the air is dispersed in all directions, until the energy of the system thus set in motion is exhausted.

The patterns of the motion of the air so developed are known as sound waves. These sound waves have the same characteristic patterns of motion, as the elastic body which initiates them.

The speed of these sound waves in traveling through the air is approximately 1100 feet per second.

The number of vibrations made by an elastic body in one second, is the frequency of vibration. Likewise, the number of sound waves propogated by the frequency of these vibrations, is the frequency of the sound wave. This is the number of recurrent waves which pass a certain point in a given second.

The wavelength of a sound wave, is the distance that a sound wave travels in order to complete one cycle. Since this distance is dependent on the speed with which the compression and subsequent rarefication of the air molecules is accomplished, it is easily seen that short sound waves are the product of extremely fast vibrational patterns, and long sound waves are the product of slower patterns.

As sound waves are propogated in the free medium of the air, they travel outward in all directions equally at once. Thus a sound wave is a spherical wave shape.

Sound waves traveling in the air, are modified in several ways by the environmental control. They may be forced to vary their direction due to a change in the relative velocity of the several layers of air which may have a different temperature. Sound waves traveling over the surface of the earth, may therefore be bent downward, or upward due to these temperature differences. This bending of the direction of the sound wave is termed refraction.

Sound waves may also meet obstacles and be required to pass around them. Sound passes around the corner of a building, or over a hill, or in an open window. It is not necessary to see the source of a sound in order to hear it. Since the ratio of the wave length of the sound in the audiofrequency range, is very large compared to most obstacles encountered, the change of direction caused by obstacles is for the most part not too great. Otherwise, we would have much difficulty in the propagation of sound. The change of direction due to obstacles is known as diffraction.

If a sound wave meets a heavy, rigid obstacle such as a wall, it will be reflected. When the wave is reflected, it is a perfect image of the sound source, and retains exactly the same energy as the original sound source. This situation is termed reflection.

When sound waves meet a soft material or a porous substance, the numerous small passages in the material so formed, cause a slipping of adjacent layers of air due to the particle velocity of the air; and due to the viscosity of air, this slipping produces a kind of friction in the air, which thus dissipates its energy as heat, and effectively diminishes the strength of the sound wave. This situation is termed absorption.

A sound wave travels in the transmission medium such as air, until its energy is lost. In a theoretical situation, this loss of energy could be so small as to be almost negligible, provided there were no obstacles encountered. The term transmission of sound, simply implies the movement of the action of the sound wave from the source, along a spherical front, in all directions. However, no sound wave is free from the effects of the various modifications which have been listed. In practically all situations, sound waves meet with one or more of these modifiers. The mechanisms of modification, reflection, and absorption are never complete, however, and some sound passes through almost all reflective or absorbing obstacles. The amount of sound which passes through these two modifications, is defined in terms of the remaining portion, and the situation is measured in terms of transmission loss, or the decrease in power of a sound, in transmission from one point to another.

THE CHARACTERISTICS OF SOUND WAVES

The sound waves caused by the vibrational action of elastic bodies assume the characteristics of this vibrational action.

These characteristics are frequency, intensity and partial structure.

The frequency of a sound wave, is determined by the frequency of the cycles of vibration of the elastic body, and has been shown to follow this pattern as established by the vibrator.

The intensity of the sound wave, is produced by the amplitude of vibrational action of the elastic vibrational body, and is dependent therefore on the forces of energy supplied for sustaining and initiating the vibrational cycles. This intensity is measured as sound pressure in the sound wave, which is the amount of displacement of the air particles accomplished by alternate compression and rarefaction situations. This pressure is measured by units termed dynes. Dynes are units of force or mechanomotive force, which for this purpose is usually computed as the force per square centimeter.

The partial structure of the sound waves, is a reflection of the several primary and secondary vibrational actions of the elastic vibrational body.

These several vibrational actions depend on the size, shape, material and method of initiating vibration in the elastic body.

The primary motion of the vibrating body, produces the shape for the sound wave which is termed the fundamental. The secondary vibrations produce the shape for the sound wave termed partials.

A vibrating body does not vibrate randomly, but according

to a certain pattern, whereby the secondary vibrations which are the strongest, are all in direct relationship to the primary vibrating motion.

The vibrating shapes which are formed in the sound wave by these patterns of vibration, in the vibrating body, have been shown by the Fourier theorem to be the only possible sound wave action which can be propogated by this means. It is thus possible to analyze a sound wave, and to determine the vibrational pattern of the initial sound source or vibrating elastic body. The strength and relative distribution of these secondary vibrational patterns, with relation to the primary vibrational pattern, provides the distinguishing characteristics of the sound, which is termed its tonal character.

The dimensions of a sound wave enable us to study the differences between the several vibrational patterns of musical instruments, and provide a means for reference and measurement. These dimensional characteristics allow the sound wave to be recorded by several electronic instrumentation means, and to be drawn as a curved graph which may be analyzed with great precision. These sound curve graphs are what is termed the projection of a uniform circular motion.

The simplest form of vibratory motion, is illustrated by a swinging pendulum, which as it makes a back and forth movement, swings through a certain arc, depending on its length and on the distance by which it is displaced before it is allowed to swing. This is illustrated by Figure 1.

Pendulum P is at rest at point A. If it is displaced to point B, and then allowed to swing, it will swing back to point A, and then a distance equal to the distance from A to B, in the opposite direction or to point C. This action is described by a law known as Hooke's Law which states that "a body displaced from a position of rest, will tend to return to the position of rest, with a force which is proportional to the force of displacement".

In the case of the pendulum, the force required to displace it to point B, is off-set by the weight of the pendulum when it is released, and the pendulum then reurns to the point of rest at point A, but due to the proportional force of its weight will continue on past point A and travel to point C, which is a distance directly proportional to the force required to displace its weight to point B, in the first place.

If no further force is applied, the pendulum will gradually swing back and forth, through proportionally decreasing arcs on either side of point A, until it finally comes to rest again. This action of the pendulum simply swinging back and forth, is described as simple harmonic motion. The distance that it. swings in its complete arc, is its amplitude of motion, and the time that it takes to complete one arc is its frequency of motion. The greatest arc, or the first swing that the pendulum makes at its release from the initial displacement to point B, is its arc of greatest amplitude. Note that even though the arcs which are subsequently traveled by the pendulum, decrease in length as the force is exhausted, that the time of each arc remains the same. Therefore, frequency is not dependent on amplitude. The weight of the pendulum, and its force of displacement, determines its amplitude of motion. The time of each arc, or the time of vibration, or frequency, is dependent on the length of the string from which the weight is suspended. The shorter the string, the faster the same weight pendulum will move through its arc of amplitude; and the longer the string, the slower the

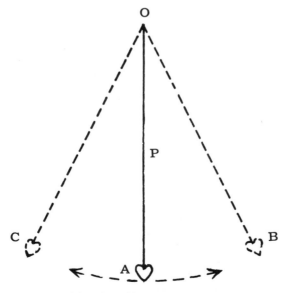

Simple Vibratory Motion

same weight pendulum will move, even though the amplitude of its arc can be controlled by a force of displacement equal in both cases.

If the pendulum is suspended over a piece of paper, which may be moved under it at a constant speed, and some device for allowing the tip of the pendulum to mark its arc, is provided, the motion of the pendulum will be recorded as a curved line on the paper. This line, or curve represents a projection of the uniform circular motion which the pendulum is making as it swings back and forth. This motion is termed simple harmonic motion and the resulting curve is a sine wave curve.

Imagine that point P moves around the circle ABCD, at a uniform speed like the hand of a clock. At some point where P is at any instant, perpendicular lines may be drawn to the diameters AC and BD, and Px and Py. Now as P moves steadily around the circumference of the circle, x moves back and forth along DB, and y moves up and down along AC. The time that P takes to complete one circumference of the circle, is the fre-

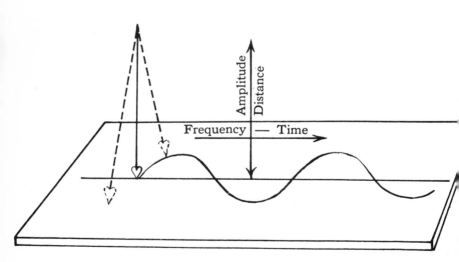

Sine Wave Curve

Simple Harmonic Motion

quency of the motion, and the radius PO is the amplitude of this motion. If the pendulum is suspended over the moving paper, PO will be shown as the extent, or height and depth, of the curve. The distance from one point on the complete curve from its beginning, on a central reference line, to a return to another point on the reference line, after the pendulum has swung to both sides of the line as far as it will go, will represent the distance traveled by P around the circumference of the circle. PO will therefore be the amplitude of motion, and the time of P through ABCD, returning to P will be the frequency of the motion.

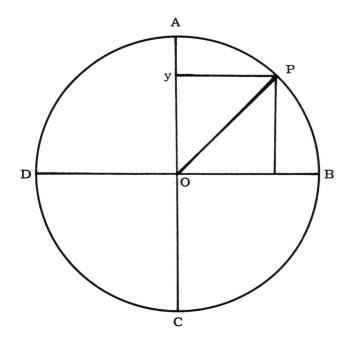

Geometric Analysis of the Projection of

Uniform Circular Motion

A curve of simple harmonic motion, drawn as follows, is termed a simple sinusoidal curve. The distance **A** to **B**, is the amplitude, and the distance **F** to **F**¹ is the frequency.

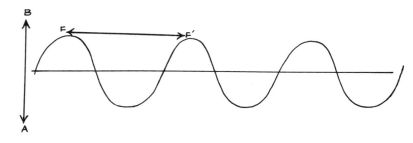

Sine Wave Curve Projection

It can further be imagined that a number of pendulums of different weights, and with different lengths of string, could all be placed in motion with different forces of displacement applied to them all at the same time. If a number of such motions were recorded at the same time, it is evident that the curve, on the paper, would be of a more complex design. Certain distances would be added to others, and certain times would be added to others, in such a way that the resulting curve representing all of the motions, would represent a combination of their several effects. This is precisely the situation with the complex patterns which are obtained from the recording of vibrations observed as emanating from musical instruments, as sound sources.

Since the complex curve is the result of the effects of the number of simple curves, of which it is composed, the complex curve may be analyzed into its respective simple components by a system of computation devised by the mathematician Fourier. By such an analyzation the various weights, and lengths of string, and displacement forces acting on each of the many pendulums which produced the curve, could be determined. In this same way, the vibrations from a musical instrument may be analyzed and determined as to relationship and presence.

Fourier's Theorem states that 'any single-valued periodic function whatever, can be expressed as a summation of simple harmonic terms having frequencies which are multiples of that given function'. Stated in this way, it is obvious that the harmonic motions which can be determined by an application of this theorem to any curve represented as the vibrational pattern of a musical instrument, will yield the harmonic series, and the relative strengths of the members of this series, present in the tone of the instrument. While this in itself is still not enough to satisfy the demands of the musical ear, it does provide a solid basis for preliminary investigation and description, which are usable for reference.

Vibrational actions of elastic bodies are divided into two main categories, that of vibrational production by means of transverse vibration and that of longitudinal vibration. Both of these vibrational categories however, produce sound waves which are similar in wave action through the transmission medium, even though they are initiated by different modes of vibration, in the elastic body.

The vibration of a string is transverse and assumes the following pattern. This vibration is in turn amplified by the elastic body of the instrument, which in turn transmits the vibrating action to the air.

The vibration of a bar, or of an air column enclosed in a tube is longitudinal, and is initiated by a driving force of either a vibrating reed attached to one end, or a series of puffs of air caused by blowing across the end of the pipe. These longitudinal vibrations of the air column are transmitted to the air at the end of the tube, or through the vents in the side of it and the sound wave is formed. The action of the bar is similar over its surface.

In both cases, the resulting sound wave in the open air is formed, and proceeds through the transmission medium subsequently in the same way, even though its initiation was achieved by different means.

The other characteristics of the sound wave, frequency and intensity, are no different in their initiation at the vibrating source. Only the transverse, or longitudinal differences of sound source vibration are notable as sound production generation differences. The effect of this difference, provides for the several methods of tone production possible by musical instruments, which provide the variety of tonal attributes required for musical expression.

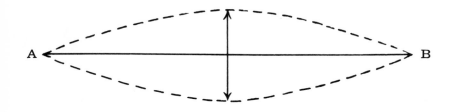

String Vibration — Transverse

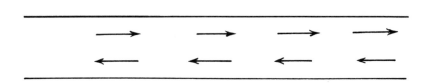

Air Column Vibration — Longitudinal

CHAPTER III

Some Quantitative and Qualitative Aspects of Musical Tone

Judgement of tone is the reasoned analysis of sound based on information received by the auditory sensation. Measurement is the recording of data obtained by means of calibrated instrumentation designed to accept information provided by natural phenomena. The interpretation of musical tone must be accomplished not by noting the inadequacies of either method as opposed to the other but by the supplementation of the information provided by both, and evaluated by intelligent recognition.

Present methods and techniques for the measurement of sound permit the analysis of musical tone as acoustical phenomena. It is equally true that no one is certain at present that those aspects of the sound wave which are customarily measured are the aspects of primary importance in the auditory perception of musical tone. It is necessary that a correlation be made between these observations and the judgement of the ear. This can be accomplished by the cooperation of the scientist and the musician.

The first step in the direction of such cooperation lies in the understanding of the problem and in the willingness of each party to accept each other's techniques as supplementary to his own. There should be no desire to mechanize music nor to reject blindly the fact that sound is the basis of music. It is not unfair to the musician to say that the scientist already knows much more about sound than does the musician, but it is also true that the musician is much better equipped to employ sound in a particular and specialized manner than is the scientist. They both have much to offer each other through such cooperation; and the common gain, which will be the result of such combined effort, is a contribution both to science and to art.

Let us examine the present possibilities for the investigation of musical tone quality on the basis of what can be observed as physical phenomena of sound, in order to place the problem in a better perspective.

Suppose, for example, that it is desired to communicate information to another musician, in another part of the world, six months from now, concerning a clarinet tone which is to be played at this present time. This information is to be complete information, which will include all phases of what we may be able to say or to show about it. The simple technique of recording it with absolute fidelity and then merely playing it for the recipient of the information is not enough in this case. True, if the recording is as perfect as we can obtain, and the playback is also perfect, we will have transmitted the identical sound of the clarinet across the intervening interval of time. This accomplishment, however, is simply a time-stretching elaboration of the same kind of communication which invokes the use of a qualitative vocabulary. We have been able to retain the clarinet tone of the present for future reference, but information which is needed for analysis and for better understanding of it is just as surely missing as if the recipient of the information had been present at the recording. Nothing has been lost, but nothing has been gained.

In addition to the perfect preservation of the presently played clarinet tone for future reference, it is also possible to provide other information concerning it by means of other techniques.

It is possible to present information in the form of a picture of the tone for purposes of visual analysis. It is possible to present information which will show visually and measure accurately the harmonic content, the amplitude and intensity, the frequency, the build-up and decay, and the comparative differences between all musical tones and this specific clarinet tone, or the similarities of this tone to others which have been played at any time and recorded for reference.

Whether this additional information will be of value to the musician or not will depend on the way in which it is used. The potentialities of communication are considered as self-evident.

THE PROBLEM OF COMMUNICATION

Communication is a basic characteristic of human beings. Man accomplishes communication by several means, by gesture, by pictorial indication, of which writing is a sub-script, and by sound, of which word noises and musical tones are primary categories. Of these means of communication, the matter of musical tone, its physical characteristics and its psychological implications, has never been adequately studied in order to realize the tremendous yield which is potential through proper use of the techniques of research available.[1]

A few of the results which may be anticipated from an adequate study of musical tone are better communication by means of this method of man's expression, better performance of the art of music, better and perhaps new instruments of music, better teaching of music, a more adequate terminology concerning the art of music, and a powerful technique for the study of psychic aspects of the human being when the physical side of music and musical tone is better known. There are undoubtedly valuable therapeutic possibilities which have only been touched upon so far by a few pioneers in this field.[2]

The basic physical property of music is sound—without which there can be no music. The production of sound for musical purposes is accomplished by the use of musical instruments, which are simply sound producers. The province of the study of such sound production, by such sound producers, for such purposes, is properly the science of musical acoustics. The human additives of the performer are limited by the physical considerations involved in this relationship. As the physical malformation of the cleft palate interferes with proper vocal production, so does the stuttering or stammering of the musical instrument interfere with proper and desirable musical tone production.

The savage with his reed flute cannot play Mozart's *Concerto in D,* not only because he knows nothing of Mozart, but also

---

[1]H. F. Olson, *Musical Engineering* (New York: McGraw-Hill, 1952), p. vi.

[2]Lewis, Burris-Meyer, and Cardinell, "Music As an Aid to Healing," *Journal of the Acoustical Society of America,* XIX (July 1947), 544-546.

because his reed flute will not do it. We have here no quarrel with his expression as far as it goes, his simple melodies and his emotional satisfaction, but we cannot fail to acknowledge the vast potential of expressive possibilities implied by the development of civilization.

What the limitations of the various musical instruments may be no matter what their present degree of refinement, should properly be determined by first attending to a study of the means used for musical sound production. The application of scientific techniques and methodology in the study of the physical characteristics of musical instruments is undeniably an exploitation of the aforementioned potential of expression.[3] Present knowledge concerning musical instruments is limited to the heritage of craft which has come down through the years with all of the mythology developed by tradition. By scientific determination, it should be possible to cut through this maze of contradiction and contra-distinction to basic principles of fact which would clarify and lead to a better understanding of the art of music in terms of reasonable, logical, and factual evidence concerning the tools of the musician, musical instruments.

The Qualitative Vocabulary of Music

The qualitative aspects of music have long been the subject of discussion among musicians. An extensive vocabulary for this purpose has been developed.[4] But for the individual musician, the interpretive possibilities of musical expression have led to the formation of an individual subjectivism as concerns each and every musical term encountered, a fact which has provided him a communicative escape mechanism, based on the single standard of individual taste.[5]

Words are not music, and music is not of words, although the expressed qualitative esthetic experience may be parallel.[6] If a musician would talk about music, he must use the words

---

[3]H. Fletcher, "An Institute of Musical Science—A Suggestion," *Journal of the Acoustical Society of America,* XIS ,July 1947), 527-531.

[4]R. W. Young, "Some Problems for Postwar Musical Acoustics," *Journal of the Acoustical Society of America,* XVI (October 1944), 105.

[5]D. H. Parker, *Principles of Aesthetics* (New York: Silver Burdett Co., 1920), p. 176.

of the only vocabulary so far at his disposal, and he must reserve a place of retreat which is conveniently provided by his personal taste. That he retreats so often is easily understandable; he might welcome a new vocabulary which would make his retreat less often necessary.

Now the human mind is a complex thing, and we know that the complexities of communication are fascinating as well as baffling. There is no reason to suppose that the qualitative vocabulary is going to be discarded; its boundaries are likely to increase with every musician who is born. However, description of the processes of music in terms of the already established vocabulary of the physical and biological sciences cannot fail to increase the probability of clearer thinking, more accurate analysis, and more efficient communication.

THE QUANTITATIVE VOCABULARY

The development of a quantitative vocabulary depends on the application of scientific techniques to the physical phenomena which are used in the art of music. The application of these techniques to the physical phenomena of music is no different from such applications in other fields of investigation. It is desired very simply to establish first of all a language of size. For this purpose, the problem may be designated as a problem in the measurement of the qualities of music, which qualities are those defined as the aspects of the phenomena of music which are measurable.

The terminology of music is usefully divided into three categories: first, terminology concerning the instrument; second, terminology concerning the player; and third, terminology concerning auditors other than the player.

THE DIMENSIONS OF MUSIC

The use of the physical phenomenon of sound for the purposes of music is conveniently considered as a dimensional relationship which provides us with specific operational limits.

Sound, as natural phenomenon, is the result of vibration. It is defined as "an alteration in pressure, stress, particle displace-

---

[6]Parker, PP. 185, 255.

ment, particle velocity, etc., which is propagated in an elastic
material, or the superposition of such propagated alterations."[7]

We live surrounded by air. The motion of this air around us
constitutes a central interest which is primary to everything
that we do. This air moves about us in various ways, and when
caused to move by the vibration of some elastic body, whether
accidental or deliberate, results in the activation of our sensory
equipment with particular reference to the ear, in such a way
that the sense-perception of this air-motion causes us to experience what is known as the sensation of hearing. Psychologically, sound is for us a sensation produced by vibration.
According to a second definition, "Sound is also an auditory
sensation, usually evoked by the alterations described above."[8]
This dichotomy of concept is of particular significance to the
problem of musical analysis and immediately suggests the need
for correlation if better understanding is to be achieved.

Three things are needed to accomplish the sound-cycle for us
as human beings, a vibration producer or sound maker, a
medium which can carry the vibrations produced by the vibration maker (in this case air), and a receiving instrument for
the produced and carried vibrations, such as the human ear.[9]

Every material body which has the necessary properties for
vibration has a time of vibration most natural to it depending
on its size, its weight, and the stresses under which it may be
vibrating. This time of vibration is called its natural period of
vibration. It is the time necessary for the body to complete one
back and forth movement or one vibration.

Vibration, or oscillation, is defined as "the variation, usually
with time, of the magnitude of a quantity with respect to a
specified reference when the magnitude is alternately greater
and smaller than the reference."[10] A periodic quantity is defined
as "an oscillating quantity the values of which recur for equal

---

[7]American Standard Acoustical Terminology: 1.040. Hereinafter abbrev-
iated to ASAT.

[8]ASAT: 1.045.

[9]Bartholomew, *Acoustics of Music* (New York: Prentice-Hall, Inc.,
1942), p. 2.

[10]ASAT: 1.040.

increments of the independent variable,"[11] and a period or primitive period of a periodic quantity is "the smallest value of the increment of the independent variable for which the function repeats itself."[12] A cycle is defined as "the complete sequence of values of a periodic quantity which occur during a period."[13] and the frequency of the periodic quantity, "in which time is the independent variable, is the number of periods occuring in unit time."[14] The number of cycles which a body may complete in one second is designated as its fundamental frequency, "the frequency . . . which has the same period as the periodic quantity."[15]

Bodies with short periods thus vibrate more frequently in the same time than do bodies with longer periods. Their frequency of vibration is said therefore to be greater. In order to produce audible sound, or the sensation of hearing, vibrating bodies must have some frequency between approximately twenty and twenty thousand cycles per second. This is the natural limitation of the human ear and consequently the sound limit of the frequencies used in music.

In order to be used as sound in music, the frequency of vibration, within these limits, must be produced in such a manner that it is continuous and steady for a long enough time interval to be used as a point of reference. This steady-state of vibration at a certain frequency allows the sound to be described as having a certain pitch. Pitch is defined as "that attribute of auditory sensation in terms of which sounds may be ordered on a scale extending from low to high, such as a musical scale."[16] The musician refers to the steady-state frequency of a tone primarily as its pitch.

The wideness of range of movement made by any body during its period of vibration constitutes its amplitude of vibration. The result of amplitude is what the musician refers to as

---

[11]ASAT: 1.045.

[12]ASAT: 1.050.

[13]ASAT: 1.055.

[14]ASAT: 1.050.

[15]ASAT: 1.095.

[16]ASAT: 5.005.

THE DIMENSIONS OF MUSIC

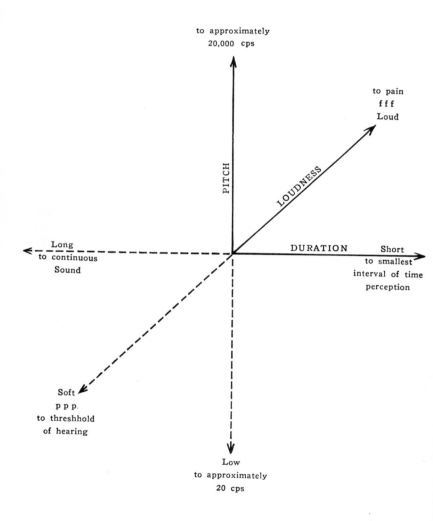

Figure 1.

the loudness of the pitch. Amplitude is defined as "the largest value which the quantity attains."[17] Loudness is defined as "the intensive attribute of an auditory sensation, in terms of which sounds may be ordered on a scale extending from soft to loud."[18]

The duration of a steady-state of certain frequency permits the use of the sound for longer or shorter intervals of time if the sound producer is properly controlled. This permits the use of the sound for musical purposes for intervals of greater or less duration. Thus, individual sounds may be given what musicians call a rhythmic relationship.

On the basis of this brief analysis of the properties of sound and its use in music, a plot of three dimensions of music may be constructed, as in Figure 1. There is no note which may be played or sung as used in music which does not fall in this three-dimensional plot.

MUSICAL NOTATION

In order to determine a sequence of sounds for communication as music and in order to preserve the sequences and combinations of sounds as art forms it has been necessary to devise a notation for this purpose.

The notation of the sounds used in music accomplishes three guide dimensions, pitch, duration and dynamic value.

These are provided by using note symbols which indicate relative values of duration, placed or positioned on a musical staff of five lines, and four spaces. The position of the note symbols indicates either higher or lower frequencies. Additional frequencies which are either higher or lower than the limited space of the music staff permits, are indicated by using portions of supplementary lines above and below which are termed ledger lines. In addition, the music staff may be modified by a sign which shifts its whole function higher or lower.

Dynamic values, or the force of the sounds to be produced are indicated by modifying terms of relative value from 'soft' or weak, to 'loud' or forceful. These are generally placed either above or below the music staff position of the note symbol to be so modified.

---

[17]ASAT: 1.070.
[18]ASAT: 5.015.

Letter names are assigned to the several lines and spaces of the music staff, and to allow for frequencies which are not accounted for by the several letter names **A, B, C, D, E, F,** and **G** which are those used, modifying signs such as the sharp, flat and natural signs are placed in front of the letters so modified.

In addition to the relative duration of musical tones indicated by the type of note symbol used, the speed with which the tones are to be produced with relation to each other is indicated by another modifying indication termed Tempo Marking. This is commonly based on the value of the kind of symbol which will be used to indicate a basic value of one second or an integral portion of a second of time. The use of the second as a basic time value and its subdivisions is conveniently determined by an ingenious time counter called a metronome, which can be adjusted to produce all of the divisions or multiples of time divisions of a second throughout a range of approximately a two-second interval to as fast as four times per second.

An additional dimension of notation which is used to indicate the type of musical sound desired is appropriately designated simply by naming the instrument on which the music is to be played. While this may seem to be an extremely simple matter, it should be remembered that not all musical instruments can produce all of the sounds that may be notated. Neither can all musical instruments produce the sequences or combinations of sounds which may be required for musical expression, in the same manner or with the same technical facility. Composers of music are quite well aware of this through bitter experience, and the art of music in its development has demonstrated the increasing need for accurate notating and precise designation of types of sound and their possible sequences. In early music, much of it was considered interchangeable, not only between instruments but between voice and instruments. Such is far from the case in instrumental musical practice both in performance and composition today. In fact, a whole history of musical development could be written and based on the increasing precision of notation as a major factor in the metamorphosis of its techniques of expression.

The symbols of musical notation and their use have been designed by practical experimentation and usage. The system was not all at once planned and provided as a complete technique. What has been accomplished is a notation which is easily seen by the eye at a glance, and by ready identification is quickly and efficiently transformed by the practicing musician into the necessary required sounds on his instrument. What may seem simple by comparison to symbolic notation of certain other techniques is a simplicity which is absolutely requisite to the coordination of eye, hand and ear for the performance of music. The resulting notation has stood the test of time and is not about to be supplanted by another system although efforts in this direction have been occasionally advanced. That musical notation is practical and usable has been proven. That it is complete, and perfect, is highly questionable, but that a system other than that which is in general use could accomplish the task assigned to it will need to be demonstrated more rigorously than heretofore. Music notation is truly a universal language, since its symbols are used throughout the entire world of western music, and its beautiful simplicity of direction and understandability is its great strength.

The symbolizing of sound as a reference for the selection of sounds to be used for musical purposes provides a communicative device that is a sophisticated link between the phenomena of nature and the expression of an art.

Sounds may be represented by written symbols that constitute a language of permanence despite the impermanance of the sound itself. These symbols enable the repetition of a sound pattern and allow a whole framework of sound construction to be devised, and utilized in a manner which would otherwise be impossible.

The notation of music is an extremely simple written language by comparison to the other written language systems such as verbal or mathematical. The symbols are few, and the limitations of their direction are great. The wonder of the art is often not that it has so little to work with, but that with such economy of expression, so much can be said.

The whole of western musical notation, which is the only system with which we are concerned, contains symbolwise, not more than twelve basic scale tone indications and their duplications. Modifications of these twelve symbols is accomplished by no more than five additional symbols and further modification is completed by not more than a few dozen or so additional symbols. In addition, there are verbal indications and descriptions, which although used with the notation symbols are essentially verbal, and cannot be considered as uniquely a part of the system.

There is indeed, a fourth dimension, of tone-quality, which is inherent in the production and the use of sound for music. However, this characteristic is infinitely variable along each of the axiis of our graph and cannot be notated, nor is expected to be, by any player or composer. At this point the verbal modifications to which reference was made above apply. Most of the profound personal differences of opinion concerning the performance of music stem from this fourth dimensional concept. There is virtually no possibility of a disagreement between musicians as to the time duration value of a quarter note at 60 metronome—this simply means that there is to be one sound played for exactly one second's duration. Likewise, there can be no disagreement as to the plot on our graph which calls for A 440, meaning a sound which has exactly 440 cycles per second as its pitch number. As to the dimension of dynamics, or the soft-loud axiis, there is not quite the same exactness possible, but there certainly is a general agreement possible on the differences of a great volume or loudness of sound as compared to a little volume or a soft sound, relative as the comparison may be.

At the level of the fourth dimension, or the quality, or the 'style' so to speak, of the sound to be used, almost no two musicians will find perfect accord. This is precisely for the reason that at this point there is no value reference which can be assigned and compared to an objective standard without much time consuming effort and elaborate technological procedures. That this can be accomplished in a laboratory situation is very true, and that musicians are intellectually and tempermentally allergic to such procedures is well known. The musician prefers the wholly personal evaluation of his music in this area and is not at all happy with anything which may demonstrate that what he calls a 'dark' sound is in reality a 'bright' sound if relative values are impartially assigned to the factors which will be used for calculation. The great glee with which 'musical' ears have been deceived by laboratory instrumentation display, not alone in this area, but even at the other levels of our common dimensions of pitch and duration, is fun for the scientist perhaps, but is a matter of unnecessary sadism as concerns the sensitive musician. That there is such an area in the art of music is perhaps what makes it an art—and there is no cause to disturb the personal state of imbalance, even though at times it may seem to be confusing to the layman. The effectiveness of expression is not going to be achieved by a computer system, just as the art of music is not going to supplant the living musician by means of an electronic analogue. The usefulness of an approach to the art by discovering more about it from the perspectives provided by a study of its physical phenomena, should not be based on a desire to prove the ineptness of its exponents as artists. The fourth dimension of music therefore, while not notated with the exactness which we may expect of the others, is nevertheless of equal value, although at a different level.

Timbre or tone quality is defined as "that attribute of auditory sensation in terms of which a listener can judge that two sounds similarly presented and having the same loudness and pitch are dissimilar."[19] It is the characteristic which enables a musician to judge that he is hearing a clarinet for example, instead of a violin, or an oboe instead of a French horn, even though they may be playing the same pitch at the same dynamic level.

Any body used as a sound producing medium for musical purposes vibrates in a number of secondary motions in addition to the basic motion of its natural period. These secondary motions also produce vibrations, and hence sounds, although usually fainter than the principal vibration. The basic pitch produced by the basic motion is called the fundamental, and the secondary sounds are in music called harmonics, overtones, or partials.

The fundamental tone is defined as "the component in a periodic wave corresponding to the fundamental frequency, or the component tone of lowest pitch in a complex tone."[20] A tone is defined as "a sound wave capable of exciting an auditory sensation having pitch, or a sound sensation having pitch."[21] A

---

[19]ASAT: 6.050.

[20]ASAT: 1.095.

[21]ASAT: 6.005.

simple tone is defined as "a sound wave, the instantaneous sound pressure of which is a simple sinusoidal function of the time, or a sound sensation characterized by its singleness of pitch."[22] A complex tone is defined as "a sound wave produced by the combination of simple sinusoidal components of different frequencies, or a sound sensation characterized by more than one pitch."[23]

An overtone is defined as "a physical component of a complex sound having a frequency higher than that of the basic frequency, or a component of a complex tone having a pitch higher than that of the fundamental pitch."[24] A partial is defined as "a physical component of a complex tone, or a component of a sound sensation which may be distinguished as a simple tone than cannot be further analyzed by the ear and which contributes to the character of the sound."[25] A harmonic is defined as "a partial whose frequency is an integral multiple of the fundamental frequency."[26] It is inaccurate to use these terms as synonyms, which is a common weakness of the qualitative vocabulary.

The sum total of the various motions in a vibrating body with respect to their strength and to the possibilities of their combination is apparently what the human ear uses as its basis for the judgement of what the musician calls tone quality. It is apparent that in addition to our simple three-dimensional limit of sound as used in music and shown in Figure 1, that we must reckon with another property of musical sound which is present under all conditions for the production of music.

As an example of the quantitative measurement of sound as used in music, the matter of tone quality is of prime importance because it represents an area of great interest of which at present not too much is known. The qualitative vocabulary of music has in some measure been able to function with respect to the three-dimensional limits of sound as described in the

---

[22]ASAT: 6.010.

[23]ASAT: 6.015.

[24]ASAT: 6.025.

[25]ASAT: 6.030.

[26]ASAT: 6.035.

discussion of pitch, dynamics, and rhythm, but in the case of tone quality the breakdown is obvious.

Generally speaking, as indicated previously, musical ears do not disagree too violently with respect to matters of pitch, or intonation, as it is commonly called. Neither is there any particular difficulty in reaching agreement concerning rhythmical subdivisions or dynamic variations. But as to tone quality, its nature, its description, its differences, and its effect, musicians all but become intelligible. Here is the point of greatest need for a quantitative vocabulary, and here is the opportunity for the most significant application of scientific techniques.

The term tone quality is used by musicians for the purposes of describing first, the tone production of the musical instrument, its nature or function; second, methods and mannerisms of individual performance, the control of the instrument by the player, or the function of the player; and third, certain conceptual and emotional values which may be the effect of musical expression.

Tone quality in the first sense, as applied to what the instrument produces, may be referred to by such descriptive terms as dull, heavy, dark, bright, light, brilliant, etc.

When tone quality is referred to in the second sense, in terms of the sound as controlled by the player due to certain physical activities on his part, the same descriptive words may again be employed but modified by personal reference as in the phrases, "so and so's tone is" or "so and so's sound is."

Or again, if tone quality is referred to in the third sense, as concerns a description of the effect of musical expression, the same words may again be used, but modified in such a way as to express an imaginative concept such as "the transparent, light sound of the strings," or the "stinging brilliance of the trumpets," or "the dark sonorities of tonal architecture."

Thus if a musician is confronted with the blunt term, tone quality, he may think of his instrument in terms of its mechanical function, or of the sound which he produces when playing it, or of the subtle differences which he imagines may be achieved when the instrument is being played by him for the purpose of producing some special effect of style in the expression of music.

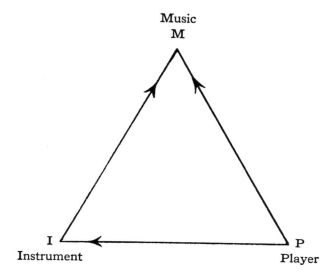

Figure. 2

The interrelations of these categories of definition are illustrated by Figure 2. The arrows represent the several uses of the same descriptive terms applied under different modes of usage. Tone quality in the first usage, that having to do with what the instrument may produce as its function (that is, what it is designed for, with the implied limitation of this efficiency), is a consideration of the player with respect to the instrument as a purely mechanical construction. This may be represented symbolically as $P \rightarrow I$.

This mechanical function of the instrument in terms of its own efficiency has a potential capacity as concerns the production of sound for the purposes of music, which in this case is its total value as a mechanical construction, $I \rightarrow M$.

The mechanical function of the instrument as controlled by the player for the expression of music is a sum total of the mechanical efficiency of the instrument and the physical control of the player, $P \rightarrow I \rightarrow M$.

The sound used for the expression of music as an art, although a product of this psychoacoustical activity, is regarded as an independent phenomenon when the considerations of the player are directed toward it in terms of musical expression, $P \rightarrow M$.

If a substitution for the player, P, in Figure 2 is made by an audience, A, as in Figure 3, the effect of the mechanical efficiency of the instrument and the physical activity of the player is that of a sum total of PI, and PI becomes a complex factor which may be written symbolically as (PI). The effect of the music in this case is $M \rightarrow A$, and the total effect of a of the music in this case is $M \rightarrow A$, and the total effect of the complex situation may be expressed as $[(PI) \rightarrow M] + [M \rightarrow A] + [(PI) \rightarrow A]$ equals $[(PI) M] + [(PI) A]$ equals $[(PI) M \rightarrow A]$.

Tone quality may therefore be described as in Figure 2 by the player in terms of I, $[P \rightarrow I]$, or $[P \rightarrow I \rightarrow M]$; and in Figure 3 by the audience as characteristic of the instrument alone, or due to any of the following relationships: $[A \rightarrow I]$, $[A \rightarrow P]$, $[A \rightarrow (PI)]$, $[(PI) \rightarrow M]$, or $[M \rightarrow A]$.

This dilemma of understanding among musicians according to their use of the descriptive possibilities of the term tone quality emphasizes the need for quantitative analysis.

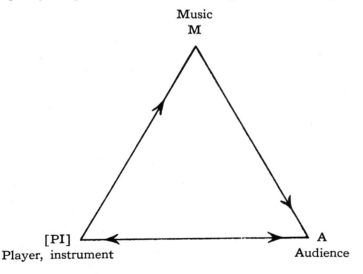

Figure 3.

CLASSIFICATION OF MUSICAL INSTRUMENTS

There are two general classifications of musical instruments which are immediately recognizable. There are those instruments in which the tone production is greatly dependent on the player and there are those instruments in which the tone production is more or less a mechanical function of the instrument itself, this function being controlled by the player. Obviously, this classification of instruments is mechanical, but it provides us with the means of separating the functions of the player and the instrument for further analysis.

In attempting to describe the tone quality of instruments of the first category, we are much more concerned with what the player does than we are when describing the tone quality of instruments of the second category. With regard to the description of intonation, we are exclusively concerned with what the player does with instruments of the first category. A pre-set instrument of the second category leaves the player with no control over this matter whatsoever, while in the former case, intonation presents one of the greatest difficulties of performance.

Most of the violent disagreements concerning the definition of tone quality spring from this difference in musical instruments. To the degree that the player has control of the tone generation of his instrument, and to the degree of flexibility of adjustment which the instrument possesses, the more difficult is becomes to define and measure musical instrument tone quality. Discussions of this nature are too often referred to as simply psychoacoustical problems. While it is true that they are, there is considerably more than psychoacoustical values involved, and the correlation of a quantitative analysis is to be desired.

THE JUDGMENT OF TONE QUALITY

In addition to the description of musical instrument tone quality by the use of terms such as dull, heavy, dark, light, bright, brilliant, etc. (as applied to the three references: the instrument, the player, and the music), the musician quite simply uses as a basis for first judgment on hearing a musical tone, the terms good or bad. This first quick and automatic judgement is based on acceptance or rejection of the tone as being worthy of further description. Good tones merit further discussion and classification according to the extent of the qualitative vocabulary, while bad tones need improvement before their subleties are discussed.

If some basis of this first judgment of the musician can be established to the effect that there is a measurable difference between tones qualitatively referred to as good and bad, and if this quantitative difference can then be correlated with and substantiated by the musician's ear, we will have a least limited our scope of reference and can proceed further.

MEASUREMENT OF TONE QUALITY

In the first analysis of physical data concerning musical tone it is found that in order for a sound to be defined as a musical tone that it must have a fixed, or measurable frequency which has a duration sufficient for reference and which has a defiinite, or measurable intensity. The frequency, the duration, and the intensity can be accurately measured by scientific instruments and can less accurately be determined by the ear.

It is simple enough to collect physical data concerning musical tone, but it is not a simple matter to determine what these data may mean in terms of the ear. The scientific instrument for measurement is analytic, the ear is synthetic. The ear subtracts, adds, selects that which it wishes to hear—it even may add certain components of its own to the sound which is to be described, but it hears as a whole. The scientific instrument is impartial; the ear is prejudiced by all of the concomitant factors of the complex associations of thinking which make up the nature of the human being.

No instrument of sound measurement can be substituted for the human ear, nor can the human ear ever analyze sound with the impartial reference of a sound measurement device. Certain differences of sound for the ear are, however, the same differences for the measuring device, and the reference to these differences constitutes our quantitative vocabulary.

If the sound produced by a musical instrument does not possess the properties which satisfy its definition as a musical tone with respect to the measurement of the scientific instrument nor to the 'hearing' of the ear, there are but two alternatives which may be in effect: the musical instrument is at fault mechanically, or the player is not exercising the degree of control possible and necessary for the proper mechanical functioning of the instrument.

CONCLUSION

Since by definition a musical instrument is a sound producer designed to produce musical tones, the nature of the instrument plus the efficiency of the mechanical function of the instrument plus the efficiency of the player's control (which is a skill quotient) gives musical tones of a particular quality. Introduced variables of design, mechanical function, and player's control all produce differences in tone quality.

The nature of the instrument, the mechanical function of the instrument, as well as the player's control, all may be measured by instruments and be heard by the ear, and introduced variables may also be measured and may be heard.

It can be argued that art is self sufficient and complete in itself. It should also be said that the materials of art, the colors of the painter, the words of the poet, and the musical tones of the musician are dependent on physical phenomena without which art could not be. Better and more complete understanding of these materials and their uses cannot fail to increase the efficiency of the artistic process and might perhaps give rise to a broader scope of artistic development simply on the basis of the added freedom of the mind which comes about through greater understanding.

CHAPTER IV

The Acoustics of the Clarinet

The clarinet is an instrument which utilizes the air column, contained in the tube of its instrument body, as a source of vibrations for musical purposes.

The air in wind instruments must be excited into vibration in order to radiate sound. This air in the instrument, which is called the air column, is of the shape of the walls which contain it. The air column must be excited into vibration by energy applied from an external source.

When an energy source is applied to the air column, and excites it into vibration, a complex situation results. The energy source must conform to certain requirements in order to assure the efficient vibration of the air column. The shape of the air column, and its mass, determine the fundamental frequency of the sound produced. The shape of the air column has a reactance effect on the energy source, which must be perfectly balanced in order to assure the complementary efficiency necessary to enable a control of the sound for musical purposes.

In order to establish the knowledge necessary to obtain the control and to maintain the functioning of any of the air column instruments for musical purposes, it is therefore necessary to understand, at least in a very general manner, several basic acoustical phenomena. It is necessary to understand the basic behavior of air columns as vibrators; the effect of their shape and size; the effect of the energy source which excites their vibrations, and in turn, the reactance effect of the air column on the energy source.

The air column in the body of the clarinet is the air column with which we are concerned in this instance, and coupled to it as an integral part of the system is the top portion of it, which constitutes the energy source for exciting the vibrations of the air column of the instrument; and of course the breath of the player, which is the regenerative or steady supply source required to sustain the conditions of vibration. Such general knowledge of acoustical phenomena quite naturally then leads to a determination of the proper dimensions and shape of the air column for the clarinet, as concerns the dimensions and shape of the bore of the tube; the proper dimensions and adjustments required for the mouthpiece cavity for the instrument, which constitutes the upper portion of the bore; and the adjustment and proper dimensions of the reed, which when held on the mouthpiece and activated by the breath provides the energy source necessary for the sound.

The behavior of a vibrating system depends on the forces which act between the particles of which it is constituted. In the case of the air column, air molecules have been found to act much as infinitely smooth balls, which may exert a push against each other, but have no possibility of effecting a shearing or sidewise motion on each other. For this reason, the air particles of an air column bump against each other in such a way as to cause what are known as longitudinal vibrations, or vibrations which occur along the direction of a line which would be drawn through the centers of a string of these balls. This is the opposite vibrational pattern to that which is found in a vibrating string, where the sidewise motion, or shear effect, of the particles which compose the string, is the line of direction for the vibration, which in this case is termed transverse, or at right angles to the vibrator.

When the air of an air column, or any other air in a cavity is excited into vibration by the application of a sound energy source, it has been found that the fundamental pitch, or the lowest sound obtainable from such a system, is jointly determined by the size and the shape of the cavity. The larger the cavity or air mass, the lower the fundamental pitch, and the smaller the cavity or air mass, the higher the pitch. In addition to the size however, the shape of the air cavity has the effect of providing a potential difference in the possible vibrational modes to which the air cavity will respond. Therefore, while the fundamental frequency is determined by both the size and the shape of an air cavity, the frequency ratios of the various possible modes of vibration for the air cavity is dependent on the shape of the cavity alone.

The shape of the air cavity used for the tube of a clarinet is that of a cylinder, and for this shape of cavity, the potential modes of vibrational frequency in ratio to the fundamental frequency, is that of the stopped pipe, or a pipe which is open at one end and closed at the other.

The vibration in an air column instrument is as we have noted, longitudinal in direction. This longitudinal direction of a sound wave is often referred to as a plane wave shape. In a simple parallel walled pipe, such vibrations are obviously presented to the outside atmosphere at the end of the pipe. Sound energy contained in the pipe or tube is thus radiated into the medium surrounding it, or the outside air, and damping of the pipe oscillations takes place due to loss of energy when they meet the outside air. When the sound waves meet the open air at the end of a pipe, they are reflected back again, but there is a loss of energy each time that they meet the open air. Otherwise, vibrations in the pipe would be maintained indefinitely. This loss of energy at the open end of a pipe, causes the frequency of the wave to drop slightly, and actually lowers the pitch of the sound. This effect is known as the end-effect, and in practice creates a situation which makes the pitch of any pipe slightly lower than it would be assumed to be, from a theoretical calculation of its basic length.

When sound waves are initiated in a pipe they travel along it longitudinally until they meet the open air where they are reflected back into the pipe and to the opposite end. If a pipe or tube is open at both ends, it is termed an open pipe; if open at one end and closed at the other, it is termed a closed pipe. A comparison of the sound wave action in these two types of pipe is important in showing the results of the shape of the pipe on the ratio of vibrational potential of the various modes to the fundamental frequency as determined by the length of the pipe. The clarinet is of course a 'closed' pipe, and the effect of its shape is noted by this comparison. Before proceeding with the discussion it is necessary to make very clear a matter which has always been apparently quite confusing to wind instrument players when they wish to refer to the sizes and shapes of their various instruments' air column, and to describe the results practically.

It will be seen in the succeeding description of open and

closed pipes that the difference between the two, results in a different ratio of the various vibrational frequencies to the fundamental frequency. At the same time, this difference will be seen to be the same basic difference, which is described as being the result of the difference in shape of a pipe, when the cylindrical and the conical shapes are compared. The clarinet and oboe are both closed pipes, that is closed at one end where the player plays on the reed. Both of these instruments act as closed pipes as far as practical performance is concerned. However, since one is conical, and the other cylindrical, the vibrational modes with respect to the fundamental is different. It must be emphasized that the shape of the pipe therefore, is the real governing factor with respect to the musical instrument result which is obtained. Therefore, while an oboe is a closed pipe, its conical shape causes it to act as an open pipe, while a clarinet, due to its cylindrical shape, acts as a closed pipe both according to the description of simple closed pipes, as well as due to its cylindrical shape as compared to the oboe.

We will therefore discuss first the open and the closed pipes, and then describe the conical pipe situation. The cylindrical pipe shape, is used for the basic discussion of both open and closed pipes, for the reason that the simple plane wave formula for the equation can be calculated as a simple cross section of the pipe at any point throughout the length of a cylindrical pipe, which is not the case with the conical pipe, which changes in diameter throughout its length.

Pipes Open at Both Ends—Open Pipes

A pulse of compression in the form of energy is initiated at one end of the pipe, and travels to the opposite end. At this point it is reflected from the open air with a reversal in phase. The reversal in phase simply means that a compression is reflected as a rarifaction and vice versa.

Compression is the force of squeezing the air molecules closer together, and rarifaction is the opposite, increasing the space between them. The wave reflected as a rarifaction, again traverses the length of the pipe back to its original starting point. Here, it is reflected again, with a subsequent reversal of phase again, which means that it is again a compression, and consequently a cycle has been completed. It is obvious that the

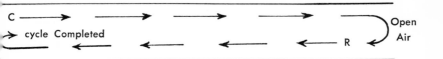

C → cycle Completed   Open Air   R

Pulse is generated at one end of pipe as C or Compression-Wave travels length of pipe and is reflected as R or Rarifaction at opposite end. Wave returns to original end of pipe and is again reflected with change of phase, becoming a compression again and completing the cycle.

initial state of the wave is therefore repeated after two complete traverses of length of the pipe.

PIPES CLOSED AT ONE END AND OPEN AT THE OTHER— CLOSED PIPES.

In the case of the closed pipe, it will be seen that the ends are different, or asymmetrical, as compared to the open pipe situation. Since it does not matter which end of the pipe is open, and which closed for purposes of the theory, the reversal of a closed pipe does not make a different situation.

In this case, the initial energy pulse provided at one end, must traverse the pipe four times, in order to attain a completion of the cycle. If it begins at the open end, it is reflected from the closed end without a change in phase, since there was no open air to change it. It must make two traverses of the pipe length before it can have a change of phase. Exactly the same situation prevails if the initial energy pulse occurs at the closed end, as in the case of the clarinet. The pulse must travel the length of the pipe where it reverses phase, then back to the closed end, where it is reflected in the same phase, and then again to the open end where it completes the cycle.

The velocity of sound divided by the frequency equals the wave-length of the sound. The velocity of sound in air has been

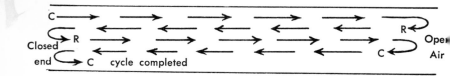

Pulse is generated at closed end of pipe as a Compression. Wave travels length of pipe and is reflected with change of phase as a Rarifaction. Wave travels back to closed end where it is reflected in the same phase as a Rarifaction. Wave returns to open end where it is reflected with change of phase as a Compression. Wave returns to closed end completing the cycle.

calculated to equal approximately 1100 feet per second. Therefore, for example, if we wish to determine the wave-length for the pitch of **A** 220, we may do so the following simple formula:

$$\frac{1100}{220} = 5.1 \text{ or the wavelength in feet}$$

Since the sound wave must travel twice the length of the open pipe before a cycle is completed, as has been shown, it is necessary to divide the wave length as obtained above, by 2 in order to determine the length of an open pipe which will produce this pitch.

Therefore $\dfrac{5.1}{2} = 2.5 +$ or approximately 2½ feet in length.

For the closed pipe, since the sound wave must travel four times the length of the pipe before the cycle is completed, it will be necessary to divide the wave-length by 4, as follows:

$$\frac{5.1}{4} = 1.2 + \text{ or approximately 1 and 2/10 feet in length.}$$

Formulas for these two calculations can be conveniently expressed as follows;

V = velocity of sound
F = frequency of sound
W = wave-length

therefore:

$$\text{length of open pipe} = \frac{V}{F} = \frac{W}{2}$$

$$\text{length of closed pipe} = \frac{V}{F} = \frac{W}{4}$$

However, the calculation for the length of the pipe depends on another acoustical phenomenon which must be accounted for. This is known as the 'end-correction'. _p.49_

END CORRECTION

In the theory of pipes, it has been assumed that the end of a pipe at the open air is a true antinode. In other words, that the reflection of the sound wave from the open end will be perfectly accomplished. This is not truly correct, since some sound energy escapes at each reflection, and is radiated in the form of spherical waves from the end of the pipe. The air beyond the end of the pipe is therefore in vibration to a certain extent, and the extent of this vibration is greater than the length of the pipe itself. This additional length, added to the basic length of the pipe, is termed the effective length. For this reason, musical instruments must be calculated in length to include this end effect, and an end correction must be applied if the instrument is to have a proper scale. The bells of the woodwind instruments, particularly that of the clarinet, accomplishes this correction, in addition to encouraging the formation of spherical sound wave patterns more smoothly radiated into the open air. Any lack of understanding of the effect of the clarinet bell, is based on a lack of appreciation for this acoustical phenomena.

It is obvious that with each length of pipe used for a pitch, as the tone holes are opened or closed, that a certain 'end correction' will need to be applied. This effect determines the practical placement of the tone holes of the instrument.*

Therefore, in order to more properly calculate the length of the pipe required for a certain pitch it is necessary to have an additional formula which will yield the 'effective length'.

It has been calculated that the necessary end-correction for a closed pipe without a flange is 0.62R where R equals the radius of the bore measurement. For a closed pipe with a flange, or a 'bell' as in the case of the clarinet, the end-correction calculation is given as 0.82R where R is the radius of the bore measurement.

Therefore, the simple formulas for length must be revised as follows for a closed pipe as used for the clarinet:

$$\frac{V}{F} = \frac{W}{4} + 0.82R$$

In the case of a clarinet with a bore of 14.5 millimeters, this end-correction would theoretically be the length of the pipe plus 6.0+ millimeters.

The end effect lowers all frequencies, of all tones of the pipe. The end correction depends on the wave length. Consequently, the various partials of the same pipe are not exactly a harmonic series. This is more theoretical in value than practical however, and an end correction applied to tune the fundamental length of the pipe, is the basis for the practical calculation of the tuning of musical instruments of this design.

SHAPE OF THE PIPE

As has been indicated however, the shape of the air-cavity as well as its size determines the resonant frequencies. It is therefore necessary to be informed on this matter as concerns the cylindrical and conical shapes used for wind instrument pipes.

CYLINDRICAL PIPES

The harmonic resonant frequency of a cylindrical pipe is expressed as follows:

N = the fundamental frequency of the pipe
s = the series of potential vibrational modes
L = the length of the pipe
V = the velocity of sound

*For a discussion of tone-hole placement on the clarinet see Chapter XI, part 2, The Tuning of the Clarinet.

therefore $N_s = \dfrac{sV}{4L}$ and s is an odd integer

This represents a series of odd harmonics or frequencies and is the situation found in the cylindrical tube of the clarinet.

CONICAL PIPES

In the case of the conical pipe, the simple plane wave theory which has been applied to the parallel walled pipes, is no longer possible. In this case, the sound wave traveling along the pipe, will be either spherically divergent or convergent, depending on the direction of the conical slant. In the case of the oboe, this slant will be divergent, or traveling on a slant from the closed end to the open air, along a tube which increases in diameter from one small end to the larger.

The theory of propagation of spherical sound waves is extremely complicated, and is not easy to reduce for simple display, in the same manner as that of the parallel walled pipe formula. This is for the reason each subsequent diameter of a conical pipe is slightly greater, or less than the one next to it, when measured from any point, whereas in the parallel walled pipe all diameter sections are the same. In order to account for the motion of the sound wave along a conical pipe therefore, it is necessary to calculate the expansion of the sound wave, so to speak, at each diameter, in addition to each distance which it travels longitudinally along the pipe. This requires equations of motion and of continuity, which must be reduced to a general equation, and combined with velocity potential function, in order to describe the situation.

When this is done, however, the calculation yields a formula which shows that the harmonic series for a cone is the same as for an open parallel walled pipe with the same length as the slant length of the cone. This explains the harmonic series of the oboe, as compared to the clarinet, due to the differences in their bore shape, and not to the fact that they are both closed at one end.

The harmonic resonant frequency of a conical pipe is expressed as follows:

N = the fundamental frequency of the pipe
s = the series of potential vibrational modes

L = the length of the pipe
V = the velocity of the sound

therefore: $N_s = \dfrac{sV}{2L}$ and s equals s^1, s^2, s^3 etc.

It is thus seen ,that the open pipe contains the complete harmonic series of frequencies. It should be noted that a pipe closed at both ends, acts in the same manner as a pipe open at both ends, since the reflection of the sound wave will reverse its phase in the same manner, due to the similarity of the reflective end. It may be simply said therefore, that an open pipe means a pipe that has the same kind of ends, which reflect the wave in the same manner, whether they are open to the air, or closed. This is a symmetrical system of acoustical reflection.

When an air column is excited into vibration by means of an energy initiation, the vibration of the air column acts according to the acoustical laws which we have observed. The continuation of vibration in the air column or a condition of sustained vibration, can only be accomplished if a regenerative or continual replenishing source of energy initiation is available. The air column loses its energy vibration as supplied by the energy source, both to friction, and to radiation into the surrounding air.

In wind instruments, it is necessary for the energy to be renewed by approximately from one to five per cent of the amplitude of each cycle of vibration, or the sustained vibration of the air column cannot be maintained.

In addition, it has been found that the energy to be regenerated, must be supplied in a very definite way, at a very precise time, in order to meet the requirements of an air column vibration.

Since vibration of an air column represents pressure variations, which consist of the two conditions of compression and rarifaction, sufficient energy to accommodate the needs of the mass of air to be affected by this pressure requirement, as well as the timing of the application of the energy pulse must be exact.

It has been observed that if the natural frequency of the energy source is higher than the air column vibration, that the energy vibration will be naturally affected by the pressure variation of the column's vibrations, so that it moves back and forth in phase with these vibrations. On the other hand, if the energy source has a lower frequency than that of the air column vibration, the energy source will move back and forth out of phase or in opposition to these vibrations.

Consequently, it will be concluded that the clarinet reed, which acts as the energy source for the clarinet air column, must have a higher frequency of vibration than that of the modes of vibration present in the air column, or it will not be able to move in phase with the pressure variations present in the instrument, and will therefore, be unable to supply the regenerative energy required to sustain the vibration system.

The air mass of the clarinet air column, driven by the spring in the form of the clarinet reed, acts according to very definite principles. It can readily be understood that a large mass would require a weaker spring. Furthermore, if the mass to be driven is to be driven at a below-natural frequency level, it is easily understood that the weaker the spring, the greater the amplitude, or movement, that can be forced on it by any given magnitude of driving force.

In a self-sustaining system, such as that of the clarinet, the mass of the reed itself is important. The forces available for driving the reed are small, and consequently the reed must be quite flexible, and capable of much freedom in movement if it is to be moved enough by the several forces, in order to have it work as a valve action, to supply the regenerative pulses necessary to the sustaining system.

The total driving force of the clarinet reed depends also on its exposed area. A wide reed will be moved greater distances than a narrow one of the same mass, if they are mounted in the same way, with respect to the air column which they are to drive. Therefore, it is perfectly proper to deduce that the mass per unit area of the reed must be less than some certain amount if it is to respond properly to the pressure variations of the air column, which it is driving. The position, design and mounting of the clarinet reed, as well as the shape, size, and design, of the mouthpiece to which it is attached, must therefore correspond exactly to the requirements of the air column of the clarinet on which the driving system is to work.

The reed and mouthpiece of the clarinet, when attached to the body of the clarinet, actually add to the size of the air column of the instrument, as can easily be seen, and consequently provide additional air space, so to speak, which lowers the vibrational modes of the air column of the instrument alone. The fact is, that musical wind instruments of this design, always play lower in pitch when excited with a reed, than would be true if calculation is made of the vibrational modes of the air column alone, or with the reed clamped in a closed position.

This lowering of pitch is not more than a fraction of a semi-tone in the lower register of the clarinet, but is much more in the higher register, particularly for those pitches which are near to the reed's own natural frequency.

The tone generation system of the clarinet, which consists of the reed, mouthpiece and ligature, can be blown without the body of the instrument. The pressure of breath, and the tension of the embouchure, in such a case, indicates that the frequency of this tone generation system depends on the breath pressure and the embouchure tension. The Bernouille principle of aero-dynamics, explains the vibration of the thin edge of the reed under breath pressure, and embouchure tension. The blown frequencies possible with the tone generation system of the clarinet alone, are always higher than the frequencies to be produced on the clarinet when the reed mouthpiece and ligature generation system is attached to it. This of course, proves the theory of the requirements of the air column for sustained vibration, in that the frequency of the energy source must be higher than the vibrational modes of the air column to be excited. The tension of the embouchure, and the breath pressure required, to produce various pitches on the clarinet, are also seen as perfectly reasonable adjustments to be made when the instrument is played under normal conditions. The relaxation of the embouchure necessary for the low register, and the delicacy of breath pressure noted for tonal control and emission, are seen to be directly related to this theoretical analysis, and practically followed in playing the instrument.

A valve, such as the clarinet reed, provides puffs of air, for the sustained vibrations in the clarinet air column, which are timed at a definite frequency, to match the requirements of the theory as previously discussed. These puffs of air, not only have the potential requirement to match the fundamental frequency of the air column shape to be accommodated, but also must have the proper shape to meet the complete vibrational mode potential of the clarinet air column.

In our discussion of open and closed pipes, it was indicated that the shape of the air column determined the harmonic potential of the system, and that the closed pipe or the parallel walled, or cylindrical construction, of the clarinet, produced a pattern consisting of strong odd harmonics.

The valve action of a reed has been observed to provide shapes of puffs of air, which basically contain the potentials for different harmonic patterns. If a valve flies open and shut very abruptly, and admits the air for only about one-twentieth of a cycle of vibration, it has a potential of producing approximately equal amounts of all of the harmonics.

If a valve flies open abruptly, and remains open for about one-fourth of a cycle, and then shuts abruptly, it has the potential of producing a harmonic pattern which is quite different from the former. A valve opening for only one-eighth of a cycle, again produces a different pattern.

On the clarinet, when played under normal conditions, the reed valve opens and shuts more or less sharply, and for various portions of the cycle, according to the musician's desire for one kind or another of tone-quality, as well as because of the requirement of the system itself. This explains the reason for one player sounding differently from another, even though he plays the same reed and mouthpiece, on the same instrument. It also accounts for the 'feel' of performance that the individual player may have, as well as for the particular individual preference in reed voicing.

Because the harmonic frequency supplied by the tone generating system of the clarinet, matches the resonating or vibrational mode potential of a musical horn, all of the vibrational modes of the air column system are excited by the reed. However, the musical result is that which is obtained by the dampening effect of each of these modes, according to the shape of the air column involved. The shape of the air column reacts in turn, on the vibration pattern of the reed, which is the energy supplier for the sustaining system, and is so dominant, that in practice the tone-generating system of the clarinet is absolutely required to match the requirements of the clarinet to which it is attached, or the results are extremely inefficient. Intonation, tone quality, ease of performance, flexibility, articulation, and dynamic control, are all affected by this reactance between the air column of the instrument and the tone generating system.

As a practical application of the previous theory, it can be observed that for the three recipes of tone puffs as described, three different mouthpiece shapes and their corresponding reed styles could be prescribed. The first, a short-open lay, the second, a longer and closer lay and the third, a medium open, medium length lay. The corresponding calculation of the air column, and design of the clarinet on which these mouthpieces would be used, would necessarily be somewhat different for ideal results. The added control of the player, as concerns his embouchure and breath pressure control, are the only possible means of rectifying the situation to provide a means of mixing the several factors involved.

It is therefore necessary to make a detailed study of the acoustical mechanics of the tone-generating system which follows in the next chapter.

The reader will have undoubtedly noted the omission of a discussion of the materials of construction used for the design of the clarinet. It must be emphasized that this omission of comment is deliberate, and is so, for two very definite and pertinent reasons.

First, the material of the tube which surrounds an air-column, has only a secondary effect on the acoustical results which are obtained by its size, shape and characteristically generated vibrational action, irrespective of the method of such tone-generation. There is no effect as concerns the basic acoustical mechanics of the situation with regard to the material used for the walls of the contained air-column. Any attempt to describe secondary effects, which are largely subjective in nature as concerns the player, would only confuse the anticipated clarity of the presentation of acoustical facts.

Secondly, a discussion of materials used for the construction of clarinets, with their characteristics in terms of acoustical reflection, absorption, diffusion, diffraction and transmission, would occupy an inordinate space which it is impossible to encompass in this book.

CHAPTER V

The Acoustical Mechanics of the Tone-Generating System of the Clarinet

When a vibrating body is coupled to another body, either by being directly connected to it, or by means of an intermediate medium such as the air, the motion or vibration of the first body is transmitted to the second.

If, at the same time, the vibration of the first body happens to be exactly of such a pattern that it coincides with the potential vibration pattern of the second, the resulting vibrational excitation is greatly increased and we have the phenomenon of resonance. Resonance simply means that the potential frequency of any body which would occur if that body were excited into vibration, has had this precise vibration transmitted to it by another vibrating body.

The clarinet reed, which is set into vibration by the breath of the player, transmits its vibrations to the air column in the body of the clarinet. The resonant frequency of the air column is then initiated in response to the vibrations of the reed. There are several of these resonance frequencies which depend on the size and shape of the air cavity in the clarinet, and in addition, these resonant frequencies occur in their different orders as the tone-holes of the instrument are opened and closed to provide the several lengths of pipe required for the several pitches which are produced for musical purposes.

Three factors determine the vibration of a vibrating body such as the clarinet reed. These are mass or m, stiffness or s, and resistance, or r. As the mass is increased, the vibrations become slower; as the stiffness is increased, the vibrations become faster; and as the resistance to the motion is increased, the vibrations die out sooner, or are 'damped' as acoustically described.

The law of proportional vibration, or Hooke's law, states that the restoring force is proportional to the displacement. That is, the elasticity of the reed after being set into vibration, will cause it to spring back a distance equal to the distance from which it has been displaced by the breath action of the player, acting according to the Bernouille principle of aerodynamics.

Hooke's law permits an equation to describe the action of the reed as coupled to the air-column of the clarinet. A situation in which there would be little if any resistance would allow the following equation:

$$F = \frac{1}{2\pi} \sqrt{\frac{S}{m}}$$

If the resistance is considerable, the frequency is decreased and the amplitude of the vibration is decreased accordingly. The characteristic of "damped" vibration, is that the ratio of the maximum strength of each frequency described, is in direct proportion to the time between the first vibration and the second, and is also equal to the same amount of time between any two subsequent vibrations. This is shown by the following illustration:

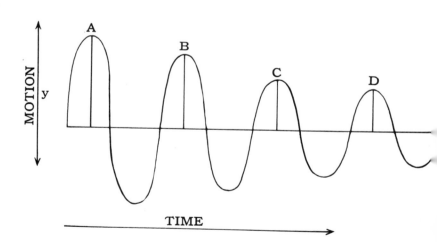

Damping of Vibratory Motion
Decay of Sound Wave

This fact allows a measure of the time which it takes for a vibration to be damped, or to 'decay'. The limits of the waves shown in the illustration can be designated by y, and described as a function of the time t, by the following equation:

$$y = Ae \frac{rt}{2M}$$

where A is the initial or greatest amplitude, r is resistance, and m, mass. The natural logarithm of the ratio of A to B is termed the logarithmic decay per cycle and the equation which illustrates it is as follows:

$$k = \frac{rT}{2M}$$

therefore, if the resistance r, the mass, m, and the period or T of the system are known, the logarithmic decay may be found.

The ratio r/2m is known as the damping factor of any such system and its reciprocal is called the modulus of decay or the time constant of the system. This constant is the time in which the amplitude falls a proportion of its value equal to 1/e or 1/2.718.

It has been demonstrated that a critical situation of damping occurs when the values are:

$$r = 2\sqrt{Sm}$$

In this situation the system returns to its original position without once passing beyond this point. This is to say, that no vibration can occur whenever the situation is such that the damping is critical.

In the case of forced vibration, which is the result of the vibrations of the reed being forced onto the air-column of the clarinet causing it to respond by its resonance frequencies, the system is not allowed to come to rest but is maintained in vibration due to the application of periodic force, or continued vibration of the reed, which in turn is dependent on the continuation of the breath and embouchure pressure of the player.

When the system is at first placed into action, as at the beginning of a tone played on the clarinet, the natural acoustics of the situation respond with two effects. First, when an external force is applied to a potential vibrating system, there occurs a sudden and immediate response known as the transient, and this quickly is damped, due to the action of the vibrating body, which has been impelled to act by the force of another. Second, a stage of vibration develops, which is termed the steady-state response. This steady-state response continues and is maintained by the continued application of the periodic force. Whenever a system at rest is set into motion by a constant periodic force, these two stages of vibrational pattern are noted. The time taken for the vibrating system to reach the steady-state, depends on the speed with which the transients are damped. The same condition occurs, when the periodic force is removed from the vibrating system, for the reason that the vibrating body must go through the stages which are present wherever a condition of resistance is present.

The action of the clarinet reed as an initiating impulse for the vibration of the air-column of the clarinet, is thus seen as the sudden application of a periodic force to a system, and the response of the clarinet as a vibrating system will be understood to go through a transient state, before finally achieving a steady-state of tone. The reverse will also be seen to be the case when the breath pressure and embouchure pressure are removed, and the tone of the instrument is stopped. This illustrates the action also of the articulation of the clarinet, where the periodic force is interrupted by the tongue. It is extremely important to note that the breath and embouchure must be maintained at a perfect level of activity while the tongue interrupts the action of the reed, or that the result will be highly uncontrolled, and will certainly not allow the system to return to its steady-state of tone, without undue transient response.

Another acoustical law, which operates in this situation indicates that the transient response is really the natural period of frequency for the system, while the steady-state is the frequency of the driving force. Thus it will be understood that the initial response of the clarinet to the impulse provided by the reed action, will at first be a transient which contains all of the several resonant frequencies of the air-column as it is particularly shaped, by the fingering involved. Then, as the steady-state is reached, the frequency of the reed will be assumed, as a resonant response of the air-column, and the resonant frequency of the air-column as presented by the fingering being used will in turn cause the reed to comply.

When a force with a constant period operates to drive a system into vibration, the amplitude of the vibrations, and consequently, the velocity of the vibrating particles, depend on the direct relationship of the frequency of the driving force to the natural frequency of the system. When resonance occurs, the frequencies of the two, the driving force and the system acted upon, are the same or at a maximum. But as the driving force, departs more and more from the natural frequency of the system driven, the velocity of the particles decreases.

The response of the system to a driving force, or in the case of the clarinet, the air-column to the reed and mouthpiece combination, is thus seen to be responsible for the different effect of the several fingerings possible. The frequency of the driving force or the reed, while complying with the imposed effect of the air-column does not of course, follow it as to the frequency of the pitch being produced other than in a general manner due to the inherent, necessity for the reed to act as a driving force under its own conditions of action. Hence, as the difference between the driving frequency and the response of the system increases, the damping is seen to increase, and with the approach of the resonant frequency areas, the resonance maximum is approached. The efficiency of the tone-generating system therefore is a critical one as to design. The differences in the 'feel' of response to the different notes on the clarinet to the player is explained by this acoustical phenomenon. Differences between reeds, mouthpieces and combinations of these with instruments are also largely the result of this situation.

If two equal forces are applied to a particle, they cancel each other and the result is no motion. Thus, if two equal vibration patterns are established one by initiation, and the other by reflection of vibration from some source, the result is that the sound vibration patterns cancel each other. This result is termed a standing wave, or point of no motion when it occurs within a contained air space such as the tube of the clarinet body.

The walls of the clarinet, being hard and smooth, reflect the waves of vibration of the air-column and in addition, the vibrations traveling longitudinally through the pipe are reflected from the open air at the end of the tube at the bell, or at any open tone-hole in such a way, that at points along the tube, there occur standing waves.

When a vibration pattern is not exactly cancelled by an equal reflected vibration, the effect is to diminish the sound or to increase it, depending on the proportional strength of the initial and the reflected wave.

Therefore, certain resonances are attained in the tube of the clarinet by this means in addition to the simple concept of the resonant frequency phenomenon of forced vibration. Again, in this case, it will be readily understood that factors such as sound reflection, and the attendant standing wave patterns within the tube of the clarinet, will have some effect on the efficiency of the tone-generating system.

It is thus seen that the tremendous flexibility of the tone-generating system and the design of the clarinet as a vibrator to receive the impulses provided, must be controlled by the breath and embouchure of the player, in order to have it operate as a system. The functions of the air-column and air-cavity as provided by changes in this air-column by the several shapes provided by the fingering of the tone-holes of the instrument, and the driving force of the reed as a transducer for achieving vibration of the air-coulmn of the instrument are at every instant controlled by the breath and embouchure of the player.

This explanation will help the clarinetist to understand the several differences of response and feel of the different registers, and different individual tones as he plays them, and to further explain differences between mouthpieces, reeds, and instruments which provide multiple choices in variation. The matching of the functions is extremely critical, and a reed designed for one mouthpiece can not possibly function efficiently on another; nor can a mouthpiece of certain dimension, be accomodated either by an instrument, or a reed, of a mis-matching dimension. Furthermore, the player must also have a certain matching of breath control, or blowing, and embouchure, to accomodate the differences presented by different measurements of the other factors involved.

Arriving at a useable system therefore, is not at all an easy matter of simple calculation, but must be an adaption and matching of the several factors, which is attained by procedures as described in the discussion of the reed, mouthpiece and ligature adjustment, as the tone-generating system of the clarinet.

The design, operation, and control of the Tone Generating System of the clarinet is a problem of Acoustical Mechanics. The system consists of the mouthpiece, the reed and the ligature. The mouthpiece is designed to accept the reed which is secured to it by the ligature. The design of the mouthpiece is determined by the acoustical results required, the design of the reed is determined by the design of the mouthpiece. The ligature must hold the reed on the mouthpiece in such a way as to permit the functioning of the system with maximum efficiency.

The physical actions of the player, which for tone-generating purposes consists of the embouchure, the breath and the use of the tongue for articulation, are applied to this system. While it is true that a great flexibility of individual physical characteristics is possible, and indeed desirable in the performance of music, it cannot be too strongly emphasized, that there is not an unlimited range of possibilities available. The player controls the instrument to the extent of the acoustical mechanical design of the instrument, and the instrument controls the player to the extent of the acoustical mechanical design of the instrument.

The reed is a wooden spring. The mouthpiece is a springboard for this spring, which is slightly curved at the tip, in such a way, that a small space between the flat back of the thin end of the reed, and the curved portion of the mouthpiece, permits the spring to function, and to vibrate across the space provided.

When air pressure, supplied by the breath of the player, is applied to this system, provided the reed-spring has been placed in a state of tension, or 'spring-loaded' by the embouchure pressure of the player, the velocity of the air particles past the reed into the mouthpiece chamber is increased, and a lowering of air pressure results, which sucks the reed *towards* the mouthpiece surface. This increase in air-particle velocity is increased by the principle of the venturi, or narrowed air channel design, of the windway of the mouthpiece. When the opening between the reed and the surface of the mouthpiece is thus made smaller, the velocity of the air entering the aperture is decreased, to the extent that the area of lowered air pressure is equalized by the air in the instrument, and the natural spring action of the reed pulls it back away from the surface of the mouthpiece. This spring action of the reed is not only strong enough to cause it to return to its primary position of rest, but to continue on beyond this point, where it is then overcome by the inertia of the material mass of the reed, and is then returned by the embouchure, or lip pressure of the player, again to its primary position. The embouchure is seen therefore, as a control limit of the vibrating potential of the reed spring. From the primary position thus obtained by this cycle of events, the air pressure then initiates another cycle, and the cyclic series continues as long as the system remains in a state of balanced operation. The whole action of the system is essentially what is known as an action of mechanics as described by the Bernoulli theorem.

The occurrence of a number of these cycles as described, in a rapid series, induces a resulting vibration in the air column contained in the tube of the clarinet. The tone generating system therefore acts as a transducer in producing the tone of the instrument.

The mouthpiece of the clarinet is constructed in such a way, that the portion of it nearest the instrument terminates in a conically shaped segment, which is the upper end of the bore of the instrument. The length of this conical segment, must correspond to the correct acoustical length of the entire bore, and its diameter must also be properly calculated for the instrument on which it is to be used. This is a very important matter and one which is not too well-known or considered by most players. It is the primary reason for certain mouthpieces being unsatisfactory on certain makes of clarinet. It is not possible to interchange mouthpieces with the most efficient result, unless a calculation of this segment is made and accommodated. The intonation pattern of the instrument is changed by modifications of this conical segment.

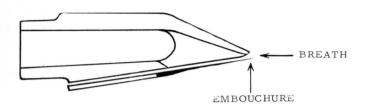

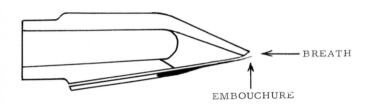

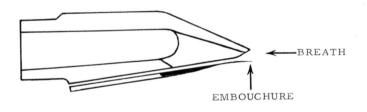

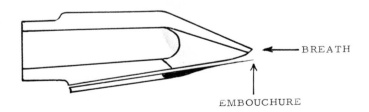

CYCLE OF VIBRATING ACTION
OF THE CLARINET REED.

The tuning of the clarinet depends on the length of its bore. The bore of the instrument terminates at the end of this conical segment within the mouthpiece. The depth of this bore within the mouthpiece may be used as a means for lowering or raising the pitch of the whole instrument. The overall length of a mouthpiece does not determine its pitch, but rather the depth or length of this conical bore segment. It will be appreciated that the enlargement of this bore segment will provide for an enlargement of the bore at a critical point. Enlarging this bore flattens the pitch of the whole instrument. The fitting of the mouthpiece to the instrument on which it is to be used, is therefore a process which involves the whole bore measurement and cannot be disregarded. Mouthpieces, while interchangeable to a certain degree of tolerance, require fitting to the specific instrument on which they are to be used, for maximum efficiency.

The narrow channel leading from the opening of the mouthpiece under the reed into the conical portion aforementioned is termed the 'wind-way' of the mouthpiece, and is what is known in mechanics as a venturi, or air-flow direction channel. It serves the purpose of shaping and directing, as well as accelerating, the air-flow required for the tone-generating system to acquire its power. The shaping of this venturi must be calculated with respect to the proportions of the bore of the instrument, and to the shape, size and contour of the reed to be used, as well as to the curvature of the mouthpiece opening.

The baffle of the mouthpiece, is that portion of the windway just inside the tip end of the mouthpiece, which develops into the whole venturi shape, that leads into the chamber of the mouthpiece. The shape of the baffle must be such, that the least impedance possible is offered to the breath as it enters the windway channel. The shape of this baffle, when established as part of a properly formed venturi, is not varied according to the facing curve of a mouthpiece. The attempt to vary the baffle shape, is not a successful control of the design. It is true that when the baffle shape is changed, that a different response of the mouthpiece is noted. This is the unfortunate aspect of the situation, which misleads many players into thinking that the change of the baffle will remedy difficulties.

The changes in response caused by reshaping the baffle, either as a steeper or a more gentle curve, changes the whole venturi

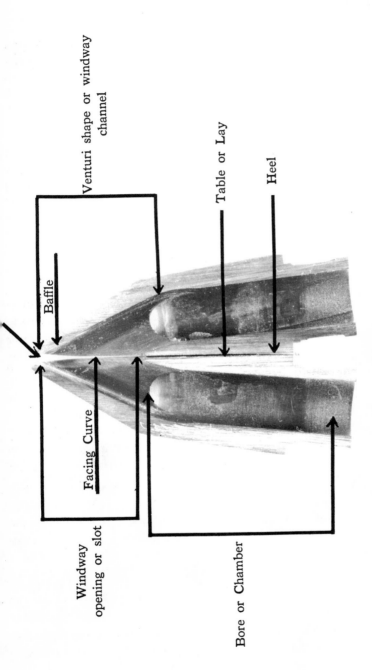

Venturi shape or windway channel

Table or Lay

Heel

Baffle

Facing Curve

Windway opening or slot

Bore or Chamber

Mouthpiece Showing interior design with design components identified.

pattern. If a change in design is desired, this requires a design of the venturi which will include the baffle shape. This is the most difficult control which the maker of commercial mouthpieces has to contend with for the uniformity of his product. Commercial curve measurements, for the facing, and commercial table measurements, can be accurately made by machining. The curve of the venturi, including the baffle, must be very carefully made by handwork, since it is impossible to design a machine which will provide the contour of the interior shape of the mouthpiece. The practice of grinding or polishing the baffle of the mouthpiece with a small wheel, as is often done, does not guarantee any uniformity with accuracy. Indeed, most mouthpiece makers are unaware of the required venturi shape as being of such critical importance as a factor, and take little care with it other than to provide a smooth finish for the interior of the windway at this point.

The venturi shape necessary for the best results is a gently-sloped flat curve which corresponds to the requirements of the chamber. The shape as established remains constant, no matter what facing is applied to the mouthpiece subsequently. There is no venturi design which will accommodate the same whole venturi shape and a 'high' or 'low' baffle design. The situation here is comparable to the balance of measurements necessary for other requirements of design. There is no such thing as a 'round' square, or a 'square' triangle. If this point can be established, the player will be sensitized to the problem of the venturi shape and extremely careful concerning any modifications which he might be tempted to make himself. The baffle shape, is the manner by which a mouthpiece is 'voiced', in the same way that a reed is 'voiced.' It is a delicate handmade adjustment.

The Bernoulli effect of the reed, and the venturi effect of the mouthpiece windway, lead the generated vibrations into the body of the clarinet in such a manner as to act as a transducer for the required vibratory response of the instrument, as a musical sound producer. It is important to note that this transducer situation produces air puffs provided by this reed-mouthpiece mechanism, so to speak. The shape of the puffs of air determine the subsequent development of the tone-quality—the power and the distribution of the partials in the sound, and an effect on the intonation (due to the shaping). There is an effect of the embouchure on the air-puff shape, and the reed contour also affects it. The whole matter of 'reed-voicing,' or reed adjustment is an effort to achieve just the proper shape of air-puff desired, which will be easily and efficiently received by the instrument under the air pressure as delivered by the player. These factors are all interrelated and balanced.

It is possible that the vibrating shape of the reed is similar to the shaping of a vibrating string as to nodal distribution. This is with consideration to the loaded or non-symmetrical string, heavier at one end, but with a gradual and uniformly decreasing load throughout its length. This shaping would explain the voicing of the reed, with relation to the mouthpiece shape, that it is used to accommodate—also the adaptation of the embouchure formation and pressure on the reed . . . this is to say how much, and at what point.

If the shape of the air column is comparable to the 'shape' of the string, and the shape of the air column is determined by the influence of the reed, as the shape of the string is determined by where it is plucked, then we have a definite possibility of analyzing the possible results of the modification of the reed-mouthpiece, embouchure-blowing system of tone generation.

It is particularly important to emphasize that the measurements given in the present discussion are examples of the interrelation of an efficient system of design. The subsequent equations developed here are indicative of the general situation and must be applied to any specific design problem. Reference is made to the later chapter on the Measurement and Design of Musical Instruments. *See foot note on following page.

The dimensions of the mouthpiece model shown in the photograph are as follows:

W — 32 mm: windway length from center of tip to center of square window in facing.

TL — 40.5 mm: flat table from square window to heel

O — 92 mm: from tip to end of tenon (bore length)

D^1 — 14.6 mm: diameter of bore at tenon

D^2 — 14.4 mm: diameter of bore at beginning of heel (upper end)

D^3 — 13.9 mm: diameter at point where enlargement begins (E)

D^4 — 14.3 mm: diameter at greatest point of enlargement (E^1) at the opposite end of slant (S) beginning of cone taper shaping

D^5 — 12.6 mm: depth of windway slot at point where S begins to baffle edge opposite—therefore S^1B

C — 56 mm: length of cone from tenon to tip of cone taper (end of clarinet bore)

CT — 10. mm: total length of cone taper from point D^4 to center of cone taper tip CT

FACING CURVE MEASUREMENTS

.000 of an inch	½ millimeters
.0015	32
.002	30
.004	28
.008	22
.010	20 plus
.012	20
.020	13
tip	106 plus (in 1/100 mm.)

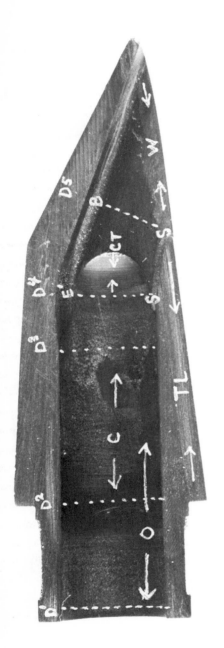

*[An interesting study of the clarinet mouthpiece has been made by Walter L. Wehner and published under the title of "The Effect of Interior Shape and Size of Clarinet Mouthpieces on Intonation and Tone Quality." Journal of Research in Music Education Volume XI, No. 2, Fall 1963. While the results of this investigation supply no new facts concerning the design or construction of mouthpieces they do prove the relationship of the several factors involved and support the necessity for a balance of acoustical factors for maximum efficiency.]

The tone-generating system of an air column instrument supplies the partial structure of the tone which is to be produced. No partial note introduced to the instrument by the tone-generating system alone can be produced in the tone of the instrument. The resonant cavity of the instrument acts as a selective band filter for the partials present in the generated tone and permits by selectivity the partials which are to be the strongest in the tone. The resonant cavity is therefore the control agent for the tonal character of the instrument but must of course have the partials as produced by the tone-generating system available for its selective action. Therefore, noise components of the tone generating system are excluded from the tone subsequently produced by the air column of the instrument.

It is thus seen that the conical pipe and the cylindrical pipe with their respective acoustical properties act as the tone quality determinant for the instrument. The tone generation system must provide the most complete partial structure possible for the most efficient results and must also have the capacity to sustain the production of this structure for the whole acoustical system of tone production to function for the time required to be usable as a means for music.

The resonant frequency of the pipe or air column is in fact the determinant for what is known as the formant of the tone. The changes in resonant frequency caused by the opening or closing of aperatures in the pipe including the nodal vibrational patterns due to provisions for initiating these modes, exert a constantly shifting effect. The tone-generating system must be stable and flexible enough to adapt to the requirements as caused by this situation.

The bore dimensions of an instrument of the same general characteristics may therefore be seen to effect a certain difference of pattern within the characteristic tolerances between the instruments which may be allowable. The tone-generating system will have to be designed to match or to accommodate these differences of characteristics.

Therefore, mouthpieces and reeds must match instruments in order to achieve the most efficient results. The energy of the player may be expended uselessly if the tolerances which are allowable are not realistically adjusted.

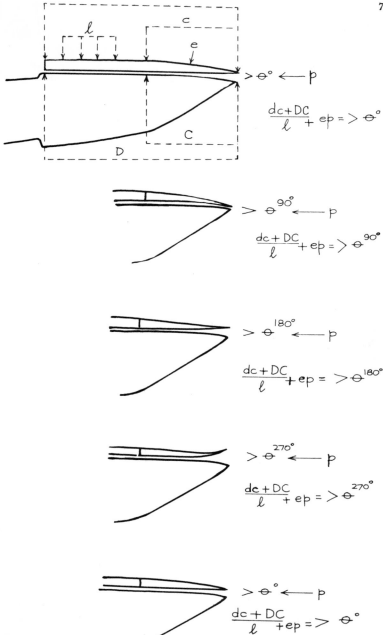

$$\frac{dc+DC}{\ell} + ep = > \theta°$$

$$\frac{dc+DC}{\ell} + ep = > \theta^{90°}$$

$$\frac{dc+DC}{\ell} + ep = > \theta^{180°}$$

$$\frac{dc+DC}{\ell} + ep = > \theta^{270°}$$

$$\frac{dc+DC}{\ell} + ep = > \theta°$$

Tests may be made of the resonant cavities of instruments and of the tone-generating system independently, and from the data obtained a matching characteristic may be evolved.

Calculation may be made according to Figure 1. The reed spring of a certain dimension 'd' with a contour 'c,' is coupled to the mouthpiece of dimension 'D' and contour 'C,' by means of the ligature which holds the reed at all points of contact equally, as 'l.'

The lip pressure or embouchure force is given as 'e' and the air or breath velocity as 'p.' Velocity of air particles are the vector $\theta°$ as the reed angle.

Therefore; $\dfrac{dc+DC}{1} = (ep) = \theta°$ at the instant the tone-

generating mechanism is initiated. As the cycle proceeds, air enters the aperture of the mouthpiece, and the reed is closed by the lowering of the air pressure due to increased velocity in the venturi or mouthpiece channel.

$$\text{and } \frac{dc+DC}{1} + (ep) = \theta° \; 90°$$

$$\text{Then: } \frac{dc+DC}{1} + (ep) = \theta \; 180° \text{ as the reed returns to}$$

normal rest position by its own elasticity potential which overcomes the displacement angle caused by the lowered air pressure in the venturi.

$$\text{Then: } \frac{dc+DC}{1} + (ep) = \theta \, 270° \text{ as the reed goes beyond}$$

the normal rest position and allows a greater air velocity to be gained. The cycle then returns to $\dfrac{dc+DC}{1} + (ep) = \theta°$, and is

repeated again and again.

The mechanical action of the reed with respect to this situation may therefore be described by the simple equation

$$\frac{dc+DC}{1} = (ep) = \pm \, \theta°$$

However, if any factor in this situation is varied, then all factors must then be varied according to the functions which each contains, as follows:

$$\text{if } \frac{d^2c + DC}{1} \text{ (ep) then } \frac{dc + DC}{1} \text{ (ep) }^2 = \pm\ \theta°$$

It is quite true that a complete theoretical description of the action of the reed could be developed from the formulas which have been established with respect to the longitudinal vibrations of bars. (see footnote)

For our present discussion however, we will continue with the simple and practical concepts required for the clarinetist to develop a perspective necessary to his understanding of the nature and action of his instrument.

Very simply, all that these equations say, is that if any factor in the tone-generating mechanism is varied that all factors must then be varied according to the functions which each contains, and that the function of the tone-generating mechanism as a whole will be varied according to the variables of its separate functions.

Now let us examine the physical situation of the problem: The reed is a wooden spring which is loaded by energy applied by embouchure pressure. In the accompanying diagram, the reed is represented by the line CB. The point of the commencement of the mouthpiece curvature, and therefore the reed spring action is denoted by the point A and the spring action as the distance AB. The point A is the point from which the reed begins its action as a spring across the gap formed by the curvature of the mouthpiece lay.

Figure 1

C——————————·——————————B

A

When force F, is applied to the reed spring AB, this spring is deflected toward the mouthpiece across the gap provided between the reed spring at rest and the curvature of the mouthpiece lay, BD. Point A acts as a fulcrum for the spring action

---

[1] A Textbook of Sound—A. Wood p. 140-144 "Longitudinal vibrations of Rods".

[2] Musical Engineering—H. Olson p. 75 section 4.6 and following.

and is known as the 'bridge' of the mouthpiece lay. It is the point from which the length of the curve of the lay is measured.

Figure 2

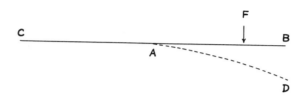

The further from B towards A that the force is applied as by F^1, F^2, F^3, F^4, the greater the force must be to deflect the reed spring the same distance BD. Also, the change in point A from A^1 to A^2, A^3, A^4, increases the force necessary for deflection. Therefore, either a change in position of F or A may increase the force required for the deflection BD. This is of course, provided that the curve from A to D remains constant. Therefore F and A are functions of BD.

Figure 3.

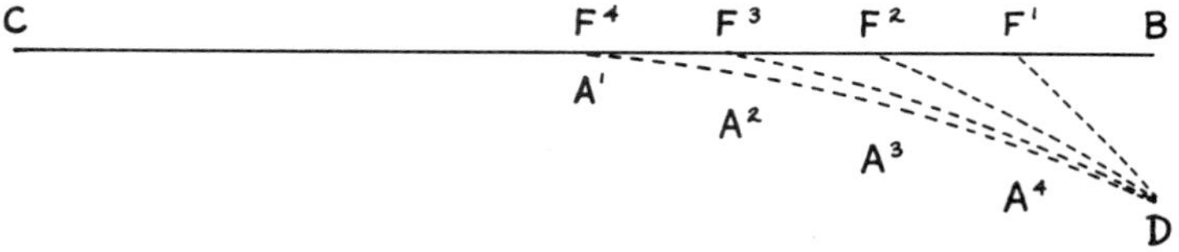

C F^4 F^3 F^2 F^1 B

A^1

A^2

A^3

A^4

D

If $\dfrac{F'}{A'} = BD$; $\displaystyle\int A^2, A^3, A^4 = \dfrac{F'}{A'}$

and $\displaystyle\int F^2, F^3, F^4 = \dfrac{A'}{F'}$ if $\dfrac{B}{D}$ is constant

If we now invert our diagram to show the position of the reed on the mouthpiece we have:

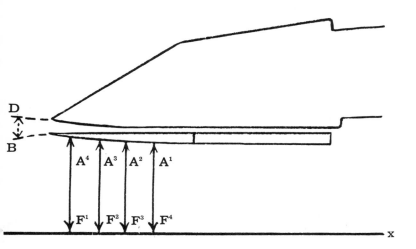

1. showing that increased pressure is needed when force is applied for points from F^1 to F^4 if A remains constant.
2. showing that increased force is necessary when A is moved from A^1 to A^4 if BD remains constant.
3. therefore F is increased by moving it along axis xy and F is increased by moving A along axis xy if Bd remains constant.

The effect of the pipe or tube of the clarinet on the reed as an anterior effect initiated as a reaction to the pulses as originated by the tone-generating mechanism, requires an adjustment to the pressure or F, and not a change in the placement of F or A.

Now in an actual situation of performance, BD does **NOT** remain constant due to the variation in the air pressure in the actual clarinet, since opening and closing apertures in the pipe cause many changes in the pattern of vibration. Nodal phases however, are caused by groupings of pitches, low, middle, lower second phase clarion, upper second phase clarion, and the altissimo or high register. These phases cause a change in reed action across the gap and BD becomes more or less, maximum or minimum. This is the change in the Bernoulli action that was mentioned before as now being under critical observation. Thus since, the gap does not stay the same—that is BD does not remain a constant, the same force cannot be applied for all pitches on the instrument. The amplitude of the reed movement across BD does change, but in broad relationship to the pitches produced. The frequency of the reed remains constant within phase shifts as a transducer for tone generation.

An excellent description of the matter in question has been supplied by Mr. Walter Vogt in an unpublished manuscript titled, "An Engineer's Look at the Clarinet". "The pressure of the 'bite' of the clarinetist increases or diminishes slightly and thereby changes minutely the point of contact of the reed against the curving lay of the mouthpiece. By this action of increased or diminished contact with the curved lay the effective length of the reed is shortened or lengthened. The change in pressure changes the aperture between the reed and the mouthpiece (or as we have noted, EB) and the playing frequency is thus increased by a small amount. This change in frequency is brought about by the resulting smaller reed opening and is not due to any change in the resonance frequency of the reed itself. This is the manner in which a clarinetist 'lips' a pitch up or down by a few vibrations.

"There is no question but that clarinetists do not move the reed in and out of the mouth in order to change the effective length of the reed. On the other hand, they maintain their embouchure position and increase or diminish the embouchure pressure as required."

"A reed is in a state of what is known as 'forced vibration', and if properly fitted to the mouthpiece, will, if held by the proper embouchure and blown with the proper breath pressure, vibrate. The tube of the mouthpiece acts as a closed pipe resonator and this length then dictates the pitch at which it will sound. The pitch of a mouthpiece and reed alone, is the result of the length of the mouthpiece and not on the method of embouchure or breath pressure, although to be sure these may be less than efficiently used and thus provide a situation which is distorted.

"However, with exactly the same embouchure and breath pressure, as used for the production of a sound with the mouth-piece alone, the mouthpiece when attached to the remainder of the tube of the clarinet will respond to the frequencies imposed by the added length of the instrument. This is further illustrated by the additional test of adding the speaker key to any pitch chosen from the fundamental register. The responsive frequency is chosen by the length and action of the tube of the instrument and not by any modification of the tone generating mechanism other than a use of it as the most efficient transducer of vibration possible".

"The clarinet tube almost instantly, probably in a matter of less than 1/50 to 1/100th of a second, rejects all frequencies that are not in tune with the resonating column and amplifies those that are in resonance. At this very instant of rejection, and therefore of attenuation of unwanted frequencies, aided by the lip tissue of the player, which acts as a damping medium, the fundamental and its associated odd numbered harmonics build up again almost instantly to the full sound level possible with the breath pressure supplied. It is the action of the breath pressure on the reed, and the reflected standing wave within the bore of the clarinet, that keeps the reed vibrating at the frequency corresponding to the length of the tube. The effective tube length is the distance from the tip of the mouthpiece to the nearest open tone-hole plus a minor end correction. The reed therefore dances to the tune called by the clarinet tube. In other words, it vibrates at the frequency required of it, and it uses only that portion of its length which is required to make its frequency match that of the standing wave". (end of quote)

Now the curve of the mouthpiece provides a space over which the reed can spring. The point of departure from a straight line from the table of the mouthpiece, which is flat, to the tip, is the point at which the leverage principle of the reed (the fulcrum) is calculated.

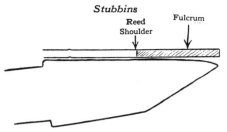

The reed is tapered since the mass of the reed body is such that it could not function otherwise on such a fulcrum.

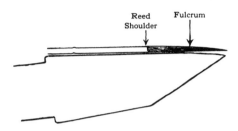

The relationship of the length of the fulcrum action is determined by the distance from the tip of the beginning of the curve of the facing. This length determines the amount of pressure necessary to bend the reed spring across the fulcrum to employ the leverage principle. The same pressure moves a greater mass with more leverage. Therefore, a longer lay or curve of facing accommodates a heavier reed with the same embouchure pressure. Also, a lighter reed, will require the same embouchure pressure if the fulcrum of the curve is moved nearer the tip of the mouthpiece.

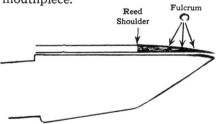

The next figure shows the mass of the reed to be moved, the fulcrum point and the pressure required for closing the gap at the tip in order to initiate the Bernoulli effect. If gap is greater, more pressure is needed—if the gap is smaller, less pressure is required. The relationships of these factors is shown.

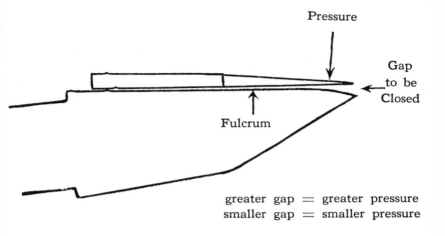

Pressure

Gap
to be
Closed

Fulcrum

greater gap = greater pressure
smaller gap = smaller pressure

p = pressure
f = fulcrum
m = mass
g = gap

$p = m + g$ f^1, f^2, f^3
$f = p + m$ g^1, g^2, g^3
$f = p + g$ m^1, m^2, m^3
$f = m + g$ p^1, p^2, p^3

1. Increase in pressure will be needed to close gap as mass to be moved increases by moving fulcrum towards tip. (shorter curve).
2. Increase in pressure will be needed as mass is increased with same fulcrum point. (heavier reed)
3. Increase in pressure will be needed as gap is increased with same mass and fulcrum point. (more open tip)
4. Decrease in pressure will be needed as mass to be moved is decreased by increased leverage obtained by moving fulcrum point further from the tip. (longer curve)
5. Decrease in pressure will be needed as mass is decreased with same fulcrum point. (lighter reed)
6. Decrease in pressure will be needed as gap is decreased with same mass and fulcrum. (closer tip)

The clarinet reed is a simple wooden spring. The proper function of this spring for its maximum efficiency is dependent on three primary dimensional characteristics. First, the uniform graduation of thickness on the horizontal and vertical axis of the spring-form which determines the contour of balance. Second, the maximum thickness and graduation of this contour from the beginning of the 'cut' or shoulder of the reed to the point where the reed is not touched by the lip of the player, which is the resistance contour. Third, the remainder of the reed from this point to the tip, the response contour, which includes the minimum thickness at the tip where the reed acts as a free agent in vibrating or 'beating' as set in this mode by the breath.

The proper graduation on the vertical and horizontal axis determine the balance or evenness of the reed and permits it to function as a spring evenly over its entire area with respect to the opening and closing of the aperture as provided by the curve of the mouthpiece.

The proper thickness of the contour of the reed from the shoulder to the point where the reed is not touched by the lip of the player provides the exact amount of resistance to embouchure pressure required by the player, and permits him to control the distance that the reed moves in opening and closing the aperture provided by the curve of the mouthpiece. We have already seen that this opening and closing is affected by the reactance of the air column in the body of the clarinet and that it does not stay as a constant due to the many variations of air pressure provided by the opening and closing of apertures in the tube. The resistance contour must be such that the player 'feels' comfortable in controlling the various pitches produced by the instrument in all registers. In other words, a good reed is one that will play all of the notes on the clarinet with a feeling of control. This feeling of control is engendered by the proper resistance contour of the reed. It must fit the mouthpiece—and it must fit the player. The final 'voicing' of a clarinet reed of pends on this very subtle adjustment—and also accounts for the great gain or loss in performance characteristics of reeds from day to day due to the changes which take place by the swelling or warping of the cane material. (See Chapter on Reed-making).

The contour of the reed from the point where it is not touched by the lip of the player to the tip and the maximum thinness of the tip, provides the exact amount of material weight or mass required to beat rapidly and evenly in the Bernoulli cycle as initiated by the breath of the player. Adequate mass is required for stability, but a minimum of mass is necessary for the most efficient result and a minimum of material fatigue of the cane.

The factors of the whole mechanical function are therefore:
overall dimensions of the reed

> length—l
> maximum thickness—t
> width—w
> taper of width—θ

contour dimensions

> flatness of the back of reed — f
> length of cut-shoulder to tip—h
> contour graduation for balance—b
> contour graduation for response—b

dimensions of the mouthpiece

> overall length
> length of windway slot
> width of windway slot (maximum and minimum
>> taper)
> flatness of table
> length of curve
> maximum opening at tip
> width, and taper of side-rails
> width of tip rail.
> Interior dimensions:
>> length and taper of chamber
>> length and width of windway
>> contour of baffle
>> shape of venturi opening from windway to
>>> chamber (which is determined by the three
>>> previous dimensions)

material variations of cane or cane factor (material of reed)

> density of material
> inherent elasticity
> porosity
> distribution and size of longitudinal rays

With a given set of measurements it is possible to develop an equation which will represent the situation:

Mouthpiece constant as C which includes interior and fac-

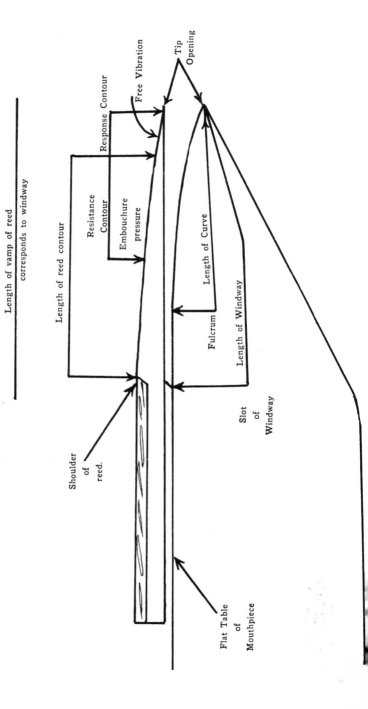

Length of vamp of reed
corresponds to windway

Length of reed contour

Response Contour

Free Vibration

Tip Opening

Resistance Contour

Embouchure pressure

Length of Curve

Fulcrum

Length of Windway

Slot of Windway

Shoulder of reed.

Flat Table of Mouthpiece

ing measurements to fit any particular instrument.
Pressure of embouchure with limits x and y which may
be considered as x being too light (permits loss on control)
and y being too tight (over-control) with respect to tone
production as P. Thus P is as x is to y or P (x)

$$\overline{y}$$

Balance contour is even or uneven with respect to the
mouthpiece, therefore it is a factor of it as B C.
Length of curve of the mouthpiece 1, requires more pressure P, if longer-maximal length lm or less pressure if
length is shorter 1-m, 1-m^1, 1-m^2 etc.
Steepness of curve of facing requires more pressure is
more pronounced, less if less pronounced. Normal curve
as N, more pronounced curve N^1, N^2, N^3, etc. N will of
course yield tip opening measurement as included in curve
plot.
Breath pressure (intensity) requires certain degree to
initiate Bernoulli reaction in reed—less breath pressure
required for less mass at tip, more for greater mass—thus
tip t varies as to BP (breath pressure) as t^1, t^2, t^3, etc.

Any given mouthpiece with an established measurement of
the relation of the balance contour of the reed requires a certain
embouchure pressure depending on the curve of the mouthpiece facing, in terms of the normal facing curve measurements
previously provided. The breath pressure will of necessity be
required to adapt to the requirements of the tip of the reed
with respect to the mass to be moved in order to initiate the
Bernouille action.

A simple equation shows this quite readily as follows:

$$C(BC) = \frac{P}{N} (BP)$$

where P is $\dfrac{x}{y}$ (1^1, 1^2, 1^3 etc.)

and N is (n^1, n^2, n^3 etc.)
and BP is t (t^1, t^2, t^3 etc.)

We can find the following effects:

1. The lip pressure must be increased as the thickness of the resistance contour section of the reed approaches the maximum.
2. The resistance contour of the reed is varied from maximum to minimum in direct relation to the length of the curve and the rapidity of the increase of its steepness.
3. The length of the curve and the steepness may be varied to affect the resistance contour—a longer curve requires a longer resistance contour and a shorter curve requires a shorter resistance contour. A steeper curve requires a more minimal resistance contour and a more gentle or slowly increasing curve will require a more maximal resistance contour.
4. The thickness of the lip of the player, or the amount of it which is placed against the reed, will determine the length of the resistance contour—the strength of the lip pressure will determine the maximal or minimal graduation of the resistance contour as well as its length.
5. The thinness of the reed at its tip (mass) varies as to the delicacy of the presentation of the breath stream and the amount of aperture available at the tip opening. A strong lip pressure requiring a strong resistance contour with a long resistance contour due to a thick lip used on a long gentle curve may require a very light response contour (or thin tip) which will give a powerful sound rich in harmonics. Increasing the thickness of the tip or the response contour will dull the upper partials and vice-versa. This is essentially the theory of the so-called German style mouthpieceas an example of the theory.

The mouthpiece and reed have been designed to be used together as a unit of tone-generation. The ligature is devised to simply hold the reed in the mouthpiece in such a way, as to allow it to act efficiently. The proper way to assembly this tone-generating mechanism is to assemble it according to its design for accomplishing the purpose for which it is intended. This is very simple if the instructions are followed, whether or not the reed itself needs certain adjustments, which again must be made according to the needs of the mechanical system. If the proper assembly of the tone-generating mechanism is accomplished, the primary demands of the mechanics of the instrument will be satisfied and better results obtained than by assembly without proper calculation.

The windway of the average Boehm system soprano clarinet mouthpiece is approximately 32 millimeters in length. While this may vary slightly, it will be revealing for anyone who doubts this fact, to measure the length of all the clarinet mouthpieces to which he may have access. This is very simply accomplished by laying a millimeter rule across the facing of the mouthpiece and reading the measurement taken from the center of the tip-rail to square end of the windway opening at the lay of the mouthpiece. It will also be found that the length of the average clarinet reed vamp, or the cut part of the cane, will measure approximately 32 millimeters in length. This again may easily be accomplished by laying a millimeter rule on the vamp of the reed and reading the measurement from the center of the curved tip to the center of the vamp, where the bark of the reed begins.

These matching measurements are not accidental. They are measurements which have been generally adopted for the reason that this is the size reed length and the size windway which is needed for the dimensions of the instrument on which they are to be used. While very little has been said about this simple measurement matching, reed-maker and instrument makers all follow it, whether by calculation or by tradition. Curiously enough, if the acoustics of the clarinet are calculated carefully, it will also be found that these are the measurements which present themselves as the requirements for an efficient acoustical system. Whether the instrument makers and reed makers do what they do because of a result of trial and error, or whether by calculation of acoustical design, the answer checks out as the same.

If every clarinetist would undertake to make just one reed, it would be revealed to him just how important it is to have these measurements match. If the vamp of the reed is made shorter than the windway of the mouthpiece, the pitch of the instrument is raised and a change in tone-quality and tone-production is noted. If the vamp of the reed is made longer than the windway of the mouthpiece, the pitch of the instrument is lowered and a change in tone-quality and tone-production is noted. In the design of clarinets other than the Boehm system, certain modifications in mouthpiece and reed length are necessary, which further substantiates the need for exactitude in the matching measurements described. The German windway slot is longer, as is the vamp of the reed.

It should be noted that the reed is to be adjusted on a straight vertical axis and a straight horizontal axis. The tip of the reed should be adjusted in a manner so that when the reed is bent by the lip pressure that its tip will precisely meet the tip rail of the mouthpiece. Diagram shows the mechanics of this situation. Since the facing of the mouthpiece is curved to provide a distance between the flat back of the reed and the mouthpiece in order to provide a distance for the reed to vibrate, the distance of this curve is greater than the distance of the flat portion of the reed which is held above it. The distance between two points A and B is a shorter distance than the distance between two points C and D because the shortest distance between any two points is that of a straight line. When the flat back of the reed is bent to conform to the curved surface of the mouthpiece, it will be found that if the observed length of the reed has been adjusted as if these two distances

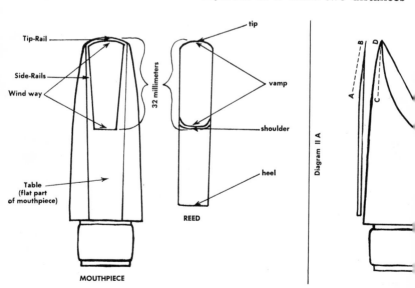

were equal, that the tip of the reed will fall inside the tip-rail of the mouthpiece when it is placed in playing position. Consequently, in order to have the flat length of the reed conform to the curved surface of the mouthpiece when it is in playing position it will be necessary to be certain that the reed is adjusted to accommodate this added length when it is observed in the rest position.

The flat portion of the mouthpiece, called the table, and the flat portion of the heel of the reed are intended to provide the mechanical seal of a flat surface against a flat surface. This is a sealing action which is strengthened by the moisturizing of the reed by saliva and if properly prepared is perfectly efficient. The ligature provides the constant, even pressure required to maintain this seal.

The flat table of the mouthpiece is of no consequence whatsoever to the mechanical action of the tone generation other than as a tool guide for the action of the reed across the gap at the tip. The table mus be flat in order not to affect the action of the curved portion of the mouthpiece lay adversely. It is in a sense, the support of the mouthpiece curve and must be mechanically perfect as a departure point for the measurement and the subsequent action quotient of the curve involved.

Likewise, the flat back of the reed acts as a support and constant base for the secure positioning of the reed and the provision of a spring base for the action of the spring portion of the reed from the shoulder to the tip.

There are no transverse vibrations of the reed throughout its length other than the several minute disturbances which run through the material along the rays of the reed from tip to butt end. These small disturbances must be damped as much as possible in order to maintain the seal of the reed against the flat portion of the mouthpiece and in no case contribute to the tone generation possibilities which are only concerned with the vibration of the reed across the gap between its flat surface and the curved portion of the mouthpiece. This has been shown in the discussion of the mechanical and acoustical action of the reed as previously described. In fact, this is precisely the major function of the ligature. A properly adjusted ligature must hold the reed without allowing the portion of it which is against the mouthpiece to vibrate at all. Theories which advance the idea that a reed should be held loosely against the mouthpiece in order to allow it to vibrate more freely are obviously working in the directly opposite manner required by the mechanics of the situation. A vibrating medium must be held firmly at its base in order to assure maximum efficiency of its vibrating portion. A loosely held vibrator is an inefficient vibrator. An easy comparison to understand is the use of an electric drill, or sander, or any other tool which is designed to abrade a material. A loosely held bit in a drill, a loose sanding disc, an insecure grip on a hammer for example —all provide inefficient loss of tool effect. No spring is a spring unless it is under tension, and less tension is readily achieved by less firmness in the support.

On the other hand, a vibrating medium must be held as firmly as possible without distorting its action. This is the reason for the possible misunderstanding of the ligature action on the reed. A too tightly adjusted ligature deforms and distorts the shape of the vibrating medium, the reed, and consequently distorts its vibrating action. A too loosely adjusted reed permits a loss of efficiency because of lack of support for the vibrating medium.

The portion of the reed from the shoulder to the butt, that portion covered by the bark of the reed, acts only as a handle for the support of the vamp or shaved portion of the reed. As the flat portion of the mouthpiece or table acts as a support for the action of the curve of the mouthpiece, so does the flat bark covered portion of the reed act as a support for the action of the vamp of the reed. The two supporting factors are bound together by the action of the ligature, which must be absolutely secure, but without a pressure which will distort or interfere with the vibrating action desired.

The ligature, since it is merely a mechanical device to hold the reed in position on the mouthpiece, must accomplish its purpose without impairing the efficiency of the situation. The ligature should be placed just below the vamp of the reed in order to allow the reed to act mechanically as it should with respect to the length of the vamp of the reed and the length of the windway of the mouthpiece. It is a fallacy to suggest that the whole length of the reed vibrates, and that it consequently should be held loosely on the lay of the mouthpiece in order to achieve this total vibration. The only portion of the reed which actually vibrates in order to initiate the pulses necessary to act as a sound generator on the air column of the clarinet, is the portion which is freely positioned above the curved portion of the mouthpiece facing. The remainder of the reed, especially that part below the vamp, or the part covered by the bark, does not vibrate. The care with which the flat part or table of the mouthpiece is constructed and the concern with making a reed with a perfectly flat back in order to achieve a perfect seal between the reed and the mouthpiece lay, is an absolute necessity.

Refacing of a mouthpiece is generally concerned with remaking the table into a perfectly flat surface. When this operation is accomplished, it may also be necessary to realign the curve since material has been removed from the mouthpiece, but the real correction is in the table and in its flatness rather than in the curve. If this simple fact is understood, a new concept of mouthpiece and reed mechanics is provided for the player and the problem does not seem so mysterious.

The lower portion of the clarinet reed acts only as a handle to support the vibrating part of the reed. Ligatures which claim the distinction of 'allowing the reed to vibrate more freely' are making a ridiculous statement with respect to the mechanics of sound production on the clarinet. A ligature is designed to hold the reed firmly on the mouthpiece lay, without distortion in such a way that it will act as a vibrating blade at its thin, shaped end.

It is for this reason that string is best used as a clarinet ligature. The great damping potential of the string acts as a perfect foil for any noise quotient of the reeds action which may be transferred along the reed fibers from the vibrating tip to the heel. The string also follows the curved contour of the bark portion of the reed in a completely perfect manner no matter what this contour may be. A string ligature, therefore, fits every reed perfectly. On the other hand, the metal ligature, in common use, cannot conform to the curvature of the bark of the reed in all cases and will only touch it in the high spots. If the metal ligature is tightened too much, it will simply distort the shape of the reed, to conform to the metal. This is the reason for using extreme caution in tightening the screws of a metal

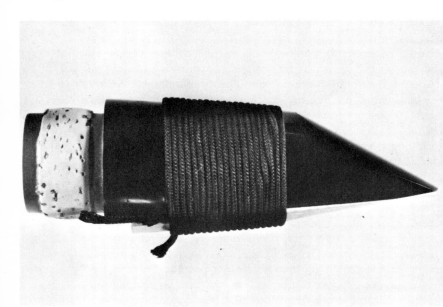

ligature. A pressure of over eighteen pounds can be easily developed by an easy turn of the metal ligature screws.

The string ligature is more difficult for the student to use, since it requires some skill and patience to learn the proper procedure of attaching the reed to the mouthpiece. The metal ligature has the decided disadvantage of being too easy to adjust —in the improper manner. If a metal ligature is used it should be very carefully adjusted according to the photograph which illustrates its proper use. The screws of the metal ligature are used OPPOSITE the reed for the simple reason that the reed is then positioned by a pull against it instead of a pressure on it. Furthermore, the pull applied by the screws of the ligature is more evenly distributed on the surface of the held portion of the reed since the metal ligature used in this way acts according to the mechanical principles of the clamp—which is exactly what it is. The reader may care to examine other mechanical uses of the clamp which will be found in numerous examples and on any appliance which he may care to observe. In every case the screw part of a clamp will be found to be on the opposite side of the clamping action itself.

When the metal ligature was first invented, it consisted of a double metal band, tightened by a single screw. The single screw was of course not placed against the reed but on the opposite side of the mouthpiece. Very few of these older ligatures may be seen today. Why the double ligature should have been reversed remains a mystery, for the action of the ligature as a mechanical device certainly has not undergone any change in principle from its original design.

A word about mouthpieces and reeds in general is in order here. Most players use a medium strength reed and a medium lay mouthpiece. There are a great many statements made, by a great many players to the contrary, but when their mouthpieces and reeds are measured it has been found that they have selected or adjusted for their own use, the same medium strength reed and mouthpiece situation which might have been anticipated. An application of the equations of balance previously developed will prove this beyond doubt to anyone who will take the time to do so.

This is not at all difficult to explain since the efficiency required of the clarinet as a musical instrument demands a certain similarity of tone-generating mechanism as well as a certain similiarity of physical actions required in playing it. With a musical instrument such as the clarinet, which requires a certain length and diameter tube required for the pitch and character of sound necessary, there are not too many variations in mechanics possible if it is desired to retain the results common to clarinet playing. So it is with the tone-generating mechanism and so it is with the physical actions of the human beings who play these instruments. Outside of a certain small range of tolerances, extreme modifications simply will not work, or if they seem to do so, will need a wide compensation in other respects. Such compensation will change the very nature and character of the instrument under question. An oboe will not sound like a clarinet, a clarinet should not sound like a flute In fact it is possible to interchange the tone-generating mechanisms on the several wind instruments and excite their respective air-columns into sound producing acoustical mechanisms. But when this is done, the instruments have changed their character and are not the instruments that they were before the experiment. The understanding and use of the acoustical mechanics of the situation should be directed towards achieving the utmost in efficiency in order to allow the performer to practice his art with the utmost freedom of expression.

CHAPTER VI

The Craft of Reed-making

The craft of clarinet reed making is a necessary accomplishment for every clarinetist.

The control of the tone production, intonation and general proficiency of performance on the instrument, is dependent on the mechanical situation provided by the construction, design, and maintainance factors involved.

The efficiency of the mechanics of the instrument is in turn dependent on the proper design and adjustment of the tone-generating system, provided by the reed and mouthpiece.

No clarinetist is any better player than his reed will allow him to be. Much of the practice time spent by students and accomplished performers as well, is spent, and should be spent, on the problem of voicing the instrument by means of the reed. If the reader is an accomplished performer, he will be the first to agree with this statement. If he is still a student, he will have already discovered the "reed problem", and will welcome any assistance offered.

The answer to the "reed problem", is to become competent in the craft of reed-making. If a clarinetist can make a reed, and has learned how to do so, and has actually accomplished this achievement, he will also have given himself the best possible training in the adjustment of commercial reeds, if he should choose to use them rather than to continue his own reed making techniques.

Here is given all of the necessary information to instruct in the basic craft of reed-making for the clarinet. There are no short-cuts, and no substitute for the work involved. There is, however, a definite method which is in accord with definite acoustical and mechanical facts.

Craftsmanship alone does not make an artist, but every artist must be a master craftsman in the control of his art. To what degree this control must function, depends on the degree of control demanded by the tools which the artist uses for the expression of his art. Certainly, the clarinet demands of every clarinetist the control of the 'voice' of his instrument, the reed.

REED CANE, THE RAW MATERIAL FOR REED-MAKING

The material used for the making of woodwind reeds is a variety of cane. There are over 600 varieties of this plant which grow in all parts of the world, but of these, only one, the Arundo Donax, has proven ideally suitable for woodwind reeds. Other varieties, of which bamboo is one, and sugar-cane another, have fibers which are either too stiff and brittle, or too pliable. The Arundo Donax has fibers which are exceedingly elastic, and which may be brought to a thin edge without collapsing under the strain of the rapid vibrations which are imposed on them by the acoustics of tone-generation by a woodwind instrument.

The clarinet sound is produced by directing a stream of breath against the thin edge of the reed as it is held on the mouthpiece of the instrument, and controlled by the player's embouchure. The thin edge of the reed thus begins a vibrating action according to the laws of aerodynamics.

While it is possible to construct a vibrating 'reed' out of many different materials, no material has as yet been devised, which meets the critical requirements of the tone generation system of woodwind instruments as satisfactorily as the natural cane.

The culture of reed cane, while interesting, is of no particular value to the reed-maker other than as concerns his requirements for the selection of mature and well-seasoned cane.

Reed cane is harvested and then seasoned for about two years. During this period the fibers dry and shrink, and the pithy interior disappears. The bark of the cane also assumes its characteristic golden mottled color, and becomes hard and compact.

After the seasoning, the cane is roughly cut into lengths of about one foot, and graded as to diameter. The proper diameter of 'tubes', as these pieces are called, should be about 22 millimeters for clarinet reeds. The walls of the tubes should be not less than 5 millimeters in thickness.

The important tests for mature cane are as follows:

1. The cane bark should have a golden yellow color. It may be mottled, spotted, or streaked with darker areas, but the overall color must be that of a shade ranging from the color of a ripe pear to that of ripe wheat. Cane which has a greenish cast, may very well mature after awhile, but is not ready for reed-making. Cane which has grey spots, or an overall grayish hue, probably contains fibers which are too coarse for the best results.

2. Tube cane should be relatively straight. The fibers of the cane which lie under the surface are of the same contour as the bark. Much tube cane will need to be discarded if a selection on this basis is to be made. In fact, about seventy-five percent of the tube cane is actually unfit for the best reed making. The commercial reed-maker, it will be understood, cannot discard this quantity of raw material, and consequently processes most of it. While it is possible to shape a crooked piece of cane into a clarinet reed, even as it is possible to saw a straight board from a crooked tree trunk, the subsequent warping of the grain in both cases will determine the result. The reed cane will warp according to its natural growth pattern. If this is crooked, the resulting reed will be crooked . . . and out of balance. No amount of adjusting or fine workmanship can straighten the crooked fibers of the reed cane. This is the primary reason that commercially made reeds play so very differently after they have been wet for the first time. The handmade reed, on the other hand, has had the benefit of careful selection of material, and the subsequent wetting and drying as it is being worked by the various processes in reed-making, give it a stability in dimension that is otherwise quite unobtainable.

3. Wetting the end grain of a piece of cut cane will cause a glowing thin, orange-hued line to appear just beneath the bark and above the fibrous portion of the cane. This is a sure test of maturity.

4. Mature cane will have a slightly sweetish taste as compared to the rather bitter taste of immature cane. Mature cane

will also give off a ripe odor when wet, and immature cane will have a grassy odor by comparison.

5. Mature cane will resist the pressure of the thumb nail and will not mark as easily as immature cane.

6. Finally, when two tubes of mature cane are struck together, the resulting sound will be a musical tone, or ring. Immature cane will produce a hollow, dull sound by comparison.

7. It is possible to test the hardness of reed cane by means of the standard Rockwell hardness factor. This is done by testing the bark for penetration both by a small needle point, and by the resistance to a rounded ball-point. The reed maker will not of course, have access to a test of this nature, but he should be comforted to learn that after extensive testing according to the Rockwell factor, that mature cane has shown to be the most favorable when selected for the Rockwell test by using the ordinary tests otherwise described. The Rockwell test suggests that the ordinary tests are of sufficient value to enable to reed maker to be assured that they are reliable. The color of the cane has something, but not too much to do with the Rockwell test result, other than that the mature coloring shows it to be the most satisfactory. It has also been found that the hardest pieces of cane are generally from material which has a less mottled or colored bark.

8. Cane is infested with a small worm which gradually eats its way along the stalk under the bark and destroys the fibers. The eggs hatch into little maggots after a long period of incubation. The eggs are laid under the bark of the cane while as yet unharvested, and while the bark is soft. Even after the cane has been completely seasoned and sawn into tubes and sometimes even after the final process of manufacturing reeds, the little bugs may be eating away merrily. Oftimes when a tube of cane is split preparatory to making the reed blanks, it will be found to have been ruined by these little animals, and full of dusty little channels, with a little worm in each one. There is no remedy for this problem, but fortunately, sound cane is more frequent than that which has been ruined by the bugs. It should be understood that these little animals are in no way harmful to man, nor do they carry any disease. They are akin to the maggot found

in the heart of palms and considered a great delicacy by some native peoples, who toast them over a fire on a stick and then eat them. The little reed maggot is far too tiny to be used in this way, but he is completely harmless, and it should be added, a connoisseur in his diet. If he likes a piece of cane, it is generally a mature and excellent piece of wood . . . and this means that other pieces from the same batch will probably be good cane as well. In this sense he is also a sort of test for good cane, and pays his way as an indicator, annoying as he may be.

PREPARATION OF REED BLANKS

A tube of cane should be selected which has a relatively straight grain. The tube is to be split lengthwise into either three or four sections depending on its diameter, and the degree of arch in its circumference. For the clarinet reed, the diameter of the tube should be not less than twenty-two millimeters and the wall thickness not less than five millimeters. Slightly thinner walled tubes may be used occasionally by splitting the tube into three instead of four sections.

The tube should be marked on the end, by measuring with a millimeter rule, and sections divided according to the three or four split. For four sections, the width of the section must be not less than fifteen millimeters. For three sections, due to the thinner wall, the sections will be approimately twenty millimeters. If the tube is oval in shape rather than round, the best portion of the oval arch should be selected as the center of a section. The arch of the circumference is very important in measuring the sections to be split. The calculation for each section should be made in such a way, as to obtain the highest possible arch in the center of each section. If only one or two good sections appear to be possible, choose the split points accordingly. It should be obvious that almost no tube will provide four sections of equal arch.

After marking the split points, the tube should be placed upright and a wedge shaped knife blade laid across the chord of the split marking, as measured from one point to another, on the circumference of the tube. A slight tap on the back of the knife blade will split the tube lengthwise very easily. Never push the knife with the hand or try and shove the tube along the knife blade with one hand. The edges of the split cane section is very sharp; sharper than a knife, and one can cut his fingers very badly by being careless.

After the tubes have been split in sections, the lower portion of the fibers must be removed to make a flat back, or lay for the reed. This is most easily accomplished by placing an ordinary plane in a vise with the blade facing upwards. It should be adjusted for a medium fine cut, and the cane section passed over it to remove the excess material. The section is best shoved across the plane blade by means of a small dowel rod, or piece of wood, in order to avoid cut fingers. Remember that the edge of the cane section is sharp, and will be even sharper after some of the fibrous portion has been removed. For this reason it is advisable to turn the section on edge after several passes across the plane blade, and take these edges down squarely. After the section has been brought to about three, or a little more than three millimeters in thickness, it should be narrowed to at least thirteen millimeters by planing the edges as described. The sections should then be sawn into lengths of approximately sixty-eight millimeters with a fine toothed coping saw. The two ends may be finally squared by filing with a large flat file. Remember to file towards the center rather than towards the edges in order to avoid tearing the fibers.

Final dimensioning of these shorter sections by tapering the width from thirteen millimeters at one end, to eleven or eleven and one-half millimeters at the other, will yield the finished blank ready for curing and sanding. The tapering of the blank is best done by pulling across 320A sandpaper with a slight pressure at the end to be used as the butt of the reed. A choice should be made as to which end of the blank is to be the tip. If certain pieces of cane are found with a slightly thickened and whorled shape of cane fibers at one end, this indicates that the tube was cut at this point just above a knot or node. When these pieces of cane are worked into blanks using this end as noted, for the butt of a reed, such reeds will generally turn out to be of superior quality. These are very choice pieces of cane.

Tools for Reed-making

Necessary minimum requirements of tools for reed-making are shown in plate 1. In the following list items marked with an asterisk are useful but optional.

        six-inch Vernier calipers*
        six-inch millimeter rule—perferably transparent
        Exacto Knife no. 5ST or no. 2, with blade no. 25
        six-inch extra narrow pillar file   o cut
        six-inch round file   o cut
        six-inch needle file   o cut
        glass plaque 4x¼x½ inches
        glass plate 4x6 inches, preferably plate glass
        small block plane*
        reed-clipper
        Dutch scraping Rush or Equisetum*
        sandpaper, grade 320A and 600 A, carborundum, wet-
          or-dry

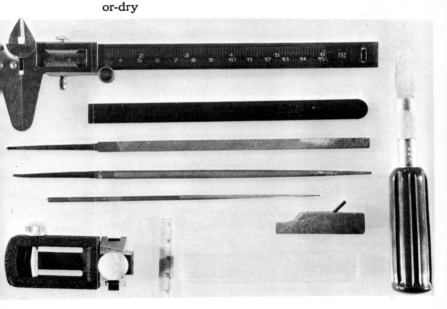

Tools for Reed Making

(Top to bottom center) Vernier Calipers; millimeter rule; 6″ extra narrow pillar file O cut; 6″ round file O cut; 6½″ needle file O cut; *(Lower, left to right)* Reed clipper; small millimeter rule; glass plaque 4x½x¼ inches; small block plane; Exacto no. 5ST knife with No. 25 blade.

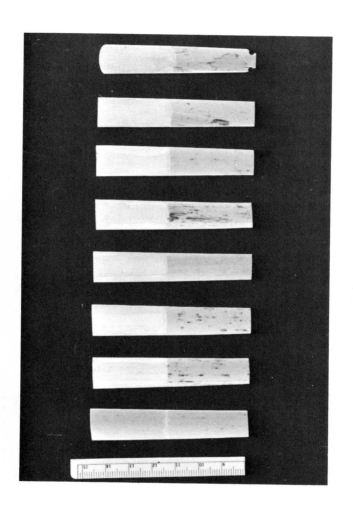

STEPS IN REED MAKING

(Steps in Reed making, left to right). Small millimeter rule; blank, carved, sized and scored; bark removed; first cut; second cut; third cut; side cuts;

CURING THE REED BLANK

The first step in preparing the reed blank for finishing, is to properly cure it. This is the process which it is impossible for the commercial reed-maker to accomplish.

The measurements of a good reed blank should be as follows before the curing process is begun:

over-all length	68 to 70 mm.
width at tip end	14 mm.
width at butt	12 mm.
thickness	3 mm. ±

It will be noted that the reed blank is tapered from a wider to a narrower end. The wider end is the tip, the narrower, the butt.

MEASURING THICKNESS OF REED BLANK

The blank should first be well wet with saliva, and laid flat side up on the large glass plate, and allowed to dry. It should then be wet again with saliva, laid against the glass on the flat side and allowed to dry. This process should be repeated three times.

After the three time wetting and drying, the reed should be wet with saliva again, and placed flat side against the glass, and this flat side observed through the glass. It will be easy to determine the flatness characteristics of the blank, since the wetness will touch the glass where the flat surface is flat, and there will be dry spots observable where the wet surface of the reed does not touch the glass. This test for flatness, will permit the maker to judge the further degree of preparation necessary, and to determine the general amount of sanding that will be required to attain a flat surface.

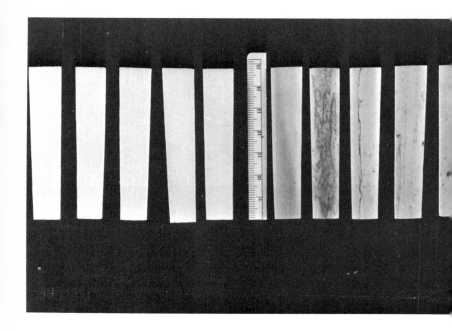

REED BLANKS CURING

(Left to right) Five Reed blanks drying with flat surface up; small millimeter rule; Five Reed blanks drying flat side down; these blanks are on large glass plate 4x6x¼ inches.

If the reed blank is badly warped, that is, if it touches the glass only in the middle, and is bowed up at both ends, or if it touches only at the ends, and is bowed in the middle, it may be that an additional wetting and drying, with a small weight placed on the reed blank, will correct this difficulty. If the blank seems to be badly warped after trying this technique, it is best to discard it, since the amount of sanding required will probably yield a reed blank too thin to properly make a good reed.

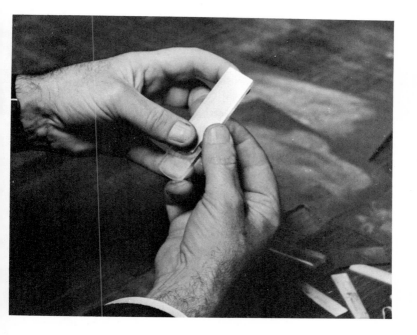

TESTING BLANK FOR FLATNESS

Testing the Reed Blank for flatness — Blank is wet with saliva and placed flat side against glass and then observed through the glass.

SANDING AND SIZING THE REED BLANK

After the blank has been cured, it is ready for the sanding of the flat side or the back of the reed. The sanding and sizing will bring the reed to the stage ready for the carving and finishing process.

The reed blank should be carefully measured once again and the thickness noted, especially at the midway point, which will be the approximate location of the shoulder of the reed. This thickness should be about three millimeters. A thicker blank will require more sanding, a thinner one less. If the blank is less than three millimeters, not enough material is present to allow for properly finishing the surface of the back of the blank.

If the measurements at this point are proper, the reed should be laid flat side down on the 320A sandpaper, and lightly rubbed back and forth with the grain of the cane, pressing evenly with the three middle fingers of the right hand.

After about six or eight strokes, the position of the blank should be reversed end for end. Be sure that the sandpaper is held flat by the spread fingers of the left hand. If the sandpaper is allowed to curl, the blank will be beveled off at the ends, and this will ruin it.

After several sets of strokes, and reversal strokes, the reed should be measured at the midway point again, with the calipers or with some other tool, such as a small piece of metal in which a two and eight tenths millimeter slot has been filed.

This sanding process should be continued with frequent measurements, until the blank is about 2.8 millimeters thick. The blank must also be measured for flatness of the back by the previously suggested wettness test.

Never sand the blank when it is wet. It must be allowed to dry each time after measurement, because the sanding of the cane while it is moist will clog the sandpaper, and cause uneven cutting of the reed. It may seem tedious to wait until the reed has dried after each testing, and for this reason it is best to work on several reed blanks at a time in rotation. While one is drying another can be worked.

After the reed blank has reached the proper thickness and

flatness, it should be sanded again on the 600A sandpaper to impart an extremely smooth surface finish. Finally, it should be rubbed to the same manner on a piece of ordinary newsprint. The newspaper will impart a very fine finish to the surface and will not remove any additional material.

At least a week should be allowed for the curing and sizing of the reed blank. It is well to prepare from six to eight blanks at a time by this process.

Sanding the flat back of the Blank — note position of fingers pressing on blank and left hand holding sand paper flat. Sanding is being done on large glass plate.

THE SCORING OF THE BLANK

The vamp or cut portion of the reed, must be made exactly

the same length as the windway of the mouthpiece on which it is to be used. The windway of the average clarinet mouthpiece is from 31 to 32 millimeters in length. The reed blank must be measured, in order that the shoulder of the finished reed will be placed at the exact distance from the tip of the reed, that corresponds to the square window cut of the windway in the mouthpiece.

Measure the length of the windway of the mouthpiece on which the reed is to be used, by laying a millimeter ruler over the mouthpiece windway, and measuring from the middle of the curved tip rail, to the edge of the square window in the table.

Lay the reed blank alongside the millimeter ruler on a flat surface, and make a light pencil mark across the bark of the blank at the length measured as the windway of the mouthpiece. Now increase this distance by exactly one millimeter and mark.

SCORING THE BLANK

The extra millimeter of length so measured will be removed later when the tip of the blank is finished, leaving the vamp of the reed the exact length of the mouthpiece windway.

Hold the reed blank in the left hand, supported by the forefinger and lay the knife blade across the bark of the cane at the pencil mark, at right angles to the blank. Carefully press the knife blade, and with a rocking motion, cut through the bark of the cane. Do not cut too deeply. This is the reason for holding the blank in the hand rather than supporting it on a hard surface and bearing down against it with too much pressure of the knife.

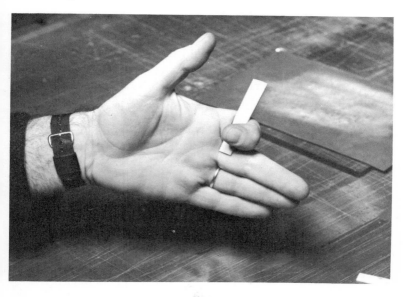

HAND POSITION FOR HOLDING THE REED BLANK

The reed blank should be held in the left hand, in the crook of the left forefinger, as formed when the forefinger is bent down to the edge of the palm. This position will be used for all of the reed cuts and carving. The reed held in this position, is pulled by the bending of the forefinger, against the knife blade, and is under control at all times.

POSITION AND USE OF THE KNIFE

The knife is held in the right hand, and guided by this hand. The reed blank, as held by the left hand, is pulled against the knife blade, as the left thumb shoves against the top edge of the knife. This enables the knife to be used as a plane blade, rather than by use as a whittling motion. The knife is held by the right hand, and pushed by the left thumb as the reed is pulled against the blade by the left forefinger. This technique will avoid any accidents with the sharp knife blade. If no pressure is applied with the right hand, the knife is under complete control at all times.

REMOVAL OF THE BARK FROM THE BLANK

The knife blade should be laid at an obtuse angle along the bark side of the reed blank, into the small nick made by the scoring. The knife blade must catch the edge of the bark where it has been scored.

With the knife in the proper position, the blade is pushed by the left thumb, and guided by the right hand, and a small sliver of the bark will be raised and removed from this shoulder point to the tip end of the blank. Do not try and remove more material than the bark alone, nor too wide a sliver at a time. By subsequent cuts of this same nature, the entire bark surface is to be removed from the shoulder of the reed to the tip.

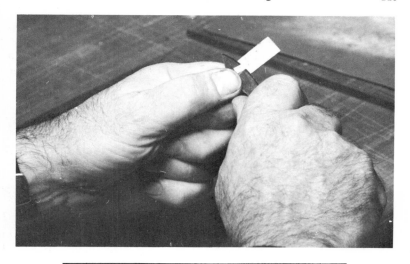

The First Cut

Beginning at the shoulder of the reed, and in the exact center, begin a cut with the knife about 4 millimeters wide and very shallow. Gradually increase the pressure on the knife by its angle, so that it cuts more deeply into the wood. As the distance from the beginning of the cut reaches about five millimeters from the shoulder, the depth of the cut should be approximately ½ millimeter, and the width about five milli-meters. Continue this even cut all the way to the tip.

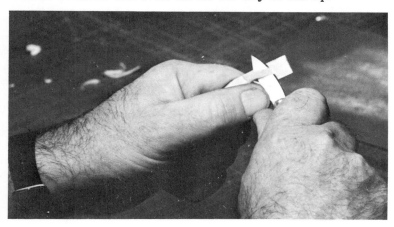

THE SECOND CUT

Measure off half of the distance between the shoulder of the reed and the tip, and lay the knife blade at this point with the hand position previously learned.

Begin a shallow cut, and increase the angle and pressure, until a cut approximately one millimeter in depth has been made. Continue this even cut to the tip until a chip of wood approximately one millimeter deep, and eight millimeters wide has been removed. This is the second cut.

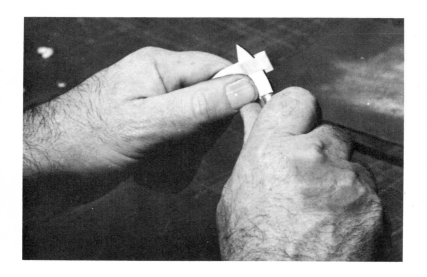

THE THIRD CUT

Measure off half the distance from the beginning of the second cut to the tip of the reed, and lay the knife blade across the reed in the same position as before.

Begin a shallow cut, and increase the pressure until a chip of wood approimately ten millimeters wide, and beveled from this point to the tip of the reed, has been removed. This is the third cut.

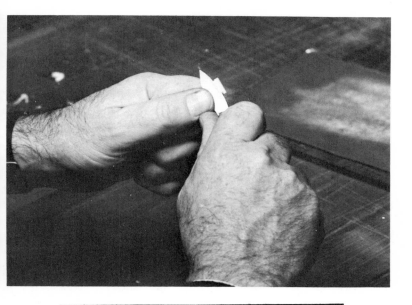

THE SIDE CUTS

Lay the knife blade at the outside right edge of the shoulder of the reed, and begin a shallow cut with the blade remaining at approximately a forty-five degree angle across the edge of the reed. This will remove the large chip of raised material, which is seen as a step-down pattern formed at the side of the reed by the previously accomplished cuts. Carry this side cut all the way to the tip, finally removing the little corner of remaining bark a the very tip. Do not cut too deeply at the extreme tip of the reed, but rather try and finish the cut at the tip with an outward motion of the blade, away from the corner of the reed, at about a forty-five degree angle, in a flat plane with the surface of the reed, and gauged with the center of the reed blank as a basic vertical axis.

Repeat this procedure for the left side of the reed. Bear in mind that the knife will now be at a reverse angle, with the point turned down rather than up, since it is necessary to reach across the reed as held in the left hand.

These are the side cuts.

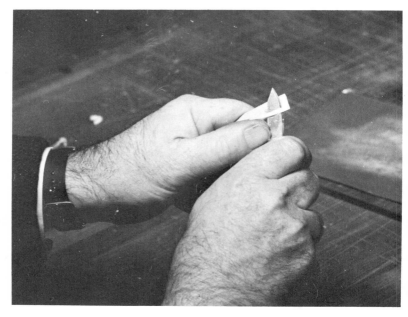

Completing the Side Cut

The Contour of the Reed

The contour of the reed is that of a leaf-spring. This contour must be carefully formed by the carving and filing operations. As these are being accomplished it is necessary to look at a rather concentrated light source through the reed in order to judge the amount of material that is being removed. Holding the reed just at the edge of the shade of an ordinary desk-lamp where the light source is shaded from the eyes except as it penetrates the reed is an ideal arrangement. Bear in mind that light transmission through wet cane is increased. The contour must be judged both when the reed is wet, and when it is dry. This is one very important reason for not attempting to finish a reed in one session of carving or filing. It is also very important to let the reed dry for at least one day, after all carving and filing have been completed, before voicing it finally.

The drawing in figure 1 shows the general shape of the contour as a leaf-spring both in the flat and as a profile. The several areas of contour are noted, which will be used as reference under 'voicing'.

In figure 2, the topography of the contour is shown as the average from measurements made from a large number of reeds. Such measurements of thickness are easily accomplished with an ordinary set of micrometer calipers. This will enable anyone interested in exactly measuring the contour, to duplicate these average measurements if he should so desire. Comparative measurements between different reeds may also be based on this average scale. These measurements are given in inches rather than in the metric system in order to conform to the thickness measurement in .000 of an inch.

While measurements are useful, and do disclose information which is accurately descriptive, such measurements are not usually made by the average reed-maker. Each piece of cane is of course, different, since cane is a product of nature and is not a uniform product. A reed may measure perfectly and not play well, and a reed may not measure perfectly, but may perform beautifully. This difference will be due to certain structural stresses and strengths which are not revealed by dimensional characteristics. These measurements therefore, represent a departure point for each reed, and for each reed-maker. It can be safely said however, that the contour measurements are consistent with the spring-form shape desired and that they provide an accurate and definite model.

The carving and filing operations, with frequent reference to the shape being developed by comparison with that of a good model reed, known to play well, will soon become, with practice, a matter of skill and judgement for the reed-maker.

Two prime considerations in the forming of the contour must be borne in mind. First, the contour must be balanced, which is simply to say that it must be even on both sides. Secondly, it is extremely important that there must always be more material in the center of the reed than on either side. If the central 'spine' of the reed is not retained during the preliminary carving and filing no amount of final voicing can replace it. Remember that material may be removed, but it cannot be replaced. The operations of carving and filing are subtractive operations. At this point in reed-making it is better to leave a little extra

Figure 1

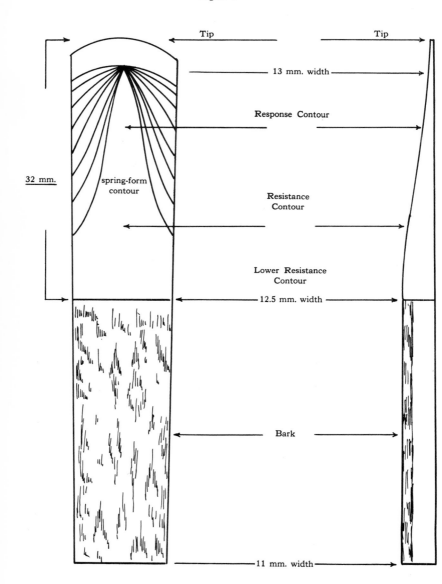

Figure 2*
Scale 1/8" = 1/32"

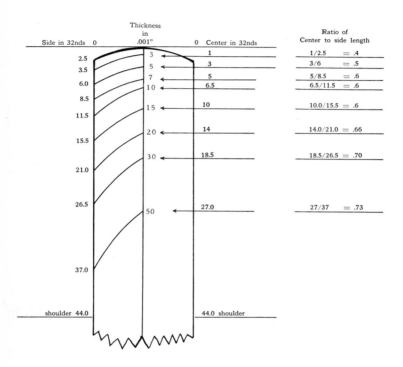

*From 'An Engineer's Look at The Clarinet' by Walter Vogt
(ms)

material to be removed later than to achieve any final dimensions.

Carving the Contour of the Vamp

After the first cuts have been made, the reed is ready for the carving of the contour.

This is accomplished by beginning the cuts about four milli-meters back from the tip of the reed towards the shoulder, and making successive small uniform chip cuts, from this point on back to the shoulder, until a uniform leaf shaped spring contour has been roughly formed.

These small cuts are accomplished with the same knife tech-nique as previously learned, but as each cut is completed, the knife is slightly rolled in the right hand, in a counter-clockwise motion, in such a manner as to finish each little cut with an up-ward sweeping motion. This prevents too deep a cut, and allows the feeling of shaping the contour, as if it were formed by peel-ing off layer after layer of the material.

Frequent examination of the reed as held up to a light, will guide the even removal of material. It is extremely important that an even amount of material is removed from each side of the reed, and that the leaf shape is as smoothly formed as possible.

The reed may be cut either wet or dry. Remember that light transmission through the cane is increased by wetness, and that judgement of the contour must be made on this basis.

The knife must not be used as a scraper, but must always be used as a cutter. The wood should be removed in small shavings, or curls, and not as dust-like scrapings. The files which will be used next, replace the old method of scraping a reed, with a scraping knife, after using the cutting knife.

The Use of the Files

Three files are used in making reeds. They are used to shape the contour, and to smooth the rougher cuts made by the carv-ing.

The extra narrow pillar file, is used after the carving has been completed. It blends the rough cuts, and brings the contour down to an approximation of its final shape. The pillar file is used at approximately an angle of 60 degrees with the vertical axis of the reed, and the cuts are begun at the shoulder, and carried along to the tip. The cuts must be made on both sides of the reed, and it will be found that the reverse cut for the left side of the reed, is the exact opposite angle from the cut made on the right side. However, care must be taken not to press too heavily on the right side, since the reed lays under the hand more conveniently in this position. A heavy stroke will also tear the cane fibers, and a number of light and easy strokes are more effective than several heavy, deep ones. It is possible to file with both a forward and backward motion of the pillar file, if the strokes are light enough.

The reed may be filed wet or dry. It is good practice to wet it somewhat, since the material will be removed faster this way with less pressure. Wetting the file itself is an easy and quite a natural technique, which will be developed. This will also help to clean the file, as it works on the material. It will be necessary to wipe off the collected material from the file occasionally. Short strokes may also be taken with the pillar file, and all rough spots on the reed vamp should be carefully worked out.

After the pillar file has been used to bring the contour to rough shape, the round file is used to shape it more accurately. This file enables the operator to more precisely remove material at the exact spot desired. A frequent inspection of the contour through the reed held to the light, will indicate the need for removing more or less material to achieve the contour.

The needle file is used in the same manner as the round file, but is even more of a precision instrument. This file is used to bring the reed tip flat, from about four millimeters from the tip to the end, and to finally shape the contour.

After some experimentation, it will be found that the three files may be used interchangeably as desired. Occasionally the pillar file may be used for a few flat strokes across the tip of the reed, even after it has been shaped by the needle file, and the needle file may be used at first filing, for the removal or shaping of some particularly rough spot, which needs careful attention.

All of these files are 0 cut, which means that their cut for material removal is exactly the same. The only difference is the size and shape of the file surface against the material. With this in mind, it will be readily understood that the variety of files is necessary, for the required flexibility of material removal.

THE PILLAR FILE

During the filing operation, it will be found most convenient
to support the reed on a small glass plaque about 4 inches long
and one-half inch wide, made of quarter inch plate glass. The
plaque is held in the left hand, with the left thumb pressed
against the butt of the reed, and holding it on the flat surface
of the glass. This position will enable the operator to reach both
sides of the reed with the file easily, since the reed will thus be
on a slightly raised surface. A small block of wood will also serve
the same purpose, but does not of course insure the perfectly

THE NEEDLEFILE

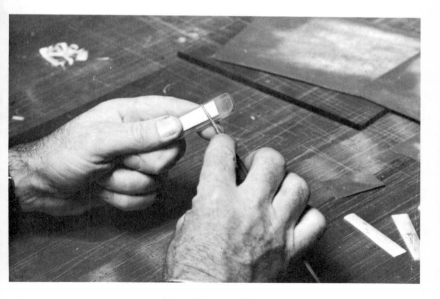

THE ROUND FILE

flat surface as does the glass. When the glass plaque is used, care should be taken not to touch the file to it beyond the reed, more than is necessary, since the file will more rapidly lose its cutting edge when worn in this manner.

NARROWING THE REED

The finished reed should be slightly narrower than the side rails of the mouthpiece, and should also be tapered towards the butt end, in such a manner that the ligature will not press against the outside edges of the reed, as it contacts the reed arch, and thus bend downwards, and spring the center of the reed away from the mouthpiece lay.

The narrowing of the reed and its taper is done by sanding the edges of the reed, at right angles to the sandpaper while it is held between the thumb and forefinger of the right hand. Always pull the reed on the sandpaper away from the tip. Never push the reed towards the tip end or it may be damaged. Slight pressure applied at the butt end as it is drawn along the sandpaper, will taper the butt to the required dimension.

A slight burr will be raised on each of the edges in this sanding process, and should be removed by laying the reed on the 600A sandpaper and lightly sanding the flat back again. A rotary motion for this sanding will be most effective.

The narrowing process should bring the reed to the following dimensions:

> tip end—13mm.
> shoulder—12.5mm.
> butt end—11mm.

FINISHING THE REED TIP

After the filing of the contour has been completed, and the reed narrowed, the tip of the reed must be clipped and shaped.

The reed should be placed in the reed-cutter, in such a manner that the cutter blade will clip the reed just below the two square corners of the reed blank tip. Care should be taken to align the reed on a perfectly straight vertical axis. Since the reed has been tapered in width, this must be allowed for in observing the adjustment. About 1 mm. of material should be removed from the tip end by the cutter. This should make the vamp of the reed the proper length, to match the mouthpiece windway. If the reed shoulder is slightly above the windway opening, the reed will tune sharp. If it is slightly below the windway, it will tune flat. This provides the possibility for an exact control of the reed in this respect. The tip may be cut or the shoulder extended to meet the needs as discovered.

NARROWING THE REED—SANDPAPER

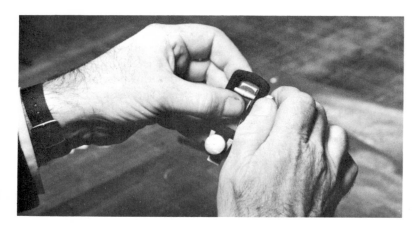

THE USE OF THE REED CUTTER

The tip of the reed may finally be shaped, to exactly conform to the tip rail of the mouthpiece, after the reed cutter has made the first cut, by carefully holding sandpaper at right angles to the tip and brushing towards the center of the reed. Never pull the sandpaper away from the center of the reed for it will tear the thin fibers.

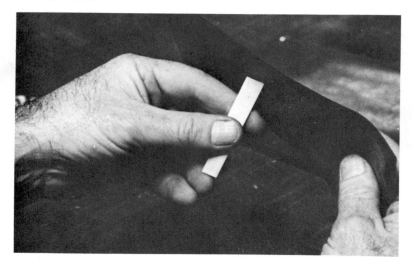

SHAPING THE REED TIP—SANDPAPER

Measurements of the Finished Reed

If the work done so far has been careful and accurate, the dimensions of the reed should be as follows:

width at tip	13 mm
width at shoulder	12.5 mm
width at butt	11 mm
overall length	68 mm
length of vamp	31 to 32 mm
thickness at shoulder	2.8 mm

Final Sanding and Polishing

After all adjustments have been made for the previous dimensions, the reed should be finally sanded and polished.

The reed should be placed flat side down on the 600A sandpaper, and a final light sanding accomplished as learned by the previous sanding operations. Be certain, however, in this final sanding, to hold the tip of the forefinger across the tip of the reed. Sand for about twelve back and forth strokes lightly, and about four or five rotary or grinding strokes.

The vamp of the reed should also be finally sanded. Cut a small oblong of the 600A sandpaper and cover the forefinger of the right hand and sand with the grain of the cane.

Follow this with a thorough rubbing of the reed with the forefinger alone.

The reed is then to be placed flat side down on an ordinary piece of newsprint, and vigorously rubbed with the sanding motion, back and forth until a high polish on the flat surface is developed. Do this when the reed is dry. A slight amount of carbon black from the newsprint will be deposited on the surface of the cane. This will not harm the reed, but will make an even finer surface. This is the only type of chemical deposit that will not affect the playing quality of the reed. Moisture saturation of the cane is not affected by the carbon black, but a stability is imparted to the cane fibers which is desirable. The vamp of the reed should also be polished in the same manner, with a small square of newsprint folded over the forefinger.

Finally, after the sanding and polishing has been completed, wet the reed well with saliva, lay it flat side down on the little glass plaque and rub with the forefinger from the shoulder to the tip until all of the moisture disappears.

The reed is now ready for testing.

SANDING THE VAMP

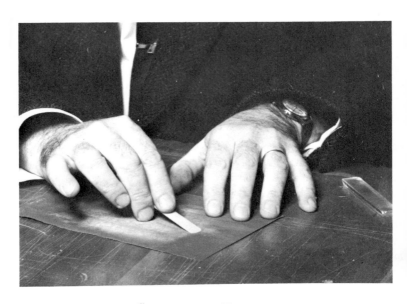

SHAPING THE TIP

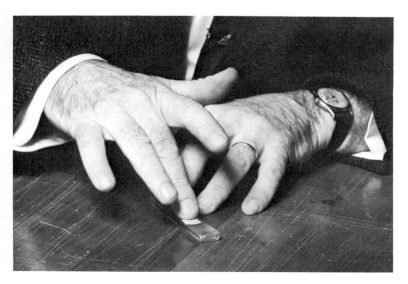

RUBBING THE REED

TESTING THE ELASTIC MODULUS

The Voicing of the Reed

The clarinet reed is a simple wooden spring. The proper function of this spring for its maximum efficiency is dependent on three primary dimensional characteristics. (See Figure 1).

First, the uniform graduation of thickness on the horizontal and vertical axiis of the spring form, which determines the contour of balance. This spring form is achieved by the carving and the filing of the reed to shape, according to the thickness pattern as seen by looking at a light through the reed, and by testing its elastic modulus with the finger as a gauge. A good reed must be basically in balance; that is, even on both sides. It must have a long smooth curve from the shoulder to the tip, as indicated by the profile contour. It must not have ridges, humps or sharp indentations.

Second, the maximum thickness and graduation of this long and evenly balanced spring form, from the beginning of the cut, or the shoulder of the reed, to the point where the reed is not touched by the players lip, but including the portion which is used as a contact area for the lip, is the resistance area or contour, and constitutes the spring strength of the reed. This is the strength felt by the player as the reed is pressed across the curve of the mouthpiece lay, to accomplish the required distance from the mouthpiece, to provide the 'spring-under-tension' edge which is set into motion by the breath. This motion of cyclic vibrational pattern of the reed is according to the Bernouille theorem of initiated motion of vibration, and is the basis for the tone-generating mechanism of the clarinet.

Third, the remainder of the reed from the point where the lip of the player does not touch, it to the tip. This is the response contour, and includes all of the tip area where the reed acts as a freely vibrating edge, across the gap of the mouthpiece formed by the curve of the lay.

The balance contour permits the reed to function as a spring on the mouthpiece. The resistance contour permits the player to sensitively control the distance that the reed moves in closing the aperture, provided by the curve of the mouthpiece lay, and the response contour provides the requisite thin edge of the proper weight and mass of material to support the vibrations, and to fit the pressure of air as supplied by the players breath.

To determine the position of these several contour areas, the player may test a reed after first smearing lip-stick on his lower lip. The lip-stick transfer on the reed will clearly show the approximate extent of the response and resistance contour areas. This test reed should be preserved for comparison when the voicing of future reeds is being accomplished. Bear in mind that different players, different mouthpieces and different facings of mouthpieces, will require new test reeds in order to act as guides for reed-making.

It is a well demonstrated acoustical fact that the opening and closing of the reed across the aperature between the reed and mouthpiece, is affected by the reactance of the air-column in the body of the instrument. This air-column does not remain constant, since it is of several different lengths according to the opening or closing of the several tone-hole apertures. If it were only necessary to play one tone on a tube of constant length, it would be an easy matter to adjust a proper reed, mouthpiece and player situation to accommodate it. However, it is necessary to play many tones, and to use many different lengths of the same tube as well as many different tone-hole aperture combinations. The resulting changes in air-pressure patterns within the tube, plus the several different lengths of air-mass involved, makes the accommodation of this situation by a single tone-generating system a very critical matter.

A good reed is easily described as one which will play all of the several tones on the instrument, with relative ease and control, and at the same time provide a characteristic tone-quality which may be used for expressive purposes in the art of music. Achieving this perfect situation is not possible, except by theoretical calculation. Achieving the closest approximation to it practically, is what is known as 'voicing' the reed. This is the final part of reed-making.

It would be very convenient if it were possible to provide a set of rules which would be infallible as to reed 'voicing'. This is utterly impossible, since each player, each mouthpiece and each instrument is different enough to make exceptions to such rules the usual rather than the unusual situation.

It is possible, however, to indicate certain general procedures which correspond to the acoustical mechanics of the situation. With practice and experience, a reed maker not only can correct difficulties, but can actually anticipate the results of his work. A good reed maker can begin and complete a reed, through the process from raw blank to finished reed, before ever testing it, and be almost certain that final 'voicing' and proper care in a short playing-in process will yield a good reed.

The following suggestions for procedure have been very carefully developed and prepared. While there is much that could be said in addition to this minimum of instruction, it is almost certain that any such addition would be directed to specific cases. Too much has been said and written about reed 'voicing' which does not prove to be true and basic to the situation. The student should use the present information as a departure point for his development of the reed 'voicing' technique. One final word. Remember, that while material may be removed from the reed, it cannot be replaced or added. Don't go too far—it is a one-way street!!

1. The balance contour as judged by the light pattern must be smooth and even. The profile contour must be smooth and even.

2. Thinning the tip area, or the response contour, will increase the brilliance of sound, and the response, until this area becomes too thin to support the vibrational stresses imposed upon it, and the air-pressure force as supplied by the breath of the player.

3. Thinning the resistance contour will increase the response, since this is the point at which the players embrochure feels the spring resistance of the reed. The response will be increased up to the point where this area becomes too thin to properly provide the desired spring tension as judged by the player's embrochure.

4. Thinning the resistance area of the reed below the point where the players lip comes into contact with the reed, or the part of the resistance area towards the shoulder of the reed, will darken the sound by providing a longer and more cushioned spring action effect. This effect will increase until a point is reached, where the reed is too thin to properly provide longitudinal support of the entire spring form length of the reed.

5. Thinning the sides of the reed below the tip area, or the

response contour, and from this point on back to the shoulder of the reed, but following the contour leaf pattern, will increase the response until the sides of the reed become too thin to support the structural vibrations of the center of the spring form.

Since the reed is to be used on a mouthpiece, the reed and mouthpiece become a unit for tone-generation, and the reed must be fitted perfectly to the mouthpiece for the most efficient results. 'Voicing' of a reed implies that it will be 'voiced', or adjusted, relative to the mouthpiece requirements. Since the mouthpiece is relatively stable in nature and is not changed whenever the reed is changed, and since the reed represents the replaceable portion of the tone generating system, the reed is the adjusted factor of the system.

No reed maker can make a perfect reed exclusive of the mouthpiece requirements, for the final end product of his labor is the use of the reed on an actual instrument, and mouthpiece.

While the embrochure and breath requirements of the player are added to the tone-generating system and must be accommodated, it is more important that the efficiency of the system be perfectly in order for the player to play, than for the player to hope to accommodate his needs by devising some mechanical adjustment to suit his physical needs. The player is more flexible and more able to adjust than is the system. This is obvious in any consideration of people related to things. For example: While chairs are made for people to sit upon, each person adapts himself to the chair in which he sits. The design of equipment must be reasonable and within a certain tolerance. A chair too high from the floor for most people ,even though it may accommodate a very few persons with extremely long legs, is not a well designed chair. On the other hand, even the person with very long legs, can and does, sit on the average chair. So it is with the musical instrument design with which we are provided. This design must be within a certain tolerance, and must be as perfectly efficient as possible. When the player is added to the situation, even though certain small modifications may be made to accommodate personal needs, the basic system retains its basic design of efficiency.

Prior to final 'voicing' of the reed and after all finishing has been completed, it is a good procedure to attach the reed to the mouthpiece, preferably with a string ligature, and permit it to form itself to the mouthpiece facing for the period of about twenty-four hours. If the reed is wet well with saliva and perfectly flattened by rubbing on the plaque with finger and then bound on the mouthpiece with the string ligature and permitted to dry, the adaptation of the reed to the mouthpiece will be ready for final testing and final 'voicing'. This is an old, old trick of reed making which is not at all practiced or known today. The reason for its not being used is simply that players do not know about the string ligature or appreciate its use.

STYLES OF REED MAKING

The French Style

The technique, general procedures, dimensions and style of reed-making which have been discussed here are according to the modified French style of playing, for use on the modified French style mouthpiece and the Boehm clarinet.

Fortunately, it is possible, within the scope of what is known broadly as the French style, to accommodate a variety and a wide range of performance requirements. This fact probably accounts for its general adoption in preference to other style of performance.

The measurements for the finished Bb soprano reed have been previously given. Measurements for the general dimensions of other clarinet reeds for this style are as follows:

Eb Soprano clarinet

overall length	60 mm
width at tip	12.1 mm
with at butt	10 mm
thickness at shoulder	2.2 mm
length of vamp	29 mm

Eb Alto clarinet

overall length	72 mm
width at tip	14 mm
width at butt	11.5 mm
thickness at shoulder	3.2 mm
length of vamp	37 mm

Bb Bass clarinet

    overall length ....80 mm

    width at tip ....18 mm

    width at butt ....14 mm

    thickness at shoulder ....3.3 mm

    length of vamp ....41 mm

The German Style Reed

The selection and preparation of the cane, forming and shaping of the blanks and general operational procedure is the same for the German style reed as it is with the French style. However, since the German style mouthpiece is of a different design, particularly as concerns the facing, it will be necessary to provide measurements to accommodate it. There is also some difference in the procedure of 'voicing' the reed, but as far as the theory discussed, the basic concepts remain as presented.

Since the German style reed is in general thicker, it is desirable to cut blanks from cane which has a wall thickness of at least 4 mm for the Bb soprano reed. While this will require more careful selection, at the same time, it will be found that a slightly larger tube diameter may be used, and this may aid the situation in the selection of otherwise wasted cane.

Measurements for the German style reed:

Soprano clarinet Bb and A

    overall length ....68-70 mm

    width at tip ....11.5 mm

    width at butt ....10 mm

    thickness at shoulder ....3.5 mm

    length of vamp ....35 mm

Eb Alto clarinet

    overall length ....72-74 mm

    width at tip ....12.5 mm

    width at butt ....12 mm

    thickness at shoulder ....4 mm

    length of vamp ....41 mm

Bb Bass clarinet

    overall length ....80-81 mm

    width at tip ....17 mm

    width at butt ....14 mm

thickness at shoulder ....4.5 mm

length of vamp ....45 mm

Eb and D soprano clarinet

overall length ....60 mm

width at tip ....12 mm

width at butt ....10 mm

thickness at shoulder ....3 mm

length of vamp ....33 mm

The German facing requires a reed which is heavier from the the shoulder to the area of the response contour. The tip is also somewhat heavier and flatter. The use of the file is a typically German technique and less carving is done with the knife. The same tools are used however, as in making the French style reed.

CHAPTER VII

The Acoustical Evolution
of the Clarinet

There is a great deal of discussion concerning the several 'schools' of clarinetistry. It is difficult to make dogmatic statements concerning areas such as the differences between the manner of playing instruments, which have developed in different countries, and by many different players, and their ideas and concepts of the proper sound of musical instruments, and the methods by which these are achieved. It is true that there are differences, and these should be noted, since there is some choice in instrumental design, and use of physical attributes of performance.

Differences can be found among string, brass and woodwind instruments, and players, to a varying degree. The resulting differences in tonal quality, and other characteristics, is not as great as it might seem to be, in the sense that the basic characteristics of the instrumental sound, and the performance is in each case sufficiently similar, that no one instrument is confused with another. The refinements of design are however, great enough to yield another dimension of musical variety, which is enough to make the interpretation of music and its appreciation, very important to those most directly concerned with this problem.

There are in fact, only two basic 'schools' of clarinetistry and of instrumental design, the French and the German. The acoustical evolution of the clarinet which follows is sufficient proof, objectively, to substantiate this statement.

The English, with a sort of desperate vanity, have attempted to refer to the art of clarinetistry in England, as a separate 'school'. There is absolutely no doubt but that the English clarinetists are to be accorded the honor of being among the finest and most accomplished exponents of the art. But to accord them recognition as a separate and original 'school' of playing, is to do them, as well as the clarinet, a disservice. English clarinetists play, and have always played, since the first introduction of the clarinet to the British Isles, according to the style of one or another of the basic 'schools', the French or the German.

English instruments, and English techniques can claim no single example of originality, although in the case of performance, the adopted, and developed excellence, is indeed unsurpassed, although certainly not unequalled.

The outstanding characteristic of English clarinetistry is its ubiquitous synthesization of the best of the original ideas and techniques devised elsewhere. This in itself, cannot but be admired, and if the English insist on a separate category of performance practice, then it may be said that perhaps the most successful synthesis of the two basic schools of clarinetistry, the French and the German, has been made by this group of generally excellent performers.

Of the Italian players, who again must be accorded no less stature than among the greatest, in terms of performance practice, there is actually no original 'school' to be discussed. The Italians have most generally followed the French in style and in instrument design.

Of the several other nationalisms concerned with the art, while there have been great players in every case, the two basic 'schools' of our designation have been the model.

As to the American 'school', there is not even a thought of claiming any such distinction of originality, even though the distortional dimension of 'jazz', if given a voice in this discussion, would probably be the only one to make such an assertion. For 'jazz', we can only pause for a moment at this point in our discussion of clarinetistry, to remark, that distortions of a basic art technique are not at all nationalistic. They are common to all of the arts, and can be found as examples throughout the history of man's creative activity.

In general, the serious exponents of clarinetistry in America follow the French 'school', with very few exceptions. However, here again, a synthesis of styles must be noted. Due to the indirect influence of three of the greatest clarinetists of all time, Joseph Schreurs, Clarence Warmelin and Gustave Langenus, the

Belgian style, which itself was a synthesis of the best aspects of the German and French ideas, was established in America, and has remained to this day, although not recognized under this name, as the finest achievement of clarinetistry in the history of performance in America.

Many performances and performers of music for the clarinet are eulogized, or condemned, almost simultaneously by persons who are sincere, and extremely sensitive in their tastes. Unfortunately, many of these persons do not understand that the differences in performance are not based on a judgment of 'good', or 'bad', but rather on differences in taste and effect. There is no possibility of performing the Brahms clarinet quintet on a German style clarinet, with a German style reed and mouthpiece, and sounding the same as performing the same composition on a French boehm clarinet, with a French style reed and mouthpiece. Therefore, the most gratifying musical performance of a German clarinetist, for example, when compared to a performance by a French clarinetist, must be evaluated in terms of an understanding of the very differences to which we refer. While we may prefer one to the other, we must appreciate the musical value, on a basis other than that of the instrumental style.

Therefore, it is important for those interested in the clarinet and clarinet playing, to be apprised of the different 'schools' of playing the instrument, and of the instrument design. A choice of performance will have to be made on the basis of taste. There is one exceedingly difficult obstacle to this accomplishment, which is easy to understand. In order to become expert enough to be able to make a choice between styles of playing is a herculean task, since the many years of performance practice required to master even one style, is the most that any one player usually experiences. After mastering one style, it is then not easy to even consider a change. Also, depending on where one finds oneself in the world, the teachers that are encountered, and the style of playing that is current during the developing years as a student, have such a deep and lasting effect, that it is quite probable that not only will one develop only one style of playing, but that he will be prejudiced against the others almost as a matter of course. A really great exponent of one or another style of playing, will almost certainly never change. A dilettante or amateur player, may experiment again and again. The really great player will not change his own style, but will be well informed enough to understand and to appreciate the great player of another style.

The evolution of the clarinet as an instrument ,with the attendant experimentation with its method of producing a musical tone, and its mechanical design, have been the contributive factors to the development of the styles of performance. From a brief consideration of this matter, it will be quite clear, that although the sound producing potentialities of the clarinet and its acoustical mechanics have remained as a base for its metamorphosis, the complexity of experimentation, and possimility of variety in the application of the acoustical mechanical principles, have not suffered from want of human ingenuity.

The 'invention' of the clarinet is credited to Johann Christopher Denner, a woodwind instrument maker of Nuremberg, Germany. Credit to this man is assigned by the historian J. G. Doppelmayr in his work *Historiche Nachricht der Nurnberghen Mathematicis und Kenstlern,* written in 1730, where he says, "At the beginning of the present century, he (Denner), invented a new sort of pipe, the so-called Clarinette, to the great satisfaction of music-lovers . . . and finally produced Chalumeaux in an improved form." It has been further established by other historians and musicologists, that the probable date of this invention was about the year 1690.

According to our best scholarly research, the Chalumeau was a rather vulgar single reed pipe which served as Denner's experimental instrument. Since it was apparently of cylindrical bore, and played with a single reed, no doubt the third partial as well as higher vibrational modes were evoked from it by players of that time. What J. C. Denner really did, must have been to obtain a kind of accidental result from the addition of two keys, to extend the limited range of this old instrument. These two keys, which were both at the top of the instrument, one for the forefinger, and one in back for the thumb, provided an extension of the instrument's range above the simple fundamental tone-hole range, by adding two pitches, which were A natural and B natural. The slight opening of one or another of these keys, which were both equidistant from the end, must have provided the sudden experience of facilitating the production of the third partial vibrational mode, and the clarinet was born.

One of Denner's sons, distinguished from him by historians as J. Denner, proceeded to improve on his father's work, and is responsible for moving the key for the thumb closer to the mouthpiece, and reducing it in size, so that it produced the pitch of Bb, instead of the B natural as before, in conjunction with the other key. This new placement was at the ventral segment of the throat partial, and was truly an acoustical refinement. J. Denner is also said to be responsible for adding a little tube of metal in the thumb key, or 'speaker' key hole, to keep moisture from collecting, and for providing a flared bell of larger dimensions, and also for reducing the size of the mouthpiece and reed.

Photograph I shows an original Denner clarinet in D, which is preserved in the Germanisches National museum in Nurnberg, Germany. The Denner clarinet is marked with the pine-tree trademark which shows clearly in the photo. This instrument is identified by Dr. J. H. Van der Meer, the director of the museum, as an instrument by Jacob Denner, the son of Johann Christoph Denner. This clarinet shows the placement of the register key, the more widely flared bell, and the more correct sizing for the mouthpiece and reed. In the author's opinion, this clarinet more truly represents the first clarinet, than would the more primitive instrument of the elder Denner, since it provides the first properly applied acoustical design necessary to the clarinet; which design was followed by succeeding makers, as basic to their work. This instrument is of boxwood, with a bore diameter of 14 mm at the barrel joint just below the mouthpiece; and also of 14 mm in the lower joint just before the bell flare begins. The length of the instrument is 54.4 cm. The finger holes are all elongated except for the next to the lowest, which is round. The two keys are of brass, with flat plates for covering the holes, and are mounted in the usual manner of these older instruments, by a brass pin holding the shoulder of the key in the raised wooden key mounting collar, carved as an integral portion of the body of the instrument.

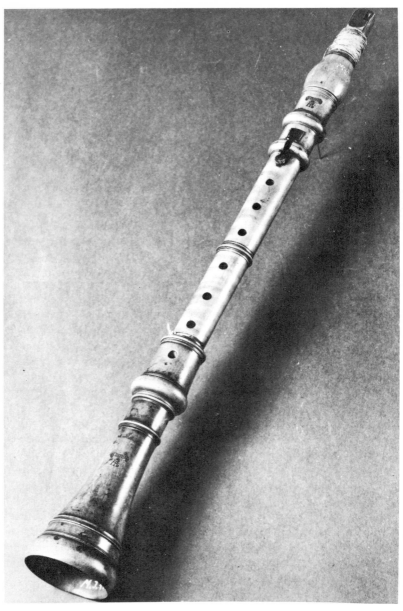

Plate I   CLARINET IN D—DENNER
GERMANISCHES NATIONALMUSEUM—NURNBERG

Photograph II shows a clarinet in D by J. G.. Zencker, also of boxwood, with a length of 54.2 cm., a bore of 14 mm just below the mouthpiece, and of 15 mm at the point just before the bell-flare. The tone-holes of this instrument are all round, except for the little finger-hole, which is bored obliquely, and thus is slightly elongated.

Photograph III is of a clarinet by D. Bauer, and is pitched in C. It has a length of 55.3 cm., with a bore of 14 mm. just below the mouthpiece, and of 14 mm at the point just before the bell-flare. All of the tone-holes are round, with the exception of the little finger holes, which are slightly elongated. This clarinet is of particular interest, since it clearly shows the plug used to stop the little finger hole not being used. These early clarinets like recorders, could be played with either hand on either joint. It was not until the third key was added, that the traditional hand-position of right hand for the lower joint, and left hand for the upper joint notes was established.

These primitive two-key clarinets were generally made in the several tonalities of D, C, and Bb. No two-keyed A clarinet has so far been discovered.

The next improvement on the key mechanism, was the addition of a long lever key for the left hand little finger, for the purpose of providing an 'accurate' B natural, at the lowest point of the third partial vibrational mode. This also extended the compass of the lower, or so called chalumeaux register, by one note.

Photographs IV and V show two three-keyed clarinets. the first in D, with a bore of 11.5 mm below the barrel joint, and 12 mm at the point just before the bell-flare. The length is 55.3 cm. The tone-holes are all round, except the little finger-hole, which is elongated. The second three-keyed clarinet is in high G or Ab, and has a length of 37.3 cm, with a bore of 11.5 mm just below the mouthpiece, and of 12 mm at the point just before the bell-flare. The tone-holes are all round, except the little finger-hole which is elongated.

All of the instruments in these five plates, are presented here through the courtesy of Dr. J. van der Meer of the Germanisches. Nationalmuseum in Nurnberg, Germany, and are probably the most interesting specimens of pre-Mozart clarinets which have been preserved.

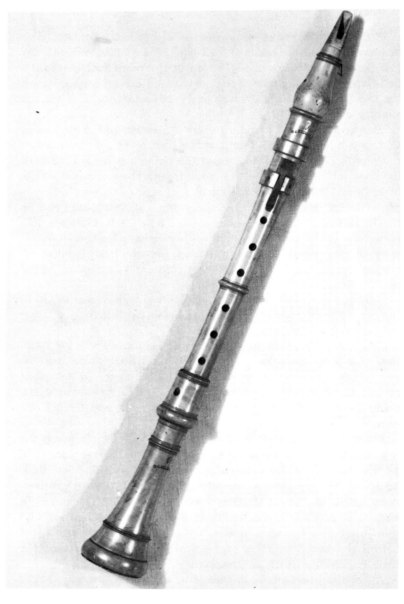

Plate II   CLARINET IN D—J. G. ZENCKER
GERMANISCHES NATIONALMUSEUM—NURNBERG

Plate III   CLARINET IN D—D. BAUER
GERMANISCHES NATIONALMUSEUM—NURNBERG

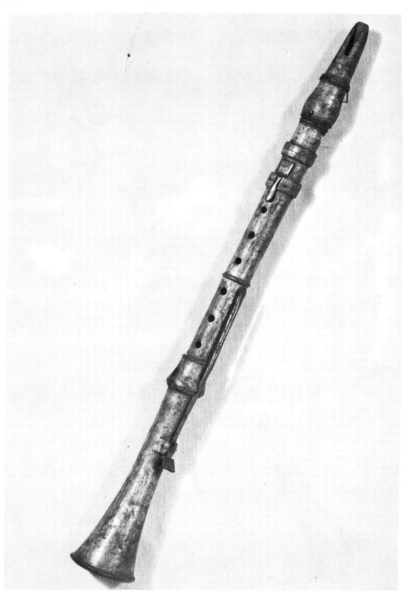

Plate IV   CLARINET IN D—THREE KEYS
GERMANISCHES NATIONALMUSEUM—NURNBERG

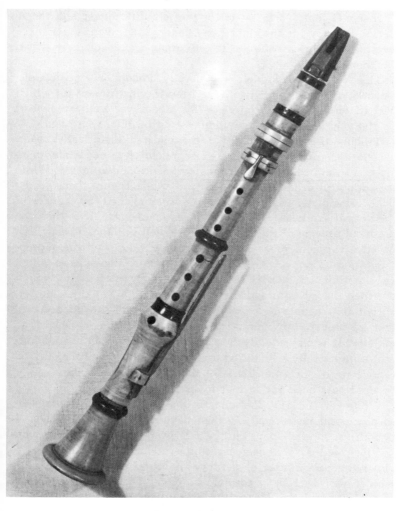

Plate V   CLARINET IN HIGH G OR (AB)—3 KEYS
GERMANISCHES NATIONALMUSEUM—NURNBERG

The addition of the third key is attributed to another of Denner's sons. The first example of an A clarinet is found in this three-keyed model.

The fourth and fifth keys to be added, were the keys for the F sharp, C sharp long levers for the left little finger and the A flat, E flat key for the right little finger. The invention of these keys is usually attributed to an organ-maker of Brunswick, Barthold Fritz.

This five-keyed model is generally known as the 'classic' clarinet, and is supposed to have been the instrument for which Mozart wrote his major works. This model was well established by the year 1770 and large numbers of this design survive.

Tracing the development of the clarinet historically, is an excellent example of the practical application of acoustical principles to the needs of musicians for musical instruments. While it is doubtful in the extreme that the application of these acoustical principles, was in any way accomplished by a careful theoretical analysis, it is nevertheless perfectly clear that the practical aspects of the situation were well in hand. Theory and practice supplement each other in many ways, and the supplementation of one by the other is of course, always true, when an experimental gain is represented. It does not matter much whether theory or practice is the first step. What does matter, is that they should agree, and that a good and true theory can, and is, proven by a practical application for evidence of its vadility. It is also equally true, that anything which is good and useful practically, should at the same time, be proven to be representative of a hard core of theoretical thought, which may be used as a basis for further investigation.

Whatever the old Chalumeaux may, or may not have been as a musical instrument, it must have been true that it was a cylindrical pipe of some kind, which was provided with a single beating reed as a tone-generating system. This situation provided the possibilities of a range of sound for the single pipe pierced with tone holes to yield all of the basic properties of an acoustical system of this nature, including the additional vibrational modes. The application of the two first keys on the Chalumeau to extend its compass upwards above the fingered tone holes, is an application of the mechanical and acoustical principles of the extension of a tone-hole system beyond the reach

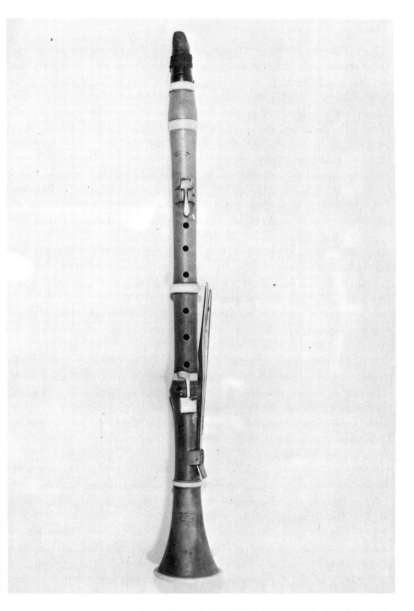

Plate VI CLASSIC FIVE KEY CLARINET. ENGLISH CIRCA 1770
STEARNS COLLECTION—UNIVERSITY OF MICHIGAN

of the fingers of the human hand alone. The discovery of the fact that there existed the secondary vibrational mode possibilities of the cylindrical pipe, as for the third partial, and possibly the fifth partial mode, undoubtedly took place before these keys were added. Primitive instruments very early in history made use of this principle, and certain primitive instruments represented in the ethnological studies of the art of music, have, and do use this possibility.

The discovery that the secondary vibrational modes could more easily be produced by slightly opening one or another of the first two keys of the Chalumeau, would be almost a certainty for the player of such an instrument to come upon as he performed his limited scale. If this be the 'invention' of the clarinet, then all credit should be given to Denner the elder for his contribution.

Much more significant however, was the moving of the key in back of this early instrument, to a position higher on the bore and closer to the mouthpiece, and the reduction of its size in order to achieve an easier and more complete activation of the third and fifth partial modes. The placing of this 'speaker' key, at a point of the ventral segment of the third partial mode, seems to be a very deliberate result either of fine experimentation or of extraordinary theoretical analysis of the action of air column vibration. Therefore, to J. Denner the son of J. C. Denner really belongs the credit for the first major acoustical advance for this type of instrument, and perhaps the first real clarinet in its own right.

The addition of a more widely-flared bell, a smaller mouthpiece and reed, and a refinement of the tone-hole placement are all acoustical developments, aimed at improving the intonation of the instrument, and its tonal emission.

The final addition of the long lever for the left little finger, and the coming to be of the three-keyed clarinet, is the next great step forward, because at this point, the final compass of the range of the clarinet was reached for the first time. This key not only provided for a tone which yielded the first note of the third partial mode accurately enough to fill in the gap between the last tone of the fundamental scale and the third partial vibrational mode, but also extended the range of the whole instrument down to its lowest tone, which has remained the same until the present. It is true of course, that additional keys have been added to extend the range downward. Stadler, the first player to perform the Concerto by Mozart is reported to have had such an early instrumental design. Many other efforts to extend the range downward have also been made, and the present day full-boehm model has the low E flat key as its lowest note. However, the range of the clarinet is generally considered to be placed at the limit provided by the third key of the three-keyed clarinet, which is low E natural, and this remains the accepted range of the clarinet today.

The three-keyed clarinet therefore, was really the first complete clarinet. The addition of the third key, also caused the position of the player's hands to be firmly established as they are presently used. Prior to the addition of this key, the lower joint of the clarinet was provided with a set of double holes, and a movable foot-joint, which permitted the player to use either hand for the tones of the lower joint simply by adjusting the position of the foot-joint to accommodate either the right or left little fingers. With the addition of the third key for the left little finger, this matter was solved once and for all and the clarinet assumed its present performance hand position.

Acoustical experiments for the improvement of the clarinet from this time on through the addition of the next two keys in order to achieve the classic model, or the five-keyed clarinet, were all devoted to the improvement of its tonal emission, and the efforts to produce a scale with more accurate intonation.

In fact, the addition of the sixth, the seventh and the eighth, ninth and tenth keys for the clarinet were all devoted to this effort to achieve better intonation and scale, rather than to make any basic acoustical change.

The next great step forward in clarinet performance practice and in acoustical achievement, came about when the players began the practice of controlling the reed with the lower rather than with the upper lip. The early clarinets were all played with the reed turned upwards and controlled with the upper lip.*

---

*An excellent resumé of discussion relevant to this matter is provided in the treatise, Clarinet Instructional Materials from 1732 to ca 1825 by Eugene Rousseau, State University of Iowa, Ph.D. 1962. pp. 123-130.

This position precluded any use of the tongue for articulation and the performance practice for the instrument was considered to be that of the human voice, with aspirations used instead of what are known as articulations in our present performance practice.

Long discussions as to the merit of both systems of performance, may be found in the early instruction books and methods of this period. The final triumph of the reed position controlled by the lower lip, and the possibilities of rapid articulation by stopping of the reed with the tongue acting as a valve, was the greatest single performance technique advancement of clarinet playing, since the establishment of the hand position by means of the addition of the third key. This technique was of course an acoustical application itself, which provided the instrument with the possibility of čontrolling the sound in a wholly new and flexible manner, which was utterly impossible prior to this time.

After the establishment of the clarinet embouchure as it is presently formed, with the reed controlled by the lower lip, numerous refinements and experiments were made by many players and makers, all devoted to the perfection of a better scale and tonal emission. The mechanics of the key action were improved, and the use of more stable and better materials for construction was explored.

Some of the examples of the workmanship of these instruments are shown in the accompanying photographs of specimens from the Stearns Collection at the University of Michigan.

Plate VII is a clarinet pitched in C by Willams, of Mons, Belgium. It has a bore of 13.2 mm. There are thirteen keys of brass, with key mountings of advanced design, comparable to that used on modern instruments, and consisting of pillars of brass or, as they are presently called, key-posts. This was a refinement which dates about the year 1840. The design of the C-F key for the little finger of the right hand, represents a particularly interesting feature of construction, since it is a platon of about the same size as one of the key cups, and of the same shape. It is mounted to act directly at a leverage point on the key arm, and is mounted below the key posts in this instance.

Plate VIII is of an instrument made of cocus wood with silver keys by an English maker. It had thirteen keys, one of which is

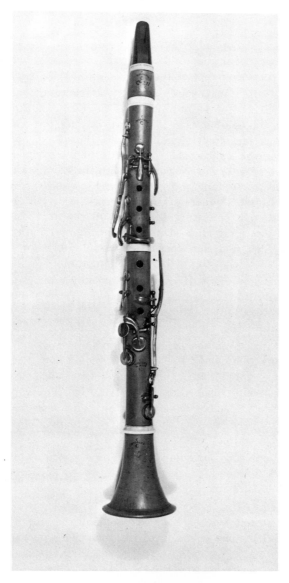

Plate VII   CLARINET IN C—WILLIAM OF MONS—13 KEYS
STEARNS COLLECTION, UNIVERSITY OF MICHIGAN

missing, and a bore of 13.9 mm. The design of the keys is very simple, with mountings of both knob and saddle, which is not unusual in instruments of this era.

Plate IX is of a German clarinet of boxwood, with thirteen keys and a bore of 14.2 mm. by Mollenhauer of Fulda, one of the better known makers. The grain of the box-wood in this specimen is particularly well defined. The keys are of brass, mounted in the knob style. The design of the register key, activated by a spatula in the rear, but with the key tone-hole on the top of the instrument and controlled by a curved ring-shaped key is not unique, but is unusual. This design was used to obviate the collection of moisture in the small register key hole, and has been used on clarinets of modern manufacture. It is an excellent idea and has been discarded largely for the reason that it is somewhat more difficult to make.

The next landmark in acoustical and mechanical design must undoubtedly be credited to the clarinetist Iwan Muller, who, in about 1808 initiated the several great changes in design and construction which truly changed the significance of the clarinet.

Muller was a pioneer in insisting on the acoustical placement of the tone holes, and the construction of key mechanism to cover them, rather than in placing the tone holes simply where the fingers could reach them. This truly brilliant application of a major acoustical principle of the air column instrument, was the basis for the monumental work of Theobald Boehm some quarter of a century later.

Muller correctly calculated the proper position of the tone holes, and designed the key mechanism to accommodate the fingers to this acoustical requirement.

He was responsible for the design of a new rounded key cup, and the stuffed leather pad, to supplant the use of a simple leather pad for the covering of the tone holes operated by the keys.

He also accomplished the first instance of alternate fingering 'for the long lever notes, by soldering additional branches on the F sharp-C sharp and the Aflat-Eflat keys, These branches were operated by the right thumb. This innovation gave impetus to the succeeding mechanical designs of every following craftsman, as the need and basic solution for a problem once indicated

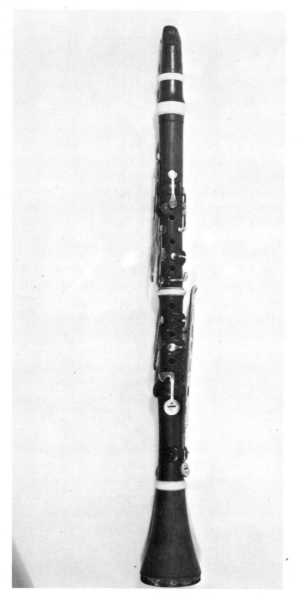

Plate VIII   13 KEY CLARINET—ENGLISH
         STEARNS COLLECTION—UNIVERSITY OF MICHIGAN

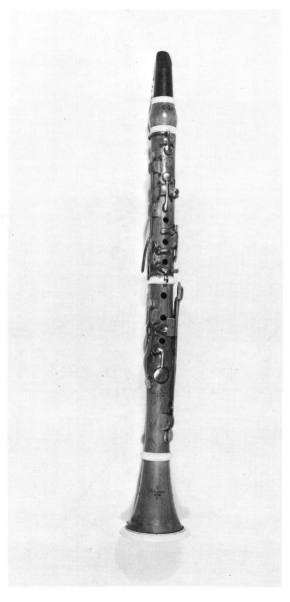

Plate **IX**   13 KEY CLARINET—GERMAN MOLLENHAUER, FULD/
STEARNS COLLECTION—UNIVERSITY OF MICHIGAN

has always accomplished. Muller deserves this as one of his greatest credits.

Muller also suffered the same rejections of his ideas which always seems to be a mark of success. In 1812 in Paris, a commission composed of musicians and players carefully considered Muller's new clarinet and rejected it on the grounds that it could play in all keys as Muller claimed! The Commission insisted that the tonalities achieved by the interchangeable pieces of the middle section of the instrument, which had until this time been used to change the pitch base, were in fact of great necessity to the subtlety of the art. As always, again, the myths of music were operating strongly in this adherence to tradition, and the members of the Commission were not of a mind to accept the idea that there was a possibility of alleviating a purely physical inconvenience, which had been necessary, due to the accommodation of the human hand to tone holes bored in the wrong place in the tube of the instrument. Consequently, they argued, and decided against the very design, which has subsequently become that of the clarinet today; a single instrument, which can play in all keys!

Muller was right of course, as is any man who follows the principles of natural physical laws in his experimentation, and his clarinet was enthusiastically accepted almost immediately following the rejection by the august and dignified "commission", by the very best players of the day, Frederic Beer, Gambaro and Hermstedt. In addition, the instrument makers immediately began a complete redesigning project of their work, and in short sequence we find the leading makers such as Bischoff in Darmstadt, Geisler in Amsterdam, Wunnenberg of Cologne and Schott of Mainz in addition to the great maker Simiot of Lyons, all who seized on, and proceeded to improve and perfect Muller's ideas.

That Muller initiated the most significant advance in design of the clarinet, cannot easily be disputed, since his new ideas can be traced through the entire development of subsequent systems, and key designs, of which there were a great number, and which persisted as the best development of the clarinet until the next significant landmark of the clarinet, the advent of the Boehm system in 1843.

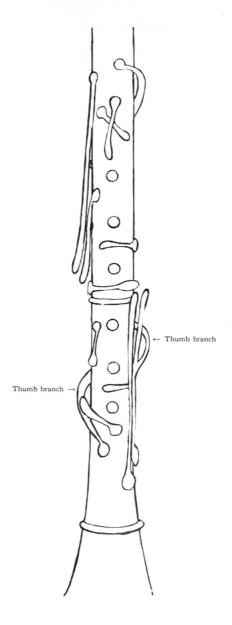

← Thumb branch

Thumb branch →

**THE IWAN MÜLLER THIRTEEN KEYED CLARINET
CIRCA 1812**

In this year, the clarinetist Klose, who had succeeded Berr as professor at the Paris Conservatoire, collaborated with the maker Auguste Buffet, in the application of the principles of the use of ring keys, as devised by Theobald Boehm. Boehm himself, had nothing to do with the Boehm clarinet, and he supplied no schemata or tone-hole design, or a key mechanism design for the clarinet. The ring key design however, had become such an integral and accepted part of his mechanical system, that when a name was assigned to the new system for the clarinet, it rather easily became the 'clarinette system boehm,' and as such has been known until the present.

Klose and Buffet started with two basic purposes, first to place the tone holes of the instrument where the laws of acoustics and not convenience of fingering demanded that they should be placed, and secondly, to contrive a mechanical key system which would serve the purpose of covering the necessary holes, and actually improve the facility of the fingering. Since both of these purposes are the avowed principles of Boehm himself in his treatise, "The Flute and Flute-Playing," it is not difficult to understand the use of his name for the clarinet design which was so successfully accomplished by the collaborators.

With the perfection of the Boehm clarinet, and the changes of bore, and mouthpiece and reed requirements which went along with this new acoustical precept, clarinet instrument-making, as well as playing, became split into two general schools, which are the only two that have persisted to the present, the French, and the German. The so-called English 'school', has never contributed any basic innovation to the clarinet, acoustical, mechanical, or style-wise, but has rather been a development which often claims, but can never prove it's originality. English players have been so generally excellent, that their accomplishments as musicians, have by far exceeded the skills of their craftsmen. It must be said in all fairness, that the English have loved and lavished their musical talents on the clarinet, second only perhaps to the French, but this love has been one of the art of music, its performance, and its composition. It is a pity perhaps, but nevertheless true, that the English mind is so creative artistically and so barren technically. But the saving grace has been the quick acceptance by the English of the obvious advantages of a good way of doing things. This basic rationality of temperment fostered Muller's contributions, and provided a strong impetus to the acceptance of these contributions at this stage of the clarinets evolution.

The Albert clarinet based on Muller's design for which the great E. J. Albert of Brussels was responsible, and the inventive design based on this system, of all of the German makers, culminating in the work of Oehler of Berlin, represents the one school, while the Boehm clarinet has conquered the rest of the world completely, including all of the Western hemisphere. The best makers of the Boehm clarinet have remained as always, in France, where Leblanc, Buffet, and Selmer, in this approximate order, have achieved the greatest renown.

Plate X shows a plain Albert system clarinet of grenadilla wood, with thirteen silver keys. The register key design, with the tone-hole on the top of the instrument, in its final stage of development, is clearly illustrated in this picture. The use of two rings on the lower joint shows the adoption of the acoustical principles of correct tone-hole placement, rather than simple finger holes.

Plate XI is one of the finest examples of the improved Albert, and is a picture of the clarinet used by the famous Belgian clarinetist Joseph Schreurs. This instrument was made by E. Albert of Brussels, and shows the refinement of the ring-key mechanism, the rollers for the keys for the little fingers, the register key on top and a separate key for both A and G# at the top of the upper joint. The springing action of the side-lever for the forefinger of the right hand, which activates the ring mechanism of the upper joint similar to the Clinton "system" one of the many examples of the copying skill of the English makers, is noted. The picture of this instrument appears here through the courtesy of Mr. Frank L. Kaspar of Ann Arbor, who for many years served as instrument repairman for Joseph Schreurs during his career with the Theodore Thomas Orchestra, which later became the Chicago Symphony Orchestra. The author also takes memorable pleasure in presenting a record of this clarinet, since Joseph Schreurs was the teacher of Clarence Warmelin, who in turn was the author's teacher.

Plate XII shows a full-Boehm clarinet made from a single piece of wood for the upper and lower joints, by the famous maker Buffet. This is the older full-boehm design, with the

Plate X   ALBERT (IMPROVED MULLER DESIGN) 13 KEYS
STEARNS COLLECTION—UNIVERSITY OF MICHIGAN

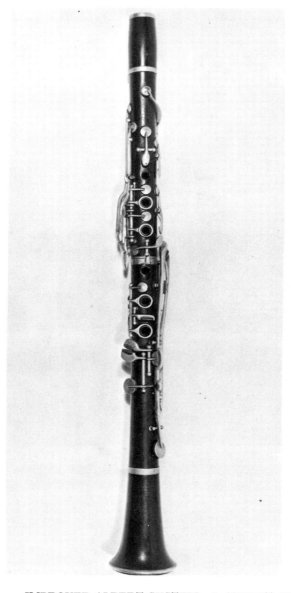

Plate XI   IMPROVED ALBERT SYSTEM. J. ALBERT, BRUSSELS
COURTESY OF FRANK L. KASPAR

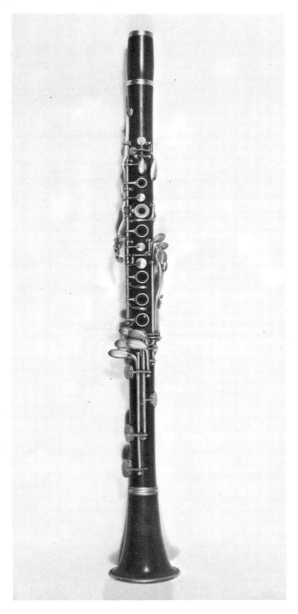

Plate XII   FULL BOEHM SYSTEM. BUFFET, PARIS
STEARNS COLLECTION—UNIVERSITY OF MICHIGAN

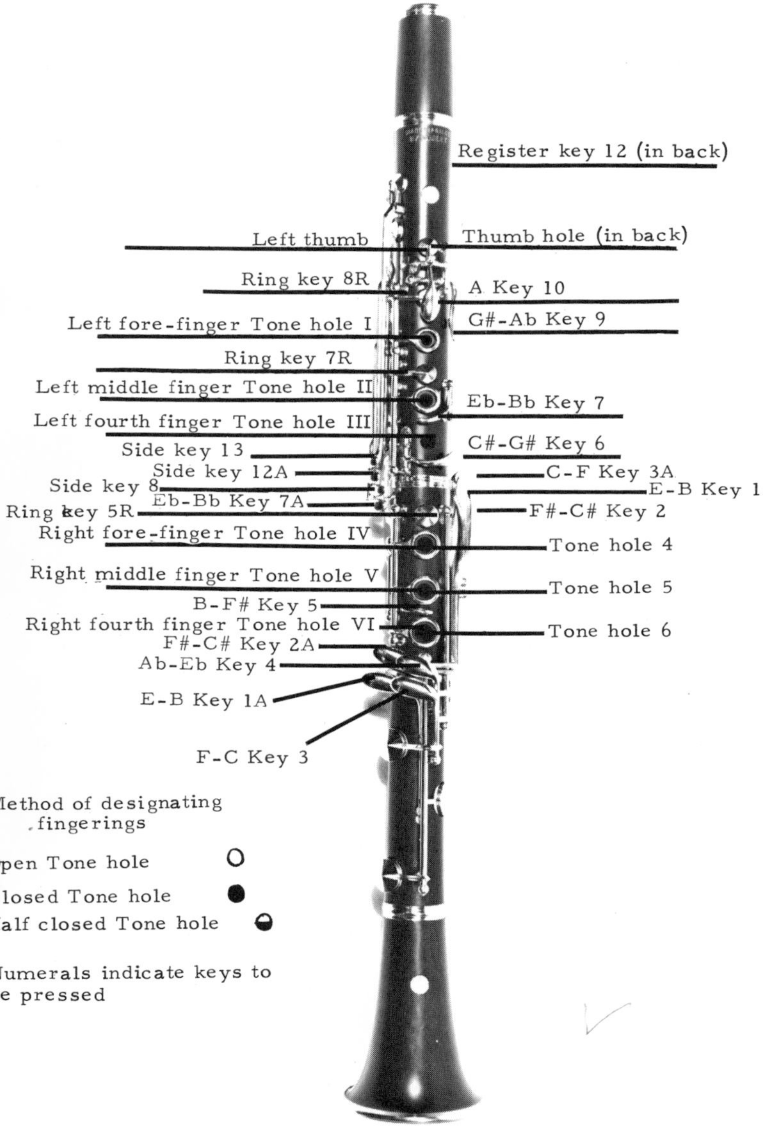

Register key 12 (in back)

Left thumb — Thumb hole (in back)

Ring key 8R — A Key 10

Left fore-finger Tone hole I — G#-Ab Key 9

Ring key 7R

Left middle finger Tone hole II — Eb-Bb Key 7

Left fourth finger Tone hole III

Side key 13 — C#-G# Key 6

Side key 12A — C-F Key 3A

Side key 8 — E-B Key 1

Ring key 5R — Eb-Bb Key 7A — F#-C# Key 2

Right fore-finger Tone hole IV — Tone hole 4

Right middle finger Tone hole V — Tone hole 5

B-F# Key 5 — Tone hole 6

Right fourth finger Tone hole VI

F#-C# Key 2A

Ab-Eb Key 4

E-B Key 1A

F-C Key 3

Method of designating
fingerings

Open Tone hole   O

Closed Tone hole   ●

Half closed Tone hole   ◑

Numerals indicate keys to
be pressed

Plate XIII   IMPROVED BOEHM. S-K CORRECTION STUBBINS MODE
NOBLET, FRANCE

"dough-nut" key for the forked Bb-Eb for the left hand. The additional low Eb-Bb key on the lower joint, the articulated G# and the extra-Eb-Ab key for the little finger of the left hand are clearly shown. As a mechanical system of fingering, the full-boehm represents the final development in mechanical dimensions of the boehm system.

There have been no significant contributions in the design of either the German, or the French or Boehm clarinet, until as recently as 1952. The acoustical correction for a more proper production of the third and fifth partial vibrational modes, and the final corrective design for the speaker key, have both been problems for all clarinet makers since the speaker key was moved up on the instrument, resized and fitted with a metal tube by J. Denner in about 1710. This new acoustical correction, invented in 1952, the S-K mechanism, has as yet only been applied to the Boehm clarinet but is perfectly adaptable to the German system as well. The Germans have long had elaborate mechanical devices for dividing the use of the speaker key as a tone hole as well as a speaker. The great maker Heckel, shows a patent device as early as 1902.

On page 132 of Woodwind Instruments and Their History by Anthony Baines published by W. W. Norton Co. 1957, an illustration of the S-K Mechanism is presented, and it is described on p. 135 as a German invention. This is a very grave error since the patent for this mechanism as illustrated, is the U. S. Patent number 2,508,550 filed August 5, 1948 and issued May 23, 1952. There is no German patent, or example of such workmanship. Since the Baines book was published (first edition) in 1957, and the U. S. Patent date is 1952, Baines was misinformed and did not give credit where it was due, to an American invention and an American Patent.

The acknowledgment of the speaker key and upper vibrational mode difficulty, has not been any secret from makers or players at any time in the history of the evolution of the clarinet, but the solutions to it, for the most part, consist of either unfortunate mechanical designs which do not function with the utmost reliability, or acoustical modifications which do not accomplish more than one half of the desired correction.

The S-K mechanism represents the completion of the Boehm design acoustically as far as possible, and will undoubtedly be a corporate part of the Boehm system as made from now on. It is not possible of course, to accomplish either mechanically or acoustically the complete results required from a single pipe which is used to play a wide range of frequencies, such as required by the design of the clarinet.

The problems of the speaker is mentioned by almost everyone who has written about the clarinet design. The solution of this matter is another landmark in the evolution of the clarinet.

As has been described in the section concerning the acoustics of the clarinet, the extension of its range by means of a speaker aperture to cause the second vibrational mode to act as a new series of fundamental tones, was the mechanical accomplishment which constituted the 'invention' of the instrument.

The S-K acoustical correction, finally allows for the separation of function of the speaker aperture, required to allow a proper use of it as a tone hole by the supplementary action of a resonance aperture, and at the same time to improve its use as a 'speaker'.

The solution of this basic difficulty of the instrument is fully described in the U. S. Patent paper, Number 2,508,550 issued on May 23, 1952, filed August 5, 1948. The accompanying illustration shows the mechanical action of the correction.

The theory involved is as follows. The effect of the speaker aperture is to provide a division of the fundamental air column in the clarinet, which causes the third partial to act as a new fundamental tone. This action of the air column is according to the principles of a vibrating air column enclosed in a cylindrical tube. Consequently, when this new vibrational mode is effected, the instrument sounds an octave plus a fifth, or a perfect twelfth, higher than the fundamental of the first vibrational mode of the whole pipe.

The requirement for a 'speaker' aperture to effect this division of the air column would ideally be at a slightly different placement, either higher or lower, on the pipe, and either slightly smaller or larger as necessary, for each tone produced by the pipe in the first vibrational mode. However, since such a mechanical arrangement to effect this would be unnecessarily complicated, and in fact, practically impossible, it is fortunate that within a small range of tolerance both as to size and placement, a speaker aperture placed near a point one third of the distance from the tone-generating system downwards on the pipe, acts for all tones of the second vibrational mode. It should be understood that the remaining vibrational modes are not, strictly speaking, ever used as fundamentals for a new vibrational mode, but are rather the upper partials of either the first or second vibrational modes, as the case may be, accomplished by a further complication in the vibrating pattern of the air column, but not directly actuated, as in the case of the second vibrational mode, by means of the speaker aperture.

The requirement as a size for the speaker aperture, has always been to initiate the second vibrational mode as a primary purpose. However, it was found, even on the first clarinets, that this speaker aperture, when used in conjunction with the first tone hole covered by a key, or what is now referred to as the A key for the left forefinger, produced a tone which was of the necessary pitch to fill in the gap between the last tone of the upper portion of the first vibrational mode, and the first tone of the second mode as actuated by the speaker aperture. The effect of using this first tone-hole key was, in fact, a use of a supplemental aperture to increase the effect of the small size of the speaker aperture, and to act as a resonance hole to free, and to lower the pitch which was produced by the speaker aperture alone. The speaker aperture, it had immediately been discovered, must be of such a small size, that it will allow the entire scale in the second vibrational mode to be produced, or it would be of little use, and therefore as a tone hole alone, unusable.

In order to demonstrate this phenomenon, it is only necessary to play one of the lower fundamental tones on the clarinet at the lower part of the scale of the first vibrational mode, such as the low E or F, and then to open the side trill key for Bb on the modern Boehm clarinet. It will be found that the emission of the twelfth, or second vibrational mode is perfectly easy, and in tune, by using this side trill key as a speaker. Testing the remaining scale of the second vibrational mode while using this same side trill key as a speaker will quickly prove that it is completely ineffective as a speaker beyond the tone of D (fourth line) treble clef. This is due simply because the size of the hole is much too large.

However, it is very well known that this same side trill key, substituted for the speaker key, and used in conjunction with the A key, will produce a steady and well-in-tune Bb third line, and is in fact the principle means of correcting it in practice for all clarinetists on the uncorrected Boehm model, as well as on the German system.

Another test should be made with respect to the size of the speaker aperture, for the upper tones of the second vibrational mode. For this test, the tones A, B and C above the staff should be attacked very softly, and the response noted. It will be immediately apparent that these several tones speak with greater difficulty of control than do others in this mode, and in fact in many cases, a very slight sounding of the fundamental from the first vibrational mode will be detected before they assume their own tonal character. This is one of the greatest difficulties for the student in his first experiences with the instrument. Tones above high C should also be tested in the same way, and the response difficulty noted. For a fine professional player this same response difficulty, represents one of the greatest concerns of performance in tone production.

Now, if the speaker key be very slightly opened, and held open by about one thickness of a split paper matchstick, so that the distance from the speaker key pad and the speaker aperture is no greater than this match-stick thickness, and then the response for each of these same test tone noted, it will be found that the response and intonation has improved greatly. This proves of course, that the speaker aperture, which was too small for the lowest tones of the second vibrational mode, is too large for the upper tones of this same mode.

It is of course, impossible to leave the matchstick correction in place, even though it is possible to employ the side trill key correction for the Bb third line. The problem, if possible, is to provide the sizing necessary to properly produce a resonant Bb third line with the usual fingering of the speaker key and the A key, and at the same time, allow the second vibrational mode to be produced more evenly than with the presently sized speaker aperture. This is exactly what the S-K mechanism accomplishes.

Again, it must be emphasized that for perfection in design, it would be necessary to have a differently sized and placed speaker hole for every tone of the first vibrational mode. But, since this is not possible, the function of the single sized speaker aperture should be one which functions best as a compromise for all of the tones of the second vibrational mode. It cannot do this and be of a size which can be used as a properly tuned and resonant Bb third line in conjunction with the A key.

The S-K mechanism provides an additional resonance hole, which is opened when Bb third line is played in the conventional manner with the speaker key and the A key. This additional resonance aperture supplements the size of the speaker aperture in such a way that the same aperture size for the production of this Bb is available, as when the side trill key is used as a alternate fingering.

In addition, by the ingenious connection of this resonance hole key to the action of the thumb ring, the resonance hole is closed, and the new smaller size speaker aperture is allowed to freely produce the twelfths of the second vibrational mode scale, in a more proper manner than heretofore.

The formula for designing the S-K mechanism is described in the patent paper. It must be understood that due to differences in bore design, and in the several sizes of tone hole apertures thus required, that there must be a proportional design for both the corrected speaker aperture size and the resonance hole. While it is not possible to enumerate all of the proportional measurements necessary for all instruments, it is possible to render an example for the size necessary in a specific case. In general, it should be remembered, that the size of the speaker aperture plus the A key tone hole and the resonance tone hole, must at least equal the correction of the emission and tuning of the Bb third line, as produced by the alternate side trill key. Furthermore, the reduction in size of the speaker aperture must be such that it improves the response of the upper portion of the second vibrational mode. This can be either the result of theoretical calculation or of practical experimentation as the case may be. The specific example provided will be of use to those skilled in the art, but will probably be simply of more interest than of use to those who are unable to interpolate.

Example of S-K acoustical correction. Measurements are in .001 of an inch and in millimeters. For a clarinet with a bore size of .590 the size of the speaker aperture will be .106 and that of the resonance aperture .116. The speaker aperture will be placed 37 mm. below the end of the upper joint, and the reson-

ance aperture 87 mm. from the end of the upper joint. The A
tone hole for this calculation, with this size bore, will in all
probability, and should properly be, .222 and for the G sharp
tone hole which also is opened as the A key is raised, the measurement will properly be .209.

A barrel joint fitted to this upper joint should properly have
as its measurements, taken three points from the upper end to
the lower, .590 (top), .591 (middle) and .589 (bottom).

A mouthpiece with the measurements given under the chapter on the tone-generating system of the clarinet, will match this
system.

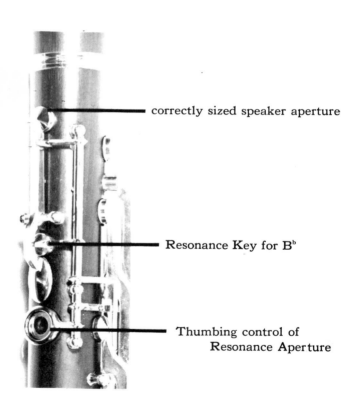

correctly sized speaker aperture

Resonance Key for B$^\flat$

Thumbing control of
Resonance Aperture

THE S-K ACOUSTICAL CORRECTION

The acoustical metamorphosis of the clarinet may be briefly charted as follows:

circa 1690 the 'invention' of the clarinet by Johann Christopher Denner by addition of the 'speaker' or register key to the Chalumeau.

circa 1710 resizing of register key and its placement higher on the instrument; also redesigning of the mouthpiece and reed as well as redesign of the bell, by J. Denner, son of Johann Christoph.

1710 to circa 1730 addition of the third key, the long lever for the left little-finger, establishing both the extent of range of the clarinet and also the traditional hand-position. These innovations attributed to another of Denner's sons.

1730 to circa 1770 addition of the fourth and fifth keys, for Ab-Eb, little finger of right hand and F#-C# long lever for little finger of left hand. Attributed to Berthold Fritz of Brunswick. This established the 'classic' model clarinet which remained the basic design through the addition of the sixth, seventh, eighth, ninth and tenth keys. Also the establishment of the modern embouchure, with the reed controlled by the lower lip.

1808 Iwan Muller's thirteen key clarinet which provided correct acoustical placement and sizing of tone-holes; the first attempts at alternate fingering mechanism, and the solution of the problem of 'pieces de rechange', for different intonation. Muller's design subsequently became the model for the school of German clarinetistry.

1839-43 collaboration of H. Klose and Auguste Buffet in the design of the Boehm clarinet, which finally placed the tone-holes in a critically correct acoustical sequence and size . . . also the mechanism for operating the new acoustical design. The Boehm clarinet design represents the base for the French School of Clarinetistry.

1952 acoustical correction of the S-K mechanism which provided a solution to the even emission and better tuned

third partials as well as the altissimo register, and sepa-
rated the functions of the 'register' key as both a speaker
and a tone-hole. The S-K correction, completes the design
of both the German and French instrumental designs,
since the basic problem solved is the same in each case.

In the intervening gaps between these landmarks of acoustical
significance, it is possible to find many designs for ingenious key
mechanisms and tone-hole placement as well as experiments in
bore dimensions, etcetera. However, to enumerate these is of
interest primarily from an historical point of view for the purpose of examining the immense amount of time and effort spent
on the perfecting the basic design of the instrument. None of
these efforts can be evaluated as comparable to the significance
of the several acoustical changes which have stimulated the activity of subsequent elaboration. For a most comprehensive list-
ing of these efforts, F. Geoffrey Rendall's 'The Clarinet' is the
best and most succinct account available.

CHAPTER VIII

The Measurement and Design
of the Clarinet

SOMETHING ABOUT MEASUREMENTS.

There is something which must be said about the measurements of design. It is the same thing which must be said about individuality and difference, and similarity and uniqueness. Things can be measured, but people cannot be measured. At the same time, no two things are identical, and in a sense, all people are similar, because they can be identified as being people.

When we say about a great man "there will never be another like him," we mean it sincerely, and there never will be in all history, any individual person with exactly the same component make-up as this certain individual. However, there will be other people, and people who will take his place, and will do the same things that he did, although in a certain individual way. But as time goes on, the great man will even be forgotten as concerns the immediate successes of the man who is now doing the same things as the great man did—and then when *he* dies, others will say, with perfect correctness, "there will never be another like him." We must thank God for the differences and the uniqueness of individuals, but at the same time we must have respect and gratitude for the thread of continuity which lends dignity to life, and permits it to continue even though one is replaced by another.

We do not destroy something fine, simply because we know that we can never make another just exactly like the fine thing. Instead, we cherish and preserve the fine thing, and hope that we can make another fine thing, even though it will not be the same exactly. Perhaps it might even be better! So it is with old Italian violins, and so it is with great paintings, and noble literature, yes, and even with clarinet reeds, and mouthpieces and instruments.

What we can do, is to examine, and measure, and describe the fine things as carefully as possible, in order to discover the relationship demonstrated by them, with reference to factors of balance and design, which are factors of quantity, and which although totally theoretical, and actually non-existent as to practical use, can nevertheless be used as descriptive generalized terms. There is no such thing as two plus two in nature, but there are many things that represent the relationship of two-ness plus twoness equalling fourness.

Things can be measured, in the sense that they have a certain stability to which we can return, time and time again. Their being so to speak, is one of repeatability. People cannot be measured in the same way, since they cannot retain their constancy of repeatability as things do, because they are living, changing quantities by their nature.

If one is asked to measure a round peg to fit a hole, it is the craftsman's task to test and try, cut and fit, until the peg just exactly fiits the hole. He then says 'this peg just fits this hole.' But it is also true that it is possible to make a peg of a certain dimension without ever having the hole, and then to make the hole to exactly the proper dimension to receive the peg, and then to test and find that the peg does fit the hole. And this process is repeatable time and time again with pegs and holes.

However, if it is desired to fit something to some person, it is another matter. It is necessary to try the thing on the person until the exact fit is obtained. But here, two matters are working in opposite directions. The thing may be stable, even though it can be changed for a better fit. The person cannot be changed, or must change to adapt to the thing which is being fitted. We have a certain constant in the thing and a variable in the person.

If two things are to be fit together, we can work with two constants and one will stay the same and repeatable, until we can get the other to match it. With persons, the thing, which is a constant, is repeatable, but the person may either vary, or not vary, depending on his individuality. Therefore, in order to fit things to people, either the person must adapt to a constant or the constant must be changed to meet he variation of the person.

Now this is all very well to say, except that we find that even with the variation in the persons, that there is a quality of sameness in our variable of people which stands as a principle of continuity. A thing may well be so very large that no person could possible adapt to it. Within this range then, there is a tolerance of repeatability or constancy for our constant thing, that must not be changed. And with the variable, the person, there is a certain limit of change which cannot be exceeded. For example, there will not be any person who has two heads who is going to play the clarinet mouthpiece to which we are trying to fit him. If he does, then we will have to have two mouthpieces, and the problem will simply be one of multiplicity, not fundamental difference.

This problem is one which the musical instrument and the person who is to play it, has constantiy as a reminder of the fluid and difficult nature of the art. People play musical instruments; musical instruments are made for people to play. Did Stradivarius make a violin for a violinist in particular or for violinists? Can violinists only play on a Stradivarius violin, or do they play on the 'violin?'

In the matter of providing measurements in order to illustrate the factors involved in the construction and design of musical instruments, we must therefore make it clear, that what is being shown, are examples of construction and design which work well, and work well enough to be called good and correct. From these examples, certain conclusions may be drawn with respect to limits of tolerance and design, and evidence provided, which shows that correct design corresponds to the abstract factors of principles of acoustics, which have been demonstrated to be repeatable constants, or laws of the relationship of things. People are in relation to things, since both people and things are concerned in the situation where people must use things, and things must be made for people to use.

Approaching the subject in this way, will perhaps provide the proper frame of reference concerning the significance of the measurement of the tools of art, as well as making clear that just because one has inherited Michelangelo's chisel and hammer, that he therefore cannot expect to chip away at a block of marble and expect the 'Pieta' to automatically become the result of his labor.

It is therefore very true that it is possible to say about any particular situation in the study and analysis of a musical instrument, "the measurements are correct—but it doesn't work well," and at the same time be able to answer "well—it doesn't measure correctly—but it works." And then to add to both statements, the real qualifying truth, by saying—,"for me."

The examples of clarinet construction and design which are presented for information in this discussion, are presented with this frame-work of reference as a basis. To expect more from such information is not intended, nor advised.

Measurements for the mouthpiece have already been given in the section dealing with the Tone-generating mechanism of the clarinet. Measurements for the reed have also been indicated under Reed-making.

The following pictures show the measurement of the clarinet bore from the end of the lower joint to the end of the conical tapered section within the mouthpiece, plate no. 1.

Plate no. 2 shows measurements of the size and placement of the tone-holes of the upper joint, and plate no. 3 shows the same for the tone-holes of the lower joint. Placement measurements are shown for the upper joint from the top of the joint and for the lower joint, from the lower end of the joint. In order to calculate the placement distance along the tube for comparison with actual tube length and bore diameter and theoretical distance for the acoustical formula shown under Tuning of the Clarinet, it is only necessary to use the following simple conversion. For placement measurements given for tone-holes of the upper joint, take measurement shown and add distance of bore for tuning barrel and mouthpiece (89. mm.), then subtract this total from 549.0 mm. This will be the actual distance from the end of the bore along the pipe, exclusive of the end correction supplied by the bell. For tone-holes of the lower joint, the measurement shown is directly comparable, exclusive of the end correction.

The end correction actual measurement, which is a bell length as shown of 109.0 mm. may be added to measurements for either joint to give a complete length comparison figure.

It will be noted that three measurements of diameter of the tuning barrel are shown. These are, measured at three points, top, center and bottom of bore, 14.9 mm. — 14.8 mm. — 14.5 mm. or a slight taper of some .4 mm. in a total distance of 34 mm.

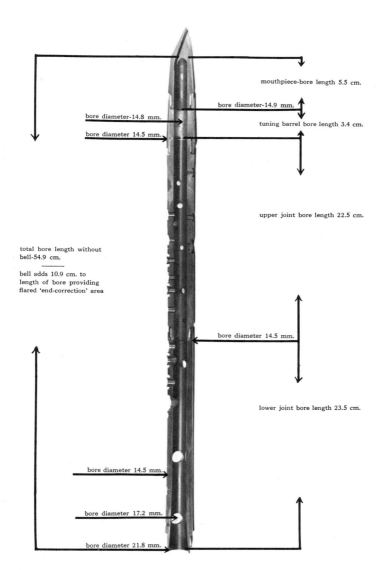

mouthpiece-bore length 5.5 cm.

bore diameter-14.9 mm.

bore diameter-14.8 mm.

tuning barrel bore length 3.4 cm.

bore diameter 14.5 mm.

upper joint bore length 22.5 cm.

total bore length without
bell-54.9 cm.

bell adds 10.9 cm. to
length of bore providing
flared 'end-correction' area

bore diameter 14.5 mm.

lower joint bore length 23.5 cm.

bore diameter 14.5 mm.

bore diameter 17.2 mm.

bore diameter 21.8 mm.

Plate No. 1
STUBBINS MODEL CLARINET MADE BY NOBLET (FRANCE)

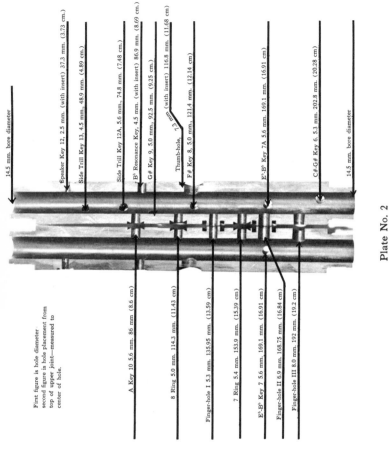

First figure is hole diameter-
second figure is hole placement from
top of upper joint—measured to
center of hole.

14.5 mm. bore diameter

Speaker Key 12, 2.5 mm. (with insert) 37.3 mm. (3.73 cm.)
Side Trill Key 13, 4.5 mm., 48.9 mm. (4.89 cm.)
Side Trill Key 12A, 5.6 mm., 74.8 mm. (7.48 cm.)
B♭ Resonance Key, 4.5 mm. (with insert) 86.9 mm. (8.69 cm.)
G# Key 9, 5.0 mm., 92.5 mm. (9.25 cm.)
Thumb-hole, 7.3 mm. (with insert) 116.8 mm. (11.68 cm)
F# Key 8, 5.0 mm., 121.4 mm. (12.14 cm.)
E♭-B♭ Key 7A 5.6 mm. 169.1 mm. (16.91 cm)
C#-G# Key 6, 5.3 mm. 202.8 mm. (20.28 cm.)
14.5 mm. bore diameter

A Key 10 5.6 mm. 86 mm. (8.6 cm)
8 Ring 5.0 mm. 114.3 mm. (11.43 cm)
Finger-hole I 5.3 mm. 135.95 mm. (13.59 cm)
7 Ring 5.4 mm. 153.9 mm. (15.39 cm)
E♭-B♭ Key 7 5.6 mm. 169.1 mm. (16.91 cm)
Finger-hole II 6.9 mm. 168.75 mm. (16.84 cm)
Finger-hole III 8.0 mm. 192 mm. (19.2 cm)

Plate No. 2
TONE HOLE DIAMETER AND PLACEMENT
UPPER JOINT

181

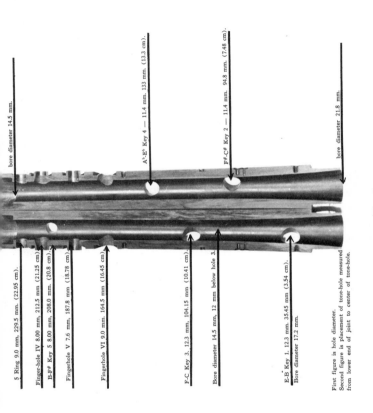

bore diameter 14.5 mm.

A♭-E♭ Key 4 — 11.4 mm. 133 mm. (13.3 cm).

F#-C# Key 2 — 11.4 mm. 94.8 mm. (7.48 cm).

bore diameter 21.8 mm.

5 Ring 9.0 mm. 229.5 mm. (22.95 cm).

Finger-hole IV 8.00 mm. 212.5 mm. (21.25 cm).

B-F# Key 5 8.00 mm. 208.0 mm. (20.8 cm).

Fingerhole V 7.6 mm. 187.8 mm. (18.78 cm).

Fingerhole VI 9.0 mm. 164.5 mm. (16.45 cm).

F-C Key 3, 12.3 mm. 104.15 mm. (10.41 cm).

Bore diameter 14.5 mm, 12 mm below hole 3.

E-B Key 1, 12.3 mm. 35.45 mm. (3.54 cm).
Bore diameter 17.2 mm.

First figure is hole diameter.
Second figure is placement of tone-hole measured
from lower end of joint to center of tone-hole.

Plate No. 3

Plate No. 3 — TONE HOLE DIAMETER AND PLACEMENT.

History of Elaboration of Design

After the advent of the clarinet as attributed to Denner, the construction of instruments according to this principle of design, immediately suggested modifications and experiments in their size and pitch range.

It is reported that a clarinet a ninth higher than the present Bb clarinet, called an ottavini, was made, and reference is made to this instrument by A. Tosoroni in his "Trattato practico di strumentazione" published in 1850. There are none of these instruments extant however. A clarinet in high Bb by an N. M. Raingo, is preserved in the Brussels Museum, and mention is made of clarinets pitched in high A, one octave higher than the present soprano A clarinet. There are no examples of these to be found.

The high Ab sopranino clarinet is still used to some extent in military bands, and is manufactured at present on special order by several makers. Of the sopranino clarinets it appears to be the most satisfactory and useful model.

Clarinets pitched in high G and F have been constructed, and the instrument in high F was widely used in German military bands and has been scored for by such composers as Beethoven and Mendelssohn. After 1800 it appears to have been supplanted by the Eb soprano clarinet, which has taken over its function, and remains the model in present usage.

The D clarinet is still used in western Europe, and has for many years been a legitimate member of the clarinet group in the widest usage. The first clarinets, as it has been mentioned, were constructed in this pitch by Denner, and as a design it would seem to have some features which recommend it more favourably than the Eb soprano. Being of a somewhat longer, and therefore a larger bore, the critical tuning problem of flexibility in intonation is an easier matter to control. The only reason for its displacement by the Eb clarinet would seem to be a desire on the part of publishers and composers to provide a more compact type of music scoring for the several groups of instruments which are the C, Bb and Eb groups. The D clarinet and the Db piccolo have had the same fate in general, and the only instruments which seem to have made any serious challenge to these three pitch groupings, are those in F, such as the Horn, the English Horn and the single instrument of the pitch of A, the A soprano clarinet. The D clarinet parts are in present day performance practice, invariably played on the Eb soprano clarinet. These scores include Richard Strauss, Mahler and Wagner. Since the transposition required is the same as that for the Bb soprano to A clarinet parts, the performers have little difficulty in this respect, and the necessity for maintaining as few instruments as possible will undoubtedly continue the practice.

The C soprano clarinet has had a long and varied career. It is scored for by Beethoven and Brahms in their symphonies and has been used in the music written for the clarinet only less frequently throughout its history than the Bb and A clarinets. Unfortunately the particular size of the C clarinet design is quite unsatisfactory acousticaly by comparison to these instruments, and since it is again an easy transposition for the Bb clarinet, the same practical considerations of performance have been applied, and it is not in general use. It is permitted to wonder if its scoring by composers was not rather a matter of convenience for them instead of an actual desire on their part for a 'tone-color'. In fact, it seems that considerable credit is given composers for an epicurean taste in tone-color which is largely read into their work by critics. Performers on instruments are a good deal more likely to know what sounds best, and which instruments sound and play better, than is a composer who at best can only have experienced the instruments for which he writes in a vicarious manner. In fact, the use of an alternate clarinet for some practical purpose at one time or another, has fooled many a conductor and provided much glee for the clarinetist who accomplished the deception.

Clarinets in B natural have been constructed, and have fallen into disuse as well, simply because of the very close pitch relationship to the more satisfactory and standard Bb model. Instrument makers can construct instruments in any pitch and have done so for many years. This is not a difficult matter for any good maker to accomplish. However, making instruments, like most other matters of manufacturing, profits most by a standardization of design wherever possible, and where the difference between designs is so very slight, and in fact represents more of an aberration from the norm than a true variety, the makers have wisely adopted the standard. It is easy enough to sit by the fire and imagine all sorts of fine differences and subtle achievements of sound production. It is another matter to have to make the instruments, and to play them. The results of the selection and practice of performers for performance sake is in every way the best for the art. Let it be truly said that the 'sit-by-the-fires' will not know the difference anyway; anymore than the average hi-fi enthusiast, whose ears cannot detect frequencies above twelve thousand cycles, nevertheless boasts of his new audio equipment that has a new high of 18,500. He cannot hear it, but he can talk about it, and may the Lord rest his soul, he is an avid fan of good music. Let us allow him his enjoyment of the illusion that he has created—but go ahead and perform our music as performers, with our practice as our guide.

Other clarinets have been made in the soprano range, such as the G and the F, but at this point the acoustical design of the instrument demands some rather difficult decisions as to construction, and usually the pitch of F, in which the old and now obsolete Bassett Horn was built, has been the dividing line between the two ranges of high or soprano clarinets, and their lower pitched relatives.

In this lower ranged group, alto instruments in F, E, Eb, D, and C have been constructed. From them has emerged the Eb alto clarinet which is the only present day survivor of the group.

At the pitch of Bb, what is known as, the bass group of clarinets begins. Actually, the so-called bass clarinet in Bb is a tenor, rather than a bass instrument, and occupies a position comparable to the violincello in the string grouping rather than as a parallel to the string bass. This design for the clarinet has yielded instruments pitched in Bb, A, G, and Eb and C of which the only present day survivor is the bass clarinet in Bb.

At the pitch of Eb, the true bass nature of the design begins and although this design is termed the contra-alto, being one octave below the alto clarinet, it is the first true bass of the group. The bass clarinets of the clarinet group are called contrabass, which is of course a misnomer again, since they are contrabass by comparison to the mis-named bass clarinet in Bb, which is a tenor instrument and to the alto clarinet in Eb. They are the only really bass instruments of the clarinet group. The only possible true contra-bass design, is that of the great bass in Bb and C.

The limitations of the acoustical design of the clarinet are quite well illustrated by the instruments which have emerged from all of this experimentation as those now in common usage. Not much has been proven by all of the experimentation, other than that it is possible to use the principles of acoustics illustrated by the clarinet as an instrument, over a wide range of pitches, and that certain of these pitches are better than others, and furthermore, that the limitations of the performer and the instrument are illustrated rather well by the experiences encountered.

The clarinets which are in common usage today and which have emerged from the numerous experimental and now obsolete or largely forgotten forms of the basic acoustical design, are the soprano Eb, Bb and A clarinets and the Bb Bass clarinet which are the accepted orchestral instrumentation grouping, and added to these, the Eb Alto and the Eb contra Alto and Bb contra-bass clarinets, which are used in the full wind ensemble.

It was discovered very early, in fact by the Mannheim school, where Mozart first heard the clarinet, that the Bb and A soprano instruments provided the timbre, flexibility of tone production and technical facility which recommended them as the most representative solo instruments. Both the Bb and A soprano instruments bear the responsibility for the greatest literature for the clarinet, and are in the truest sense, the classic design for this method of producing musical sound.

Since all clarinets have the same basic technical requisites of performance, the clarinetist will be able to use the several instruments with facility, if he will only become informed of the necessary adaptation for each of them, which is in general, a problem of size.

The notation for all of the clarinets is generally the same, that of the treble clef. However, there are some instances where it will be necessary to read both the alto and tenor clef and also the bass clef. The matter of transposition will also undoubtedly be encountered.

The relationship of the pitches of the several clarinets in common usage according to their notation and indicating the necessary transposition both for concert pitch and between their respective notations is presented in a handy reference form as follows:

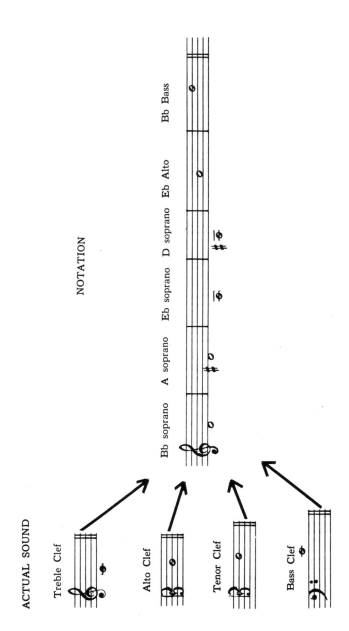

THE RELATION OF ACTUAL SOUND (CONCERT PITCH)
AND THE NOTATION FOR THE SEVERAL CLARINETS

NOMENCLATURE OF THE
KEY MECHANISM FOR THE BOEHM SYSTEM CLARINET

The nomenclature of the key mechanism for the clarinet has had many different forms. The one adopted for this text has been devised to accommodate the ambiguities which arise from the several alternate possibilities of fingering, due to the fact that the clarinet has an acoustical design which presents a unique harmonic tonal structure, as compared to the other woodwind instruments.

The necessity for the distinction between different registers of the instrument by pitch name, and by fingering as well, does not lend itself to a description of the key mechanism by pitch name alone. Therefore, numerals indicating the keys of the clarinet are used, and the keys are numbered as to the position of the tone-hole on the body of the instrument which they control. This renders the description of any possible fingering, as a precise definition, which it is impossible to confuse with any other.

A useful way of remembering the fingerings for the instrument is based on the derivation of the partials or the overblown harmonics of the instrument.

The fundamental register of the clarinet is designed for the base scale produced by the succession of tone-holes covered by the fingers, and modified by the addition or subtraction of the several keys of the mechanism which are activated either, independently or in conjunction with these tone-hole fingerings.

The fundamental register includes all tones possible without employing the harmonic possibilities of the pipe as a new fundamental, and for the clarinet, is the following indicated range as written for any of the clarinet group. The distinction made concerning the upper portion of the fundamental range by some authors, in terming it the 'middle', or the 'throat' register is not a basic description. The entire register produced as a fundamental scale before the use of a 'register', or 'speaker' key is the base for the derivation of the fingerings for the subsequent harmonic registers.

FUNDAMENTAL REGISTER

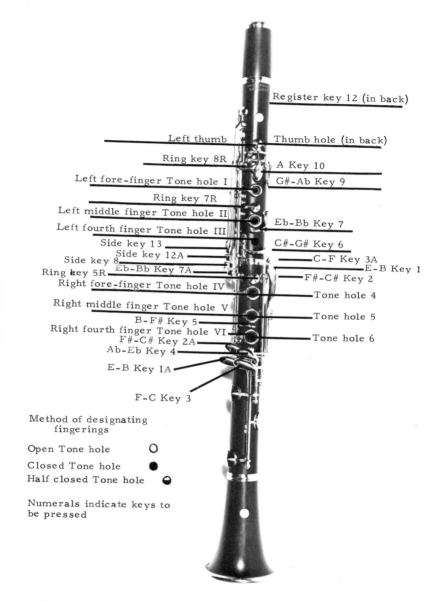

Register key 12 (in back)

Left thumb   Thumb hole (in back)

Ring key 8R

A Key 10

Left fore-finger Tone hole I

G#-Ab Key 9

Ring key 7R

Left middle finger Tone hole II

Eb-Bb Key 7

Left fourth finger Tone hole III

Side key 13

C#-G# Key 6

Side key 12A

Side key 8

C-F Key 3A

Ring key 5R

 Eb-Bb Key 7A

E-B Key 1

Right fore-finger Tone hole IV

F#-C# Key 2

Right middle finger Tone hole V

Tone hole 4

B-F# Key 5

Tone hole 5

Right fourth finger Tone hole VI

F#-C# Key 2A

Tone hole 6

Ab-Eb Key 4

E-B Key 1A

F-C Key 3

Method of designating
fingerings

Open Tone hole   O

Closed Tone hole   ●

Half closed Tone hole   ◓

Numerals indicate keys to
be pressed

NOMENCLATURE OF TONE-HOLES AND KEYS FOR FINGERINGS

The Third Harmonic register, or the 'clarion' register as it is generally termed, is the series of tones achieved by the use of the register or 'speaker' key, in conjunction with the fundamental register fingerings. This register is indicated as follows:

The Altissimo, 'high', or Fifth Harmonic register is derived from the use of the tone-hole for the first finger of the left hand, or the first tone-hole of the upper joint, an as additional 'speaker', or register key, for the derivation of these fingerings. The altissimo or 'high' register is divided into two parts, the lower altissimo and the upper altissimo, since the last interval of a perfect fourth is achieved not only in the manner as described, but also by the other means of additional forcing of the tone-generating system by the embouchure and the breath, and by what are known as 'harmonic' fingerings, which are derived from the total length of the pipe as overblown fundamental register fingerings. The resonace fingerings possible in the altissimo register are excellent examples of these 'freak' acoustical possibilities, which are in fact, better fingerings in many cases, than are occasioned by the strict adherence to the expected pattern of the design. In this case these tones are produced as the seventh harmonic.

The lower altissimo or Fifth Harmonic register is indicated as the following range:

The upper altissimo or Fifth Harmonic range is as follows:

RELATIONSHIP OF THE SEVERAL REGISTERS OF THE CLARINET

It should be noted that a very simple and graphic relationship between the several registers of the instrument, can be illustrated as follows, and the derivation of the fingerings can be easily remembered by this means; It should be noted that the registers are overlapped in each case, either by the extension of the register itself, as in the case of the fundamental, where a portion of the lower altissimo may be produced by the normal sequence of twelfths, and also the upper altissimo as a resulting seventh harmonic by alternate fingerings, or by duplication of pitch by an alternate means.

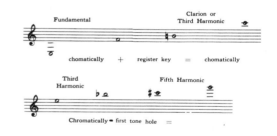

CHAPTER IX

Essentials of Clarinet Playing

Musical instruments were made by human beings to be played upon by human beings. They are not some wierd toys of a mad genius, nor is music a wierd art of some special race of men called 'talented'. In order to play music, it must be understood, as any language is understood. The symbols of its notation must be learned and the ability to translate these symbols into action must be developed. This is essentially the task of the performing musician. And, in order to put into action the language of music, a musician must develop the additional ability to use a tool of music—a music maker—or a musical instruments if you please, to produce and control and to 'express' this language of sound.

Clarinet playing is based on the same requirements that any other musical instrument needs for the expression or 'playing' of music. It is necessary to be able to produce a steady or 'musical' sound at whatever dynamic level, soft or loud, may be required. It is necessary to be able to produce this musical sound with the proper control of the required dynamic level for any musical pitch which may be within the compass of the instrument and to do this for any required duration of time, either short or long. These requirements provide us with the opportunity of constructing a nicely illustrative graph of music. This graph illustrates the dimensions of music. As you see, they are very simply a high-low axis for pitch; a short-long axis for duration; and a soft-loud axis for dynamic level. There is no note in music for the clarinet, or for that matter, any instrument with respect to its musical compass, which cannot be readily plotted on this simple graph. See the Dimensions of Music, next page.

Just as the dimensions of music notation may be indicated by the three dimensional plot for pitch, rhythm and dynamic variation, the dimensions of the technic essential to proper perform-

THE DIMENSIONS OF MUSIC

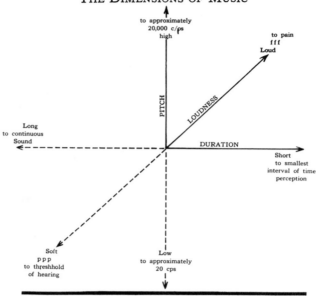

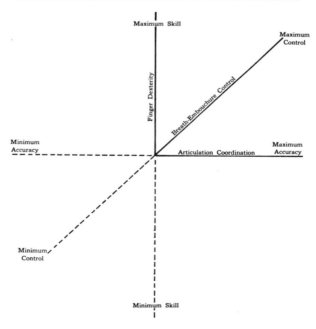

ance may be indicated as those of Breath-Embouchure control, Finger Dexterity and Articulation.

In order to accomplish the musical notes, or sequence of notes which may be plotted on our graph, the clarinetist will have to learn about the controls which he must use for his instrument for this purpose. He will have to learn the proper 'embouchure' or mouth position, in order to produce a musical tone on the clarinet and he will have to learn to use his breath to supply the sound generating mechanism of his instrument. He will also have to use his hands to properly manipulate the mechanism of the instrument for it to produce the many musical pitches of which it is capable. He will also have to use his breath and his tongue in order to provide the necessary controls for the dynamic level of the sound and the articulation necessary for the duration of the sound which he is making.

The essentials of clarinet playing as far as the physical actions of the player may be concerned are conveniently remembered as the three "T's". The *Tone* being controlled by the embouchure and the breath; the *Technique* being concerned with the manipulation of the mechanism, easily described as 'hand-position'; and the *Tongue* which is concerned with the articulation.

In the actual performance of music, none of these three can be used alone at any time and there are continually variable combinations and cross-references necessary. For example, it is impossible to produce a musical sound with the embouchure alone—or with the breath. It is also necessary to have some 'hand-position' even though a single pitch may be chosen as the single reference by which the embouchure and breath-control may be studied, as in the case of the sustained sound. Also, the attack or beginning of a sound, and its subsequent release, or ending, will certainly be concerned with what is done or it not done with the tongue. Therefore, it is imperative to understand at the outset of our discussion that although we may conveniently divide our subject matter for particular analysis, that in practice, it will always remain a matter of whole experience. We may consider each of our categories in turn, which we shall do, but let us not be so naive as to ever suppose that they can be studied or taught as unrelated.

It is also necessary to understand that the symbols of music with respect to its notation, or language of music, can never be deleted from the context of the study. They may, fortunately, be learned first, as symbols, and as a language to be translated, but their musical meaning is only achieved when they represent actual sounds.

The physical action of the player in producing a musical Tone on the clarinet is based on two major controls, the Embouchure and the Breath.

The proper Embouchure is described as follows, there are four main points in its construction;

1. The lower lip should be drawn over the lower teeth in such a manner that about one-half of the red-part of the lip covers the teeth.
2. The upper teeth should be placed on the mouthpiece about one-half inch from the tip.
3. The chin should be held flat and pointed.
4. The corners of the mouth should be pulled back in a smile position but in such a manner as to prevent any air from escaping from the sides of the mouth.

The muscular actions involved in the correct Embouchure are illustrated. A proper Embouchure is a balance of muscular action between an inward 'pressure' to place the reed of the instrument in a playing position and to hold it there, and an outward 'pull' of the facial muscles to provide a spring-like con-

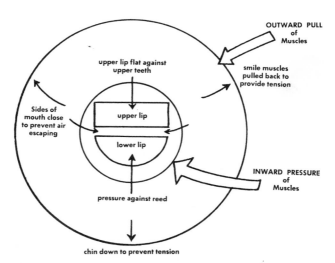

THE EMBOUCHURE

trol of the pressure exerted. If there is too much inward 'pressure' the tone will be pinched and weak; if there is too much outward 'pull', the tone will be raucous and uncontrolled. Between these two extremes lies the muscular balance required and the player will find his own 'feel' by experimentation.

The first clarinets were played with the reed turned upwards and controlled by the upper lip. The reed was not turned downwards and controlled by the lower lip in the position that it is now used until the turn of the nineteenth century[1].

With the reed in the position in which it was controlled by the upper lip, articulation by using the tongue was impossible, and considered to be undesirable. The clarinet was considered to be played as closely as possible to the singing style of the human voice. It was recommended in fact, that the tongue be held flat in the mouth, and the throat as relaxed and open as possible in order to achieve this open, free, singing style. All phrasing articulation, was accomplished by the breath and the 'hoo' aspiration as in the phrasing for vocal production.

Obviously, the limits of rapid articulation are very restrained under these conditions, and players of the present will do well to consider the tempos and the use of rapid articulation of our present style with respect to the performance of early music for the clarinet. The Stamitz concerti and, in fact, the Concerto by Mozart, may well have been performed for the first time by players using the reed controlled by the upper lip. A rendition of these compositions therefore, with fast tempos, and rapid staccato style is certainly not in character with their composer's concept[2].

With the reversal of the position of the reed, and the gain of the use of the tongue for articulation phrasing, a whole new concept of performance style was introduced. While the 'hoo' or aspiration is still possible, and is used for many phrasing pur-

---

[1] A fine description of this early style of playing and the history of it will be found in the excellent treatise, "Clarinet Instructional Materials from 1732 to 1825" by Eugene E. Rousseau, State University of Iowa, Ph.D. 1962, pp. 123-130.

[2] The Solo Clarinet Music for The Clarinet in the Eighteenth Century —Robert Austin-Titus, Ph.D., State University of Iowa, 1962, especially Chapters II and III.

poses, the rapid separation of tones which is generally termed articulation, is the basis of the present style of attack, separation and control of the spacing of the tones. This use of the tongue, much as the use of the bow for the string player becomes a matter of coordination with the finger dexterity of technic and a new dimension of articulation-coordination is thus developed.

The position of the upper lip to control the reed, when it was turned upwards, required the upper lip to be used to cover the upper teeth. Whether or not the lower teeth were allowed to come in contact with the mouthpiece or not is a question which has not been completely answered. It is true, however, that many mouthpieces from the older instruments show teeth marks. It has been generally assumed that these were caused by the upper teeth from playing in the position as presently used. However, the placement of the dates of some of these older instruments seems to support the theory that the early players may occasionally have used their lower teeth against the mouthpiece in an exact reversal of the present style.

This point is not too important however as compared to the fact that even with the turning of the reed downwards to be controlled by the lower lip, that many players continued to turn the upper lip in over the upper teeth. In fact, the so-called 'double-lip' embouchure represents simply a half-change from the early embouchure position and is probably simply the result of the incomplete adoption of the new position.

The double-lip players maintain that they achieve a sensitivity of control not permitted by the single-lip embouchure. This is due to the cushioned effect of the lips which prevents the vibrations of the tone-generating system to be felt as keenly by the player. The matter of vibration by transmission through the bones of the head to the aural centers is of course insulated by the soft tissue of the lips, and the player using the double-lip embouchure feels that he is achieving a more pure and less brilliant sound. Results observed by recording and analyzing the tones produced by both the single and double lip embouchures yield no information which would indicate that this is the case. It is not possible to tell by the analyzation of the tone structure whether the player is using one or the other embouchure.

Since the steadiness of the control of the tone-generating

system is somewhat affected by the cushion of the lips, the player using the double-lip embouchure does have some difficulty in articulation especially in the higher registers of the clarinet. Most players using double-lip embouchures cannot play well unless they support the instrument on the knee or against the body in some manner while playing. Those few players who have used the double-lip embouchure satisfactorily change to a single-lip embouchure when required to play in a standing position.

In addition to the disadvantages of the double-lip embouchure as concerns the steadiness of articulation, the lack of a steady support by the upper teeth against the mouthpiece places an added strain on the facial muscles which requires an extreme tension to achieve control. For this reason, the players of the double-lip embouchure maintain that it is very difficult to develop, an embouchure, and that it requires much more delicacy and strength of muscular effort than the usual single-lip embouchure.

Since it is possible however, to play with either a single or a double-lip embouchure, and since it is also possible to play with the reed controlled either by the lower or the upper lip, and since in the case of the single or double lip embouchures there seems to be no difference at all in the tonal results achieved as far as the performance of music is concerned, there is no reason why players should not experiment and use just the position that they, themselves, find most comfortable and satisfying.

One thing is quite true about the embouchure position, and that is that the player himself feels a difference. This in itself is often a delusion of judgment, since 'better' or 'worse' does not offer an objective difference. 'Difference' is in the player's mind, and as a subjective matter, provides no cause for discussion. So far, no player has returned to the first style of clarinet-playing, with the reed controlled by the upper lip, but no doubt this will come as a great new discovery by some as yet unborn clarinetist of the future.

For players who wish to achieve the cushioned feel afforded by the upper lip covering the upper teeth, it is possible to use a small piece of thin rubber on the mouthpiece against which the upper teeth are placed. This method of playing is finding wider acceptance from clarinetists, and seems to be a rather wise solution to the whole matter. The support is retained, the muscles are not forced unnaturally, the steadiness required is present but the resiliance of a slight cushion between the hard tooth surface and the hard mouthpiece surface is provided. The articulation is not disturbed by excessive movement of the mouthpiece due to lack of support, and the pressure required for the control of the tone-generating system is achieved by maximum result with minimum of muscular effort.

Double-lip embouchure players are like left-handed people. The world in general, is not designed for left-handed people, but they get along very well. Trying to change them is a true psychiatric matter and it is probably better to leave them alone. And of course, it is better for the rest of us that the 'left-handers' not try and prove that the world is really 'left-handed'. Ambidexterity is the only possible means of a clear and objective evaluation of either side of the question and true ambidexterity is even more rare than left-handedness.

Since the clarinet is a wind or 'breath' instrument, its tone production depends on a supply of breath provided by the player. The very simplest way to acquire the proper breath support 'feel' is for the player to take a breath, being careful not to raise the shoulders, but to allow the chest cavity to fill with air as occurs in the action of taking a deep 'sigh'. When the chest cavity has thus been filled with air, an inspiration has been made. At this point the breath should be 'locked'. This 'locked' feeling is achieved by assuming the attitude that one is going to lift a heavy weight while having the lungs full of a deep breath. The transfer from a passive deep breath to an active feeling of a deep breath is instantaneous in this case, and the player will find that this is the exact condition which is necessary at all times for the actual playing of the clarinet. The force of blowing the breath into the instrument in order to achieve the dynamic level of sound required, is a combination of the force of the breath and the embouchure control as noted above. Simply enough, when one blows harder, the loudness of the sound increases. When one blows with less force, the loudness of the sound diminishes. However, the active and controlled support of the breath remains constant since without it the steady state of the tone desired will be affected. It should also be noted that the clarinet, of all of the wind instruments will be raised in pitch as the dynamic level of the sound is reduced, and lowered in pitch as the dynamic level is increased. The tightening of the embouchure to raise the pitch and the slight loosening of the embouchure to lower it is used to off-set this natural inclination of the instrument.

BREATHING

Vibrations in an air column are initiated by the application of energy to it provided by some vibration generating mechanism. Continued vibrations are sustained by a continuous application of energy to the system.

In the case of breath musical instruments, the air column in the instrument provides the vibrational body to be activated by the vibration generating mechanism of the embouchure, reed, mouthpiece and the energy source for initial application and sustained supply is the breath of the performer.

The force or energy applied is developed by the force of the compression of a breath stream and in addition by the impedance formed by the resistance of the embouchure, reed-mouthpiece design required to accomplish the release of the energy potential of this force. Energy cannot be released inactively. It may be dissipated, absorbed, deflected, or reflected by the subsequent situation of its pattern of action, but it cannot be released without a primary requirement of force applied against a resistance.

It is necessary to understand that the breath must be applied to the breath instrument therefore in a state of compression which is achieved by the muscular action of expiration on the part of the player. Likewise, the embouchure resistance of the physical portion of the embouchure, mouthpiece, reed system must be a situation of tension in order to provide the impedance necessary to accomplish the release of energy.

Terms such as breath support, embouchure pressure, reed strength, mouthpiece resistance, response of the instrument etc., are all based on the judgment of balance among these factors, of breath compression, embouchure formation for tension, and design of instrument provided.

Therefore, the effort of the player expended against the resistance of the instrument, calibrated by the embouchure, reed, mouthpiece tone-generation system is a system of activity, and must be considered as a situation of applied force against a resistance, which in turn develops and sustains the production of a result in terms of a vibrational pattern, which induces the desired sound to be used for musical purposes.

The player's breath and embouchure force is the energy potential ,the embouchure formation, reed and mouthpiece is the calibrating device for application of the work force to the tool.

It is necessary for the player to understand the force applied to the breath instrument in terms of the physical activity of his use of the breath in order to produce the maximum result with the minimum of expenditure of effort in order to achieve the desired endurance of performance.

Breathing is the common term applied to the physical activity which accomplishes the process of respiration for animals. Respiration is the process of exchanging gases generated in the body for external gases which are required.

For life to be sustained, the gas, oxygen, is required by the animal to accomplish the chemical process of metabolism or the conversion of matter, generally in the form of what is known as food, into the necessary components of energy to build the body and also to replace the losses caused by the activity of living. Oxygen is present in the air which is external to the animal in the form of about one part oxygen to four or five parts of nitrogen and other trace gases which are known as inert gases. In the process of metabolism, carbon dioxide is generated and this gas must be exchanged for oxygen in order for the cycle to continue.

The lungs of the animal are formed of many small sac-like cells which are filled with blood-vessels with the capacity to exchange the two gases, carbon dioxide and oxygen. The lungs are filled with air when the animal breathes and consequently a supply of oxygen is thus obtained. This intake of gas is then modified by the exchange of the two gases and the carbon dioxide plus the several inert gases is exhaled to complete the breathing activity.

The whole process of intake of air, exchange of the two gases, and expelling of the air again is the process of respiration. Metabolism is the function for which the process of respiration is required.

Respiration in breathing consists of two supplemental physical actions, inspiration or in-breathing or the filling of the lungs with air, and expiration, or out-breathing, or the expelling of the waste gases from the lungs. The process of blowing a breath instrument is super-imposed on the ordinary activity of breathing for the sustaining of life.

The organs of the body concerned with this activity of respiration are of course, the lungs as the primary exchange point of the process for the gases, but this exchange is a completely involuntary matter as is the subsequent process of metabolism. The breathing of an animal as a physical action is also involuntary with respect to the quiet inspiration and expiration situation, since this is controlled by the nervous system much in the same manner as is the beat of the heart. Breathing in this respect then is not learned, nor taught, since it is a condition of living, and is either completely 'learned' at birth or the animal dies.

Both inspiration and expiration however, can also be controlled or 'forced' by definite conscious physical control exerted by the animal at will. The breath may be held for a length of time, larger or smaller amounts of breath may be taken, and larger or smaller amounts of breath may be exhaled, or the breath may be exhaled under greater or lesser pressure as the case may be. It is this conscious action and potential of control of the breathing function which concerns the breath instrument player.

Breathing is an involuntary process which can be modified by voluntary action. The action of inspiration or the taking of a breath consists of the enlargement of the chest cavity which lowers the air pressure in the lungs, by expanding them. The external air pressure of the atmosphere which is then higher than the pressure in the lungs causes the air to rush into them.

The air from the atmosphere enters the lungs by means of the air passageways of the nose, the mouth, throat and trachea. At a point in the back of the mouth at the entrance to the trachea is the very important pharynx. The pharynx is the place at which the passageways for food and for air, cross. There are four exits from the pharynx. The trachea leads air to the lungs, and is closed by the epiglottis by the action of swallowing. The exit to the nose is closed by the soft palate, which is elevated in the action of swallowing. The esophagus ,which leads to the stomach is normally collapsed by the sphincter, or binder muscle, except during swallowing, and therefore no air enters the stomach during normal breathing. The passage to the mouth is closed by the depression of the soft palate and by the tongue. Therefore, the passages for both food and for air may be used independently. In addition, air can be expelled through the mouth or through the nose independently, or at the same time.

The inhalation of air is accomplished by the expansion of the chest or by the lowering of the diaphram which is the chief muscle of inspiration. In deep breathing, the diaphram is responsible for approximately two-thirds of the total amount of air intake. The diaphram is a muscular sheet which is somewhat dome-shaped and lies between the thoracic and the abdominal cavities with a slight arch toward the thorax. Its edges are attached to the chest wall.

In the action of inspiration, the diaphram contracts by means of its muscle fibers which radiate from the center to its edges. This contraction, much like the movement of an open hand extended and then closed, causes it to flatten. As this contraction occurs, the longitudinal dimension of the chest cavity is increased, and the expansion of the lungs into this enlarged space lowers the air pressure in them. The rush of the external atmosphere to fill them then takes place.

The lungs simply follow the extended elastic wall of the thorax, since they do not contain muscles themselves. The flow and the amount of air entering into the lungs depends entirely on the capacity of the thoracic cavity since they merely expand to meet the space provided. The amount of air leaving the lungs is also entirely dependent on the reduction of size of the thoracic cavity as a reverse procedure to inhalation. The air is drawn in or forced out of the lungs strictly in accordance with the pressure differences of the air involved. The atmospheric pressure provides the initiation of the movement into the lungs and the muscular force of the reduction of the thoracic cavity provides the pressure attendant on exhalation.

Air may be inhaled either by lowering the diaphram to increase the cavity space for the lungs or by expanding the chest cavity by means of the several chest muscles. Whichever action is concerned puts air equally into all parts of the lungs. There is no such thing as putting air into the lower portion of the lungs by the contraction of the diaphram or by breathing only in the upper chest by expanding only the chest cavity. A decrease of air pressure in the lungs takes place at all parts of the lungs, and air entering them is distributed more or less equally throughout the entire lung.

It is also impossible to breathe with the chest muscles alone, or with the diaphram alone. The control of inspiration must therefore require most, if not all, of the muscles involved in the action. Pressure which might be exerted to elevate the diaphram, which would really be a pressure of abdominal muscles would also expand the chest if the chest muscles did not contract to counterbalance the pressure. In addition, a collapse of the chest wall which would increase the pressure in the lung would simply depress the diaphram unless the abdominal muscles responded with a counterbalancing pressure. It is entirely possible that many persons may think that they are breathing with the diaphram or with the chest alone, but actually the control is a much more complicated muscular movement and in every case is an applied pressure counterbalanced by another resistance.

Furthermore, the diaphram can only participate in inspiration, since it can only contract. It cannot in any possible way be made to push up against the lungs except by the abdominal muscle pressure. On the other hand, the abdominal muscles cannot participate in the action of inspiration except by relaxation. This is a process of permitting inspiration rather than inducing it. These muscles do exert a pressure in expiration, and this is the key to the breath instrument's control.

Muscular action for inspiration is an active contraction of muscles. Muscular action for expiration is a relaxation of muscles. However, the action of hastening expiration, as in breath instrument playing, requires the use of the same muscles to provide a situation known as forced expiration. The force of the expiration is accepted and controlled by the resistance of the tone-generating mechanism of the breath instrument being played.

There is a certain popular misconception concerning the matter of hyper-ventilation and its ill effects on breath instrument players that must be mentioned here. Usually the ventilation of the lungs is controlled in such a manner that the concentration of carbon dioxide in them is about 5 per cent. This amount can be increased by holding the breath, as in playing a long tone on a breath instrument, until the concentration measures about 7 per cent. Reflexes of the body are such however, that no further increase in the concentration of carbon dioxide is possible.

If on the other hand, breathing is deep and frequent for a sufficient period of time it is possible that the carbon dioxide concentration may be reduced to about 2.5 per cent. At this point the body becomes alkaline from the lack of carbonic acid and dizziness may result. If this situation is maintained, convulsions will result. There is however, absolutely no possibility of such a situation developing during the playing of breath instruments since over-breathing of this nature would require a tremendous concentration of will power and extreme voluntary effort. Such voluntary effort involved would preclude any possibility of instrumental performance at the same time. The usual metabolism of the body with respect to breathing balance takes place automatically except under such extreme conditions and there is no reason to even consider such matters as pertaining to breath instrument playing. The primary function of breathing is to obtain a supply of oxygen and dispose of carbon dioxide. The situation is such that if the carbon dioxide is disposed of, the oxygen supply takes care of itself. Since the breath instrument player is disposing of carbon dioxide by blowing into his instrument, the balance factors are provided and no harm can possibly be anticipated by the activity. It is true that at high altitudes there is a different situation than at sea level or somewhat above. Adjustment of the breathing mechanism at higher altitudes however, takes place for breath instrument playing as it does for other activities.

It is also important to remember that at the end of a normal inspiration it is still possible to inhale a little more air. This additional air intake is known as the respiratory reserve. At the end of an expiration it is also possible to exhale a little additional air. This residual volume of air is known as the expiratory reserve. Even by the greatest possible muscular effort it is impossible to exhale all of the air in the lungs. There will always be a remainder of perhaps some two cubic liters of air. This quantity is called the residual air. The residual air is of no use at all for either talking or for playing breath instruments. One other term in this connection should also be expressed and that is the difference between the maximum total possible expiration and the maximum total inspiration, which is called the vital capacity.

The activities of inspiration and expiration as applied to the matter of breath instrument playing will result in a very complicated system of reverse judgment on the part of the player which is known as sensory feedback or subsequent judgment made on the basis of what the musician calls 'feel.' Such factors as may affect this situation are the sensations of the embouchure pressure, the sound being produced, or from other sources of sensation.

The experience of breath control is best attained by the experience of playing the breath instrument concerned rather than by attempting numerous supplementary exercises aimed at establishing such control prior to its use. Understanding the physiology of the matter is a step in the right direction. Understanding the acoustics of the nature of the instrument is another. Applying the normal use of the necessary adjustment is the practice. No one needs to be taught respiration. The control of respiration as in the case of forced expiration is a natural result of applied mechanics.

Breathe naturally—Breathe deeply—Control the exhalation of the breath—Provide the muscular support, pressure or force necessary by expiration to activate the tone-generating mechanism of the instrument. This is indeed the whole matter of breathing in playing a breath instrument.

Usually there are no indications in the notation of music for the use of the breath although of course in certain studies for the instrument breathing marks have been added for the convenience of the student. However, breathing as in the case of bowing of stringed instruments is a matter of proper phrasing of music which is left by the composer to the judgement of the performer. A few simple rules in this respect have proven very helpful.

1. Breathe with the end of the musical phrase.
2. Never breathe after the leading tone whether the leading tone is that of the key signature or is an active scale step leading to the completion of a musical idea.
3. Never breathe at a bar-line simply because it is a bar-line. A

breath may be taken at the end of a bar only when the phrase ends on the last note of the bar.

4. A breath may be taken after a dotted note or a tied note in most cases, without seriously interrupting the phrase.

5. A breath may be taken before any unaccented part of a bar.

6. Breath should always be taken at a rest in the music, except during the rests which occur as the result of a series of staccato notes.

7. Several short breaths taken at convenient places will provide for the longer phrase which may follow. The wind tank, like the gas-tank, should be filled before the empty mark is reached.

8. When extended passages of technical difficulty are encountered where no application of the foregoing rules will suffice, a note may be omitted and a breath taken at the end or beginning of a phrase, provided such note is not an essential note of the melodic line. This situation generally occurs in music transcribed from music for other instruments, notably orchestral literature transcribed for band. In these cases, the performer is not at fault when he is forced to make the best of a situation where the arranger has failed to be sufficiently informed concerning the phrasing necessary for breath instruments.

9. If a breath can be taken 'in the music' and without notice on the part of the audience, it is a perfect breath, and perfect breath instrumental phrasing.

BREATH-EMBOUCHURE

The best practice to gain control of the breath-embouchure dimension of performance is accomplished by playing long or sustained tones. These should be practiced by beginning the tone as softly as possible, increasing the dynamic level to fortissimo, and then diminishing the sound again to a complete morendo. The clarinet, has a dynamic range capable of a completely smooth crescendo and diminuenedo, and this possibility should be exploited as fully as possible.

It will be noted that as the dynamic level is increased the pitch becomes sharper, and as it is decreased the pitch becomes flatter. This is the natural acoustic reaction of the clarinet. This situation may be controlled by a judicious use of the two offsetting factors of the breath-embouchure situation.

1. Increase of breath pressure flattens the pitch.
2. Tightening the embouchure pressure raises pitch.
3. Decrease of breath pressure sharpens pitch.
4. Loosening of embouchure pressure flattens pitch.

These two factors can be balanced against each other to yield a smooth and steady pitch and dynamic control. Sustained tones must be a steady-state tones. They must not waver.

While the Sustained tone is an ideal method for studying the breath-embouchure balance relationship, it is nevertheless true that most music requires more than a single tone, sustained for a period of time. The movement from one sound to another constitutes another problem which must be studied carefully. While a fine tone on one note is absolutely necessary, it must be undisturbed by the passage from one pitch to another. There are a number of practice routines which can be constructed for this purpose.

The Embouchure and Breath Control are developed best by exercises which demand slow and careful tone-production procedures. Since tone-production is the foundation of all playing requirements this type of practice is not only used as a basis for the beginner but is the routine for a good player throughout his active playing career.

There are three things which must be observed with respect to tone production. First of all, it is necessary to be able to begin a tone faultlessly on any tone possible on the instrument, and to do so at any required dynamic level. Secondly, it is necessary to be able to hold the tone so produced steadily and to color it with the required dynamic variety possible, from either a maximum to a minimum level or vice-versa. Thirdly, it is necessary to be able to release or end a tone without distorting it.

It is also necessary to be able to move smoothly from one tone to another on the instrument with respect to the first three requirements of tone production in whatever combination they may be presented.

ARTICULATION

The second dimension of clarinet playing is the use of the Tongue, for the musical result of its use or Articulation. Articulation on the clarinet is produced by the action of the tongue against the reed which produces a momentary stoppage of the vibration of the reed as well as an interruption of the air-stream, and thus produces a consequent interval of silence. The action of the tongue must be very light and quick in order to assure a minimum of interference with the normal situation of steady state tone production.

For correct articulation, the tongue must be well drawn up and back in the oral cavity and contracted to a muscular point. The motion is forward against the reed. This action may be simulated and studied by the pronunciation of the syllable 'du', bearing in mind that the explosive withdrawal of the tongue when pronouncing this syllable represents the concept necessary for the accomplishment of the initiation of the sound on the instrument. The forward motion of the tongue is really the preparatory motion involved since the withdrawal motion allows the breath to initiate the impulse of the vibration of the reed necessary for tone production. The variation in the speed of the pronunciation of the syllable 'du', provides the length of contact with the reed required for the variation in length of articulated notes.

While the tongue is in contact with the reed, there is no sound, since the vibration of the reed is damped, and the air supply is cut off. While the tongue is away from the reed there is sound, provided the air supply is constant. Therefore, the time that the tongue is in contact with the reed determines the length of the silence and the length of the articulated note. The shorter the sound, the longer the tongue is in contact with the reed, and the longer the sound, the shorter time the tongue will be in contact with the reed to interrupt its vibration and the supply of air to it. This relationship will vary with the tempo of the music and the style of articulation desired. One should think of the tongue against the reed as the normal position of rest, and the drawing away of the tongue as being a valve action in order to permit the breath to enter the instrument.

The point of contact between the tongue and the reed will vary with the individual because of the length of the tongue, but a general rule may be observed that the tongue should touch the reed below the tip, and somewhere between one-sixteenth and one-quarter of an inch from the end of the reed where it meets the tip rail of the mouthpiece.

It is possible, that the tip of the tongue may rest behind the lower teeth if this position is found to be more comfortable, and on the larger single reed instruments such as the bass clarinet this has been found to be an excellent procedure. The larger single reeds being of greater width usually respond much better if a broader surface of the tongue is presented.

The tongue must move with a light, quick recoil movement and the position of the embouchure must not be changed while articulation is in progress. This is especially true of the chin position which should remain absolutely steady.

It is possible to initiate the sound of the clarinet without using the tongue and by simply presenting the breath to the instrument with the use of a syllable such as 'hoo'. This is in fact a most desirable way to treat the first experiences in sound production. This is called an 'aspiration' and is used in clarinet playing when a soft and delicate attack is required. It is a style of articulation by default, so to speak. This style of articulation is possible on the single reed instruments alone, and is one of the truly beautiful possibilities available to performers on these instruments. The single reed instruments alone can begin a tone from nothing, and allow it to build and then die away again because of this natural phenomenon of acoustical action. The initiation of vibration in the reed takes place in this case by the gradual development of a Bernouille action in the thin end of the reed pulsed by the air stream of the breath. The use of this style of playing is not however the usual method of articulation and is used sparingly and for a special purpose. It is impossible to substitute this method of initiating the tone on the clarinet for the usual method of articulation since the speed is very limited. It is a special kind of tone production to be used in a special way. In this respect it is an advantage. When used improperly it is a great handicap.

A word should be noted at this point on the matter of single and double tonguing of wind instruments with respect to the single reed instruments. Since the reed is the tone-generator on reed instruments it acts as a transducer between the player and the air column of the instrument. The player initiates the reed vibration and the reed initiates the vibration of the air-column in the clarinet. The air column in the clarinet is not directly acted upon by the player except as it is supplied with additional air which is blown into it past the reed and permitted to enter the instrument past the pulsations of the reed. Consequently, it is not possible to articulate a single reed instrument without interfering by a stroke of the tongue which will actually contact the reed.

On instruments such as the flute, or the brass-winds, the player and the air column are in direct contact so to speak, with the player's lips in the case of the brasswinds, and the edge of the flute blow-hole in the case of the flute, as the air shaping pulse initiators. In these cases it is possible to use a number of syllable situations where the air column of the player may be influenced simply by its interruption, and the sound of the instrument consequently interrupted by intervals of silence. In the case of the flute, comparable tone initiations may be obtained by the syllables 'hoo', 'poo', 'goo', or 'du', as well as many others. Only the ability of the player to enunciate these syllables is necessary to produce a series of interrupted sound impulses in his instrument.

Double or triple tonguing then is not so much double tonguing in the sense that the tongue is accomplishing this result as it is a matter of double or triple syllabification.

The only possible parallel on the single reed instruments would be a rapid alteration between the articulation by the tongue striking the reed as in the syllable 'du' and the aspiration or the use of the syllable 'hoo'. As has been shown, the results of these two styles of tone initiation are not the same. There is then no satisfactory method of double or triple articulation for the clarinet. It is possible to develop a situation where an alternation between articulation and no articulation is used. The control of such a situation is highly questionable for musical purposes.

Articulation is developed by attaining control of the tongue. This should first be accomplished by repetition of a single tone. After this first requirement of being able to deliver the desired number of notes per beat at the indicated tempos has been accomplished, additional rhythmic patterns of repetition on single tones should be practiced in the same manner.

It will be noted that articulation is in reality a means of establishing a certain rhythmic pattern of sound. With this idea in mind it is easy to understand that it is possible to discover the rhythmic articulation pattern which the tongue is required to accomplish in any articulated passage no matter what the fingering pattern may be. The problem of articulation, after the basic control of the tongue has been established, is to coordinate the rhythmic articulation pattern with the finger pattern. When the tongue pattern is played correctly and simultaneously with the finger pattern, articulation coordination will result and the passage will be properly played. Therefore it is necessary to practice articulation coordination exercises for the final development of the correct articulation control.

Hand Position

The third dimension of Clarinet Playing is concerned with the Finger Dexterity and requires that a proper hand-position be employed. Actually, clarinet technique is more finger than hand technique. The movement of the fingers accomplishes the required manipulation of the key mechanism of the instrument and it is to the extent that this fingering is smooth and perfectly coordinated that the resulting production of the various tones possible will be controlled as desired.

Every effort to assume a comfortable and natural position should be made. The clarinet is designed to be manipulated by human hands and much thought and effort in design has gone into the fabrication of instruments which allow the fingers to act freely and to the best possible advantage. A poor hand-position can generally be described as an unnatural use of the hands and a distortion of the natural curve and flexibility of the fingers.

The clarinet should be held at an angle of approximately forty-five degrees in front of the body. This is easily determined by sitting erect on a chair and placing the bell of the clarinet on one knee, forming the embouchure with the head very slightly bent forward. This angle has a range of tolerance in adjustment and the instrument may be moved both up and down through an arc of some fifteen degrees to suit the individual. In no case however, should the angle be less than thirty or more than sixty degrees from the body. A position of the clarinet held in front of the player at an angle of position such as in playing a trumpet or the equally bad effect of holding the instrument in such a vertical position as to appear to be blowing across the top of a bottle prevents proper embouchure formation, articulation and good hand position.

The fingers should lay across the keys of the clarinet at approximately a forty-five degree angle with the vertical axis of the instrument. The left forefinger should touch the G# key

PLAYING POSITION

HAND POSITION

at the top of the upper joint with the second knuckle and the A natural key next to the G# key should be touched with the inside corner of the first knuckle of this same finger. The tip of this finger should over-lap the first tone-hole. The contact of this finger with these two keys should remain undisturbed even during the most rapid passages, unless the fingering requires that it should be removed from the instrument entirely. This position will provide a fulcrum for the left hand and will eliminate most of the unnecessary motion of the left wrist which causes a loss of efficiency in finger motion.

The right forefinger should be placed across the side keys of the instrument in such a manner that the second knuckle rests against the Eb-Bb side key.

The tips of the little fingers of both hands should touch only the tips of the long lever keys.

The third and fourth fingers of each hand should be allowed to fall naturally in place with their position guided by the position of the forefingers and the little fingers as previously described.

The left thumb is placed across the thumb-hole with the inside corner of the tip resting against the speaker key. It is necessary to be able to use the left thumb to depress the speaker key alone, cover the thumb-hole without pressing the speaker key and also to be able to cover the thumb-hole and depress the speaker key at the same time. With these three functions necessary the angled position of the thumb will provide easy access to all three positions necessary. An excellent test for the proper finger position of the left hand is to note that when the fingers of this hand are removed from the instrument and the thumb and forefinger closed together that an X should be formed. If the formation is found to be more of a cross, the finger position may be properly made and the fingers then returned to the instrument by opening the hand without moving any of the other fingers.

All of the fingers which cover tone-holes on the clarinet should cover them with the flat, fleshy part of the finger. There should be no attempt made to use the fingers as a plug to stop the tone-holes. Neither should the fingers be so flat as to be without a slight curvature or arch. The most natural position of the fingers is not flat and extended, but slightly curved. This may be observed in any hand held in a rest position. If a similar position to this rest position of the hand can be adapted to the clarinet mechanism an excellent hand position will result.

The instrument must not be held with the fingers. It must be supported by the right thumb. Of all the many difficulties encountered in playing the clarinet perhaps the clue to most of them can be directly traced to this lack of proper support. The instrument must be brought up to the player, the embouchure formed and the fingers of both hands allowed to play on the clarinet—while it is supported with the right thumb. If any attempt is made to support it with the embouchure, tone production is impossible, and if the fingers are required to support the instrument, no freedom of finger movement is possible. For this reason, players often support the clarinet with their knee, which is not disadvantageous provided the right thumb support is still the guiding factor. There is also no objection in using a neck-strap if necessary, although a neck-strap does not accommodate the clarinet as neatly as other instruments since it is likely to interfere with the action of the left thumb.

Finger movement for maximum efficiency with minimum of effort should be as conservative as possible. Movement should be precise and accurate, and in order to attain precision it is very important that the placement of the fingers should be acomplished with definitive surety. The time-honored description of this type of movement is that the fingers should be placed with a 'snap' on the keys, and removed with the same spring-like feel. The situation can be easily demonstrated by fingering the clarinet without blowing it. When the fingers are placed on the keys and tone-holes it should be possible to hear a resonance developed in the instrument as it is fingered up and down the scale. It will be noted that keys with pads are used by the mechanism to cover many of the holes while others, seven, to be exact, are covered with the pads of the fingers themselves. The resonant sound of the fingers on the tone-holes should be as evenly balanced as possible with the resonance produced by the closing of a key pad. There are certain suggestions made by some players that the fingers should be raised very gently and placed very gently in order to produce a legato effect. This is true in the sense that a rough movement of the fingers should be avoided, but it is impossible to move accurately and quickly without precision. The development of an accurate and precise finger movement can be controlled for the smooth legato passage and for the rapid passages as well if it is intelligently recognized that precision is the primary requisite of finger movement.

It is interesting to note that finger movement between two allegro notes in rapid sequence and between two notes of an adagio passage is exactly the same. The only difference is that the action is delayed by sustaining the first of the slower notes for a longer time than the first of the allegro notes. When the time arrives to change from one note to another, the change is instantaneous in both cases. For this reason, the finger movement must be as quick and precise in the slower passage as it is in the more rapid.

The phenomenon of pitch change on a woodwind instrument is very interesting. The pitch is modified by the length of the tube of the instrument and this length is provided by the various holes drilled in it laterally. There is no in-between sound possible from one length to the next unless the lower hole is gradually opened in a manner which will provide a muffled sound which really emanates from the upper of the two holes under consideration. The air-column does not act like the gradual increasing or decreasing length of a string along which one may slide the finger. Rather, it operates acoustically as a certain increment of length of the tube or air column contained in the tube. There are only these alternatives for the two adjacent holes on a woodwind instrument: the pitch produced by the length of the tube provided by the upper of the two holes: the pitch produced by the length of tube provided by the lower of the two holes: and the muffled or distorted pitch produced by a partial closing of the upper of the two holes. Actually, the closest observation of pitch change from length to length of air-column has shown that the shift in frequency is a sudden definite quantitative increment of change. It is impossible to make a smooth and uninterrupted change from length to length in an air column which is controlled in length by laterally drilled holes. It is possible by means of a sliding arrangement such as the trombone slide or slide whistle, to gradually increase the length of the tube by infinitely small degrees or increments of change. The clarinet is not constructed in this manner and any effort to finger it as if the fingers could supply the sliding effect of the trombone is merely a muffling of the sound emitted from one length of tube and is a distortion rather than a true effect of the air column length.

In this respect the acoustical action of the air column of a clarinet is somewhat similar to the acoustical action of a piano. The piano uses a different string, or set of strings for each pitch. It is therefore impossible to play any pitch in between two adjacent keys of the piano. Therefore, it follows, that it is impossible to connect two pitches on the piano in the same manner as the sliding pitch change which may be accomplished by the human voice. The clarinet, and all woodwind instruments have the same problem. The length of tube to be used for any pitch is determined by the length of tube provided by the laterally drilled holes.

It is true, that by a distortion either of embouchure, blowing or muffling by the fingers that an effect of pitch changes can be accomplished on any length of the tube much in the same manner that it is possible to change the pitch of the piano by loosening a string or set of strings with a tuning hammer as the key is repeatedly struck. This is however, not the nature of sound production desired from the instrument and is not intended by its design. In the case of the clarinet, the slight change in pitch which may be accomplished by embouchure, blowing or by what is known as intonation fingering, where certain additional keys or holes may be opened or closed in addition to a basic fingering in order to provide additional resonance or tuning is a flexibility control possible which is similar to the tuning of a piano by the adjustment of tension on the strings. This is a fortunate possibility of the acoustical system of the air column instrument. If it were not so it would be impossible to accomplish intonation. The term 'in tune' when applied to wind instruments means simply that there exists a sufficient possibility of exercising this control on the basic design of the instrument provided to permit the player to make the necessary adjustments with facility. An instrument 'in tune' means an instrument which can be played, 'in tune'.

ELABORATIONS AND MODIFICATIONS OF THE ACOUSTICAL DESIGN OF MUSICAL INSTRUMENTS

The basic designs of musical instruments are premised on acoustical principles of their use as sound producers for music.

Within certain limits it is possible to modify and to elaborate the basic designs by constructing instruments which are either larger or smaller. Limitations imposed by size are related to the ability of the human body to accommodate the physical activities of performance to the size of the instruments as well as to the most efficient function of the acoustics involved.

It is quite simple to imagine a musical instrument so very large or so very small that no human hand could reach the keys. It is also reasonable to recognize the fact that acoustics operates in much the same manner with respect to size limitations. A musical instrument doubled in size is not just the same instrument twice as large, either in performance potential or in acoustical result. The same can be said of automobiles, airplanes and typewriters. A ship which might be constructed with a length of ten miles and a draft of one mile would be utterly unoperable despite the vastness of the ocean. Limitations of size are all based on the relative relationships of physical laws to human beings and the world which they have constructed for themselves based on these laws. The best utilization of our physical powers and our physical laws is always with respect to the greatest possible efficiency of operation for the purposes intended.

So with the clarinet, as with other so-called 'families' of instruments it has been possible to construct larger or smaller versions of the basic design and with certain excellent elaborations of extension of musical tone production and additional variety of tonal timbre and musical effect. The 'family' of the stringed instruments, of the brasswinds, the flutes and the double-reeds as well as the immense variety of percussion instruments yields a wide range to the dimensions of music as a sophisticated art medium.

With the increase or diminution of size however, come the attendant problems of acoustical efficiency and accommodation of the human body to the matter of performance. These both have certain limitations which experimentally have been very broadly exploited. In the case of the clarinet, instruments have been constructed with a scale pitch of a range of almost four octaves, from the tiny soprano in Ab to the great contra-bass in C. And, as might be suspected, the results have been as anticipated. The total efficiency of the smaller instruments has

diminished with their rise in pitch scale and the larger instruments have decreased in total efficiency in the opposite direction.
The scale of the instruments with respect to size loses in
efficiency as compared with the basic design proportionally to
the increase or dimiution of this design. Only in rare instances
does the modification in size yield any increase in efficiency at
all and in these cases only because of an advantage which is
gained not so much because of increased efficiency but because
of the satisfaction derived from the greater variety of timbre
or height or depth of pitch.

In the case of certain musical instruments designs, the modifications with respect to size have given birth to new instrumental
concepts and actually to new instruments in their own right.
This is largely due however, to the extreme flexibility of certain
design characteristics. The design of stringed instruments is a
case in point, as are the brasswinds. It is true nevertheless, that
it would be possible to construct a stringed instrument with
strings so large and so long that they could not be accommodated by the human hand or a bow so very large that it simply
could not be lifted by human arm. The argument for efficiency
still holds, even though it is possible in certain design areas to
more effectually increase or diminish the basic proportions of
the instrument.

The clarinet does not enjoy this extreme flexibility of modification no matter how much we may admire the possibilities of
extension of range which it does have. In this sense, the bass
clarinet and the soprano Eb clarinet are not really new instruments in their own right but simply modified versions of the
basic clarinet design. The violin and the violincello represent
quite a different relationship in this respect and it should also be
said that the relationship of the full-size violin to the quarter
size violin for the little beginner is another case in point. The
dimiution of the strings stops at the design of the violin, and the
violin is considered the classic of design for the string family.
While larger stringed instruments constitute an extension of the
principles involved to the extent that the viola, 'cello and string
bass are considered instruments in their own right, the quarter
size violin is not regarded in the same way.

In the case of the stringed instruments, the performance techniques are quite different between the members of the group.

Cellists do not play cellos while holding them under their chins. nor do violinists play violins held vertically and supported by pegs, even though the latter technique might be possible and in certain other cultures is in fact a practice for instruments of this type. The differences of performance technique is basically a dividing line which determines an instrument to be such in its own right. In the case of the clarinet, all members of the group are played in the same manner basically, with only the modification of size as a physical consideration for the player. The mechanism of the keys is such that it is the same for each of the clarinets, and is accomplished by the same fingering technique. The flexibility which this permits as a performance factor for the player to change from one instrument to another is quite different from that required by a string player who might wish to play other instruments in his group.

The differences of performance techniques between the clarinets is therefore based on one general technique and the differences must be treated as a departure from the normal procedure of playing the 'classic' model of the group, the soprano clarinet in Bb.

In the case of the clarinet, the classic design of the Bb and A soprano clarinets has been extended on both sides, so to speak, at least to one instrument above, the Eb soprano, and to two instruments below, the alto and the bass clarinets.

Such a discussion can precipitate long and involved arguments and heated controversy but the plain facts are evident. There are in each area of musical instrument design certain 'classic' or basic designs from which modifications or elaborations are developed. In the case of the clarinet, the 'classic' design of the Bb soprano clarinet has been chosen for our theme of discussion.

In performance as well as in design, the modification for purposes of extension of range and variety of timbre is premised on the modifications of performance practices involved. The following performance suggestions are presented with this in mind. Clarinetists, unlike the players of stringed instruments, are supposed to have some facility in performance on at least the more closely adjacent instruments in their group. Therefore, the performer on the 'classic' clarinet design should be at least informed of the several performance accommodations involved in this

A^b SOPRANO CLARINET
(LEBLANC)

B^b CONTRA-BASS CLARINET
(LEBLANC)

closely associated area.

THE Eb SOPRANO CLARINET

The Eb Soprano clarinet is a higher pitched instrument than the Soprano Bb clarinet and is consequently smaller in proportion as concerns the acoustical design of bore, tone-holes, mouthpiece and reed.

The mechanism, although of necessity, designed for the smaller tone-holes and the shorter length, has been cleverly adapted in such a manner by the best makers, that the handposition may be comfortably compared to that of the larger soprano instruments. There is somewhat less distance for the fingers to move, and care must be taken that closed keys are not touched because of a lack of attention to this matter. There is otherwise no difference at all between the handposition used on the Eb clarinet and the Bb.

The mouthpiece although smaller, is shaped and constructed in such a manner as to retain the proportional difference necessary. The position of the upper teeth on the mouthpiece will proportionally be at a less distance from the tip because of this smaller size of the mouthpiece as well as the smaller sized reed. However, in the case of the Eb Soprano instrument it must be remembered that the higher pitch will require a control of the vibrating mode of the reed for the higher frequencies involved, and this will necessitate care in providing the reed with the proper amount of response area. This can only be insured by not taking too small a 'bite'. The position of the teeth for any player will therefore depend on his placement of teeth on the Bb Soprano clarinet. The problem with the Eb soprano as concerns tone-production and the control of intonation is premised on this consideration. When the greater portion of response area of the reed is exposed by the embouchure in order to provide the requisite power and partial structure of the sound, it will be noted that the control of the tone is at the very edge of a loss of control. The equation of loss of efficiency by diminution is recognized as being in action by this evidence and will be immediately ascertained by the player upon his first trial with an Eb instrument.

The use of the breath will also be noted as requiring the same general support, with even more attention to the resistance of the instrument as regards the intonation effect of increased pressure lowering and decreased pressure raising the pitch. This is for the simple reason that the Eb instrument represents the same effect noted on the Bb as the pitch of the scale becomes higher. The flexibility of the altissimo register of the B clarinet can be varied by almost a major third by means of embouchure and breath adjustment. The Eb clarinet extends this effect almost to the lowest tone possible in its scale. This added flexibility is somewhat of an advantage in adjustment possibility, but is also the subject of some concern to a player who has developed a pattern of embouchure and breath control gauged to the Bb. The shorter bore of the Eb clarinet, and the placement of the tone-holes and the effects of the consequent end-correction and tuning have all been designed to accommodate the instrument. The player has not been redesigned on the same basis. The player will have to make some experiments to determine his role in the new acoustical pattern.

The range of the Eb soprano clarinet is also found to be not as effective for its entire register as for the Bb. The top pitch effectively used for the Eb soprano is that of written high G above the staff or the sounding high altissimo C of the Bb clarinet. Tones above this may be produced but they are quite insecure and may be attained only by sacrificing the adjustment of the reed and mouthpiece for good results in the lower register. A half-step above the high G is sometimes required, and this may be played without any modification of reed or mouthpiece, but it is difficult for the player. The loss of efficiency by modification with diminution is again seen to operate in this case, since the Eb instrument loses almost a perfect fourth of its range simply by being higher-pitched.

The articulation of the Eb clarinet is the only gain in efficiency which might be counted as an asset. Since the reed is smaller, and the mouthpiece is smaller, the natural response quotient of the tone-generating system is greater by the rule of inverse proportion which is applied here. With only the very simplest adaptation of the usual tongue action for the Bb clarinet it will be discovered that the articulation speed has been increased and that a real freedom of response in this way has been attained. The smaller finger pattern, with the compactness of movement for the smaller keys also contributes to an increased articulation-coordination efficiency if the player has an adequate technique to begin with for experimentation.

It is almost redundant to remark that since the player is not redesigned, but only the instrument, as mentioned above, the anatomical characteristics of the player are limited in the dimension of size. Persons with very large hands, and large embouchure and tongue dimensions would do well not to attempt the Eb soprano clarinet as more than an experiment. Here once more the principle of diminution and efficiency is seen to operate.

The player of the Eb clarinet must be prepared to employ several transpositions. The Eb has supplanted the clarinet in D for which much of the orchestral scoring will be found. The Eb clarinet plays the D parts with the same transposition used for playing Á clarinet parts on the Bb clarinet, that is, one half-tone lower. C parts will also be required since many scores have no parts for the Eb and the usual practice is to provide this instrument with one of the soprano C parts to strengthen the ensemble. This is also done by providing the Eb clarinetist with a Bb clarinet part when no Eb part in scored. In order to be of the most use to an ensemble the Eb clarinetist should therefore be prepared to readily accomplish these several transpositions.

The fingerings for the Eb soprano clarinet for its written notation are exactly the same as for the other clarinets. Due to its flexibility of intonation control it will be necessary to carefully devise a resonance and intonation pattern of fingerings to accommodate the individual instrument however. These can only be determined by the individual player on the individual instrument and cannot be anticipated other than to advise that the regular intonation and resonance fingerings found in the fingering chart under Playing in Tune will all be directly applicable.

The Alto Clarinet

The alto clarinet occupies a position in the clarinet choir comparable to that of the viola in the string class. Its range, written in concert pitch, is

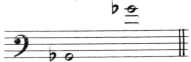

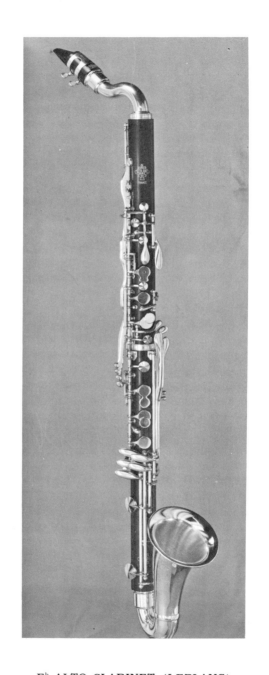

E♭ ALTO CLARINET (LEBLANC)

and as written for the instrument is

It is easier to obtain this extended harmonic register on the alto clarinet than it is on any other member of the clarinet class.

The pitch of the alto clarinet is in E-flat. Its ancestor, the Bassett horn, was pitched in F. This now obsolete instrument found considerable favor with the early composers of wind instrument music and a notable body of composition for it can be found in the works of Mozart. Its decline and subsequent abandonment was due largely to the erratic development of a standardization of orchestral instrumentation which at best has been capricious in more than several ways. There is no reason why the Basset horn should not have been perfected both acoustically and mechanically, but somewhere along the backward path of history it fell by the wayside. It may have been that the desire to simplify somewhat the score construction in groups of C, B-flat, and E-flat instrumentation caused this abandonment. Or, is may have been that, unlike the French horn which had a facility in both the pitch of E-flat and F, the necessity of constructing two instruments, an alto clarinet in E-flat and also in F did not appeal to the instrument makers, so one was chosen and the other discarded. It is also possible that the F clarinet was considered really as a *mezzo-soprano* voice, as was the now obsolete F saxophone, and that the truer alto voicing of a pitch one whole step lower, making a more decided bridging of the clarinet voicing between the soprano and the bass, caused the subsequent choice between the two. Whatever the reason, whether the choice between the E-flat and the F pitch be laid to the score of the composer, the bench of the instrument maker, or the ear of the practical musician, it is more a matter to thrill musicologists, in turning down the dusty pages of the past, than it is for our practical purposes.

The alto clarinet, which is the true alto voice of the clarinet choir, has a dark, reedy, and sonorous tone color. In fact, its sonority, note for note, is greater than that of any other of the clarinet class. It is true that the upper clarion and harmonic registers of the alto clarinet, when compared to the same pitches as reproduced on the soprano clarinet, lack the brilliance of the soprano, and it is also true that the chalumeau register of the alto clarinet, when compared with the same pitches produced on the bass clarinet, lacks the same depth as the bass. But the interesting thing about the entire range of the alto clarinet is that the register possesses an evenness and balance which surpass both the soprano and the bass voices. This is not the case with other members of the clarinet class. The others are subject to much more change in tone color between registers than is the alto, and the register changes are therefore much more violent in character. The even-tempered disposition of the alto clarinet makes it the ideal supporting instrument of the clarinet voicing and, like the viola in relation to the violin and 'cello, it does the yeoman service of being always present but not always accounted for. It adds to the sonority without disturbing; it adds to the body of the clarinet timbre without distortion. It is the perfect catalyst for blend of tone in the clarinet section.

The alto clarinet's similarity to the viola provides the perfect sonority and blend so requisite for the clarinet voicing, without which no ensemble tone can be achieved with clarinets. It is the well-nigh perfect ensemble instrument of its class and therefore indispensable in that category.

The ideal instrumentation of the wind band, which some day will be achieved, will make use of the clarinet class in the same manner in which the string class has been long used in the symphony orchestra. A balance of the requisite number of B-flat clarinets, divided into equal proportions as to first and seconds, alto and bass clarinets, and contra-bass clarinets (that is, the true contra-bass one octave lower than the B-flat bass), with the addition of E-flat and A-flat soprano clarinets in order to strengthen the harmonic register of the B-flat soprano clarinets, would present an almost perfect balance of tone color and sonority in this respect, and would permit the wind band to produce effects comparable to the sonority of the orchestra.

The problems of playing the alto clarinet are not much different from those of the soprano clarinet. The usual procedures concerning embouchure, articulation, and hand position are in order. There are, however, certain particular variations in the application of the basic procedures which should be noted.

In the first place, due to the fact that a larger air-column is involved in the production of sound on the alto clarinet, it will be found that somewhat more breath will be required to fill the tone of the instrument to the proper level. With this added quota of breath will come the necessity of a somewhat more pronounced breath support as concerns the introduction of the breath into the instrument.

In the second place, the mouthpiece and reed of the alto clarinet are larger than the mouthpiece and reed of the soprano clarinet, due to the proportions necessary to balance the larger air column of the instrument. Because of this difference in size, it will therefore be necessary to take a slightly longer 'bite' on the mouthpiece of the alto clarinet. This 'bite' will be longer by comparison, but not actually longer by relation. It will be in direct proportion to the increase in size and should be not less than five-eighths of an inch. This will permit at least one-half inch of the reed to be taken into the mouth as "free-reed."

Thirdly, due to the longer 'bite' and larger reed, the tongue will strike the reed at a slightly lower point by comparison than on the B-flat soprano, but again, this will be directly proportional to the increase in size of the reed. The action of the tongue will be the same as is usually employed in articulation on the clarinet, with the clarinet, with the exception that unorthodox methods of articulation will be found almost impossible. It will be necessary to articulate in the simple and correct style of articulation in which the tip (or about one-quarter of the end) of the tongue will strike the tip (about one-quarter inch from the end) of the reed, and the tongue will strike the reed from underneath, or from straight behind, and not from above the reed. The striking point of the tongue will be determined of course by the size of the tongue and its normal position in the mouth, which will very with each individual.

The angle of the alto clarinet mouthpiece in the mouth is correctly provided for by the angled construction of the mouthpipe or neck, and the same angle as that used in the normal soprano clarinet embouchure should be adopted. It will be found however, that if the player is accustomed to an extreme angle of the clarinet with the body, whether it be acute or obtuse, the alto clarinet will necessarily have to be held at less acute, if the angle is acute, and less obtuse, if customarily obtuse. The reason for this convergence toward the norm of the extreme angles is occasioned by the fact that the alto clarinet is held with a neck-strap as well as with the thumb-rest, and these two means of suport tend to strike a balance when holding the instrument which is usually more constant than when playing the soprano clarinet. It is qute wrong to hold either the alto or bass clarinet on the side, as in playing the saxophone. These instruments must be held directly in front of the body.

The general embouchure formation should be a little more for-ward when playing either the alto or bass clarinet. This may be considered as a fourth variation of the usual procedures. The smile muscles may be slightly relaxed and a more pronounced 'OOOO' formation of the oral cavity should be maintained. This can be illustrated by the mouth position adopted when a long, low whistle is being formed by the lips. Such an embouchure formation will prevent the common fault of exaggerated tense-ness of the embouchure and will help to avoid the breaking of the notes, B-Natural, D. E. F. and G in the clarion register, espe-cially on the attack.

A fifth variation from the accustomed style of playing the soprano clarinet will be noted in the need for several adjust-ments in hand position. Essentially the hand position when play-ing the alto and bass clarinets will be the same as on the soprano clarinet, except that larger keys must be manipulated. The covered tone-hole alto and bass clarinets have been found wholly satisfactory, and the open tone-hole models are decidedly obsolete.

Nevertheless, larger keys must be manipulated, and this in itself is a slight difference which it is necessary to become accus-tomed to in playing. The position and use of the left forefinger however, is a real difference between the soprano and the alto and bass clarinets. It will be found that on the alto and bass clarinets a plateau key similar to that found on the oboe is used for the forefinger of the left hand. The tone-hole covered by the action of this key is necessarily larger than is correct for the proper speaking of the harmonic register, but must be made so in order properly to tune the E-B and F-C Chalumeau to clarion register. Therefore, a small speaker aperture has been drilled in the finger plate which activates the pad that closes this tone-hole; this aperature is opened by a sliding motion of the fore-finger when the harmonic register is desired. Such motion causes a small aperture which makes possible the correct production of the harmonic register, without opening the entire tone-hole, and at the same time permits the use of the entire tone-hole when the aforementioned tones are played. When playing any note above C above the staff, the left forefinger must open only the small aperture, and not the entire tone-hole.

While speaking of mechanical necessities of the alto and bass clarinets it is well to mention one other matter of vital necessity which should be observed carefully in the selection of an instru-ment. This necessity is the low Eb key which should be on all alto and bass clarinets, not because of the fact that there are many low Eb's to play, but because the addition of this key in the construction of the clarinet permits an added resonance of B Natural, third line. Without the low Eb key, the resonance of this pitch is very dull, and on both the alto and bass, such dull-ness is most pronounced.

It will be found that a sixth variation in the basic application of the usual techniques is the adjustment of the reed and mouth-piece. Although these two important factors are essentially the same as the soprano clarinet, it is true that a slightly closer lay and slightly softer reed in comparison to the lay and reed used on the soprano clarinet will give better results. This is particu-larly important to those who desire to change from the soprano to the alto or the bass. The following rule will be very helpful: Whatever the strength of reed, or whatever the opening of lay used on the soprano, a slightly softer reed and closer lay should be used on the alto.

THE BASS CLARINET

The Bass clarinet which parallels, as a voice of the clarinet choir, the violincello of the string family, is a clarinet pitched one octave lower than the soprano clarinet. It has been con-structed in the several keys of C, Bb and A, the C Bass clarinet sounding one octave lower than the C soprano clarinet and the Bb and A Bass clarinets one octave lower than their soprano counterparts. Bass clarinets have also been constructed in the key of Eb, this instrument sounding one octave lower than the Eb Alto clarinet. This instrument is better known as the contra-alto clarinet. For various reasons the Bass clarinet in Bb has been more widely accepted and used than any of the others, and it is this instrument which will be commonly found in general use.

The Bass clarinet is usually written for, and reads in the soprano clef, as do all of the clarinets, but it should rightfully be written for, and read in the bass clef, as it sounds. Some composers and arrangers have recognized this fact, and it is to be hoped that the change to the bass clef will eventually become standard practice, and the instrument thus take its proper place in the score.

Because of this clef problem, the student of the Bass clarinet should be familiar with both the soprano and bass clefs, and in addition, should be able to read readily the tenor clef. The tenor clef will necessarily be employed when the bass clef reading standard is adopted for the same reason that it is now used for the 'cello and bassoon, ledger lines above the staff may thus be minimized for the convenience of composer, arranger and player.

The matter of transposition must also be dealt with, for it will be found that although the Bb Bass clarinet is the instrument most generally used, that parts for it in C and in A are in the repertoire. Therefore the Bass clarinetist must be trained in at least these two transpositions.

The range of the Bass clarinet, although lower in pitch, is nevertheless a complete clarinet range extending from the low Eb to the altissimo C as written

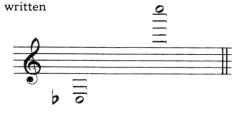

or as it sounds

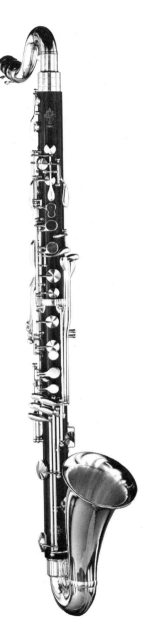

B^b BASS CLARINET
(LEBLANC)

The Bass clarinet as now constructed, is as facile and as pleasing when in competent hands, as any of the rest of the clarinet choir. Whereas it is undoubtedly a grand and noble solo voice capable of tremendous expressiveness, it is also an instrument which can be used as a complete voice within the score, in the same manner as the 'cello section of the orchestra is used. The mass effect of a section of Bass clarinets is a thrilling and perfect answer to the flexibility of the bass voice demanded as a wind counterpart of the string effect of the 'cello section, and this possibility awaits only exploitation to become as standard in wind ensemble music as is the indispensable 'cello to the orchestra.

An extended range downward has been added to the Bass clarinet in some instances, and this addition makes it even more important to the score. Bass clarinets have been constructed with additional tone-holes as an elongated lower joint and bell which increase the range to low concert Gb

It is generally standard to add the low Eb key on the bass clarinet and this is an important and necessary consideration. The bass clarinet with the low Eb key and one additional key which permits the production of a low D, or as it sounds, a concert C

is the most adequate model. This addition of the low D makes possible the performance of all violin-cello parts and is of great value in scoring. For lower notes, the contra-bass clarinet should be used.

The technical problems of playing the Bass clarinet are somewhat different from those encountered on the soprano clarinet, but are not so unique but that an explanation of them can best be made by indicating these "differences" with respect to the well-established fundamentals of clarinet playing.

First, it must be said, that because of the obviously larger physical proportions of the Bass clarinet, as compared with the soprano clarinet, that all applications of the fundamentals of clarinet playing technique must be on a larger relative scale. These applications are strictly relative, strictly greater by exact comparison in relation to size and therefore all measurable and fairly accurate as to result if correct information concerning the basic fundamentals of clarinet playing is available.

Playing the Bass clarinet requires first of all, a more sustained, supported, and powerful introduction of the breath into the instrument simply because a larger air column demands it. The breath must be more quickly and powerfully used in exhalation. This will generally mean more and deeper breaths for the performance of the same number of notes on the Bass clarinet as compared to the performance of the same passage on a soprano clarinet.

The mouthpiece of the Bass clarinet is larger than that of the soprano clarinet, as is the reed, and therefore it will be found necessary to take a longer "bite" with the upper teeth on the mouthpiece in order to obtain a correct relative embouchure. This bite of the upper teeth should never be less than ⅝ of an inch.

It will also be noted that the Bass clarinet mouthpiece meets the embouchure of the player at a more acute angle than is the case with the soprano clarinet. This is due to the curvature of the neck-pipe and must be accounted for by being very careful to hold the instrument exactly in front of the body at an angle which permits the bell of the instrument to fall easily and naturally toward the body of the player. In proper playing position, the body of the Bass clarinet actually makes an angle almost directly opposite to the angle at which the soprano clarinet is normally held. It is very important never to play with the neck of the instrument at an "above-the-horizon" level as this will most certainly result in the impossibility of maintaining the correct principles of embouchure.

The placement of the reed on the lower lip is the same as in the case of the soprano clarinet except that as the Bass clarinet reed is larger, it will rest upon a greater portion of muscular tissue. The lower teeth will however be covered by approximately the same amount of the red portion of the lower lip—

about one-half of it is the best practice.

The oral cavity is formed in the same manner as when playing the soprano clarinet, except that it will be found that slightly more relaxation of the glottis is necessary and a more pronounced 'OOOOOO' syllable should be used.

The larger reed of the Bass clarinet will also require a broader and more pronounced articulation. The position of the tongue and its stroke should be the same as used on the soprano clarinet, with the exception that it will generally be found that better results are obtained by anchoring the tip of the tongue behind the lower teeth and striking the reed with more of the central raised portion of the tongue. This is the method used by many fine players. It permits the broader surface to meet the broader reed, as well as insuring the more vigorous motion necessary to assure a definite response.

The hand position of the Bass clarinetist is the same as that of the soprano clarinetist except that it must be realized that larger keys which must be manipulated require slightly more finger action. The day of the open holes on the Bass clarinet and Alto clarinet has long since passed and therefore the problem of covering the tone holes is easier than that problem with the soprano clarinet. This advantage more than offsets the slightly greater finger action required.

Two exceptions in fingering should be noted. The first is that the first tone-hole of the instrument is equipped with an articulation key-plate somewhat similar to the plateau key for the first tone-hole of the oboe. The purpose of this mechanical arrangement is to permit a small aperture drilled in one-half of this key plate to be opened by a sliding motion of the left forefinger without allowing the entire tone hole to become uncovered. This small aperture is used to permit the easy response of the harmonic register (high C and above) and without this key arrangement, there are literally no fingerings, except the normal harmonic resultants, possible.

The second exception in fingering is the double register key which is quite often found on older Bass clarinets. When this key arrangement is used, the usual straight register key is used for the first overblown notes of the Clarion register, and the second register key is used for all notes above these. Due to peculiarities of each individual instrument it will be found that the second register will sometimes work best when used on D, sometimes on D# and sometimes on E as the first note in its series. Experimentation on the individual instrument will provide the answer in this.

Another mechanical necessity on the Bass clarinet is the low Eb key for the little finger of the right hand. This key is not added to the Bass clarinet because there are many low Eb's to be played, but because the added resonance made possible by the additional tone-hole permits both the law E natural and the B natural third line to sound clearer and more in character with the rest of the register.

For the purposes of study material, once it is recognized that the matter of range is not a limitation, all of clarinet literature is available to the Bass clarinetist. Some things will be found more suitable than others certainly, and long passages in the harmonic register are not to be wholly recommended, but under normal circumstances any clarinet literature may be played on the Bass clarinet.

Solo literature as well, may be approached with the same optimism, and fields such as the literature for the violincello can be explored with profit. Transcriptions are not to be misinterpreted as being sacriligious violations of a composer's intent. Good music is good music and great music is not always bound by the tradition of a composer's indication for which instrument he considered it to be most effective. Had the Bass clarinet enjoyed its present degree of mechanical excellence at the time much of our great music was written it would not be without a repertoire from some of the most mighty pens.

An ambitious, imaginative and serious Bass clarinetist will find that his reward for study and application to the highest principles of musicianship will be rewarded by as satisfying a musical experience as is possible with any instrument.

CHAPTER X

Intonation and Derivation
of the Scale

Intonation is the process of selecting the desired pitch frequency to be used for musical purposes. This selection is accomplished both mechanically with respect to musical instruments, and physically with respect to the activities of musicians, in the playing of their instruments.

The adjustment, design and construction of musical instruments according to a certain intonation is generally referred to as the 'tuning' of the instrument. The intonation as accomplished by the player as he performs on the musical instrument is generally referred to as the process of 'playing in tune.'

Due to the phenomena of human hearing, and the acoustical laws of nature, the formal structure of the art of music as an ordered system of sounds has been developed. This selection and ordering of sound as patterns for repetitive use and reference, is the basis of musical intonation, both for the design and construction of musical instruments, and as a guide for the selection of sound in the performance of music by the composer and the player.

DERIVATION OF THE SCALE
AND MUSICAL INTERVAL RELATIONSHIP

The sounds used in music and their combinations which have been found pleasing to the sense of hearing, and consequently used for the communication of the musical art, are derived from the natural harmonic series produced by the phenomena of vibration.

The Harmonic Series consists of tones which are produced by the vibrational pattern in the ratio of 1,2,3,4,5, etc. The Fundamental is the first of the series and the others are termed overtones, which are multiples of the Fundamental. The Harmonic Series is generally thought of as consisting of about 16 tones.

The series is therefore composed of frequency ratios between its tones of 2:1, 3:2, 4:3 5:4 etc. An interval between two tones is their spacing, or ratio of frequency. The interval of two frequencies bearing the ratio of 2:1 is termed an octave. Other intervals according to their respective ratios are therefore the prime, or unison, where the frequency bears a ratio of 1:1, on through the possible ratios which produce a second, third, fourth, fifth, sixth, seventh and finally the octave. The intervals which are most pleasing to the ear are those by which the frequency ratio may be expressed between two integers, neither of which is large.

The Harmonic Series

Although strings and air columns have certain differences of physical action, the matter of vibration and the production of fundamental tone with concurrent production of overtones is the same.

The first sixteen partials of the harmonic series constructed on C (two octaves below middle C) are as follows, although the harmonic series must not be construed to end with the sixteenth partial. Theoretically, the harmonic series may continue indefinitely. The tones bracketed are approximate in pitch, and really slightly lower in pitch, than indicated, although closer to this pitch than to the semi-tone lower.

THE HARMONIC SERIES OF THE CLARINET

No musical instrument produces all of these harmonics with equal strength, and the patterns or combinations of the harmonics accounts for the tone quality. The clarinet, for example, produces a harmonic series in which the odd numbered harmonics are more prominent than the even numbered. The harmonic pattern of the clarinet is approximately:

Theoretically, as based on the illustration of the Harmonic Series

or, as based on the lowest pitch of the clarinet

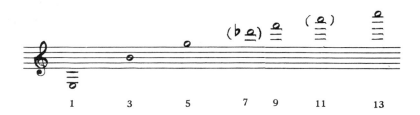

THE DERIVATION OF INTERVALS
FROM THE HARMONIC SERIES

The existence of the Harmonic Series provides us with a mathematical relationship between different musical pitches. These ratios are used as measurements of distance between pitches. The ratios of the Harmonic Series and the intervals so derived are as follows:

| 1:2 Octave | 2:3 Fifth | 3:4 Fourth | 4:5 Fifth | 5:6 Minor Third | 6:7 Indefinite |

| 7:8 Indefinite | 8:9 Major Second | 9:10 Major Second | 10:11 Indefinite | 11:12 Indefinite | 12:13 Indefinite |

| 13:14 Indefinite | 14:15 Indefinite | 15:16 Minor Second |

It will be seen from the above that several of the ratios of the Harmonic Series produce indefinite intervals. These indefinite intervals are immediately eliminated from further consideration in the formation of our system of musical theory in order to avoid confusion, and because of the existence of definite interval relationship provided by other ratios within the series which replace these indefinite intervals. For example, the ratio of 5:6 provides a definite minor third, while the 6:7 ratio provides an indefinite third. Obviously the definite minor third is chosen for the system. The other indefinite intervals are all distorted major or minor seconds and as there are definite major and minor seconds as produced by the ratios 8:9, 9:10 and 15:16, there is no reason for retaining the indefinite intervals. In the case of the two definite intervals of a major second produced by the ratios of 8:9 and 9:10 respectively, the 8:9 ratio is chosen because it is simpler.

The complete series of ratios produces the scale of Just Intonation. The definite ratios chosen for our musical system produces the scale of Tempered Intonation. The Pythagorean
Intonation is based on the ratio of the interval of the Fifth as
found in Just Intonation and proved a useable system until the
complications of musical instrument technique, both in range
and in flexibility of modulation from key to key demanded the
development of a more uniform system.

Having chosen the definite intervals from the series for
calculation, we find that the series is contracted to produce the
following table of ratios and their intervals:

$$1:2 \text{ octave}$$
$$2:3 \text{ fifth}$$
$$3:4 \text{ fourth}$$
$$4:5 \text{ major third}$$
$$5:6 \text{ minor third}$$
$$8:9 \text{ major second}$$
$$15:16 \text{ minor second}$$

These ratios constitute our working table for further calculation.

The ratios between the different members of the Harmonic
Series are arranged in sequence on the basis of the simplicity of
ratio involved. Thus, the relation of the Octave or the $1:2$ ratio
is the simplest and the complexity of ratio increases by the
series $2:3$, $3:4$, $4:5$, etc. The Octave relationship however is in
reality not a relationship of *different* tones but rather the relationship of the same tone in different register. This is easily
proven by attempting to distinguish between the two members
of an octave played simultaneously. Even the acute ear will have
more difficulty in distinguishing between these two pitches than
between any other two pitches played simultaneously. Therefore, even though it represents the simplest possible ratio, the
octave is not used as a basis for our system of musical theory,
but rather the next simplest ratio of $2:3$ or the relationship
which produces the interval of the fifth. The fifth is the
simplest possible difference between two pitches which may be
calculated from the natural ratios of the Harmonic Series and is
therefore used as the basis of musical measurement between
tones.

THE DERIVATION OF THE SCALE

The selection of certain musical pitches with the fifth as a basis of measurement, constitutes a primary Key Group of tones and is the cornerstone of the system of Musical Theory which we use. This selection of pitches is not wholly artificial and arbitrary, but represents as well the result of the appreciation of the human ear for certain sound relationships. Neither has the choice and development of these tones been a sudden and easily determined one but has rather been a slow metamorphosis.

This selection of the several members of the Key Group may be illustrated by the following. To any pitch taken as a base tone is then added the fifth above and the fifth below. Additional fifths are then added to the fifth above until a pitch is reached which would contradict the *lowest* tone of the series, or the fifth below the base note. Using C as a base note the derivation of the Key Group for C is as follows:

When these pitches are drawn together in close proximity by changing their register on the basis of the octave relationship, the result is seen to be a series of pitches which may be arraneged on the musical staff in a stepwise manner of one to each the result is seen to be a series of pitches which may be arranged on the musical staff in a stepwise manner of one to each line and space which is known as the Diatonic Scale.

Key Note

duplication
of key-note
to complete
the octave

The Patterns and Forms of the Scale

The Diatonic Scale which we have derived by our calculations is one of several forms of musical scale patterns which are in common use within the system. A scale in general may be defined as a series of consecutive pitches written on the musical staff with a span of one octave as a limit. A scale may be duplicated in another octave, either above or below, and thus extended scales may be written to the limit of an instrument's pitch range.

When a scale is constructed on the staff using each line and space only once and in consecutive order, the pattern is said to be step-wise or diatonic. Scales may be constructed in which several of the lines and spaces are used more than once in order to accommodate chromatic semi-tones. An excellent example of this usage is the chromatic scale which employs all semi-tones within the octave.

There are various patterns of semi-tones and whole tones used for the construction of scales. These patterns are all based on the natural Diatonic Scale pattern which we have derived from the basic measurement of the fifth and which pattern provides that a natural semi-tone occurs between B and C and E and F on the staff.

A scale of any of the patterns may be constructed on any degree of the staff if the pattern rules are followed. The name of the staff degree on which the scale is constructed is known as the Tonic or Key-note of the scale and the scale constructed on that note is said to be in the Key of that note. Such construction according to the basic Diatonic Scale pattern which is yielded by the basic measurement of the fifth is thus arrived at by another procedure which is somewhat simpler and quicker than the calculation required by the consecutive fifth procedure.

The Common Diatonic Scale Patterns are as follows. Note the several designations which may be used for the various scale steps. These are the same for any Diatonic Scale although illustrated only under the Major Scale.

Letter names	C	D	E	F	G	A	B	C
Numerals	1	2	3	4	5	6	7	8
Harmonic designation	Tonic	Super-Tonic	Mediant	Sub-Dominant	Dominant	Sub-Mediant	Sub-Tonic	Octave
Interval	Prime	Second	Third	Fourth	Fifth	Sixth	Seventh	Octave

THE MINOR SCALE (There are three forms of this scale)

Note: A Minor Scale is termed Relative when it is constructed
on the sixth degree of the Major Scale

A Minor Scale is termed Parallel when it is constructed
on the Tonic of the Major Scale

The Relative Minor Scale for the Key of C is A, its three
forms are as follows:

THE CHROMATIC SCALE

When a Scale is constructed on the Staff using all of the
semi-tones in consecutive order, it is termed Chromatic.

THE WHOLE-TONE SCALE

When a Scale is constructed on the staff using only whole-
tones in consecutive order, it is termed a Whole-Tone Scale.

THE CIRCLE OF KEYS

The Scales built on the various pitches of the Staff fall into a regular series, from the Key of C with no sharps or flats thru the numerical increase of these incidentals until the Keys of six sharps (F#) and six flats (Gb) are reached. This is called the Enharmonic limit of the Keys, which simply means that any pitches used in addition to those used in this series will result in duplications of the Tonic. Any pitch which may be given two letter names is called Enharmonic. Any Scale constructed beyond the Enharmonic limit would have too great a number of sharps or flats to be convenient.

The series of Keys is called the Circle of Keys and the accompanying illustration is a convenient way to remember them. The illustration is constructed to indicate Major Keys and the Relative Minor of each.

names of the Sharps
F-C-G-D-A-E

names of the Flats
B-E-A-D-G-C

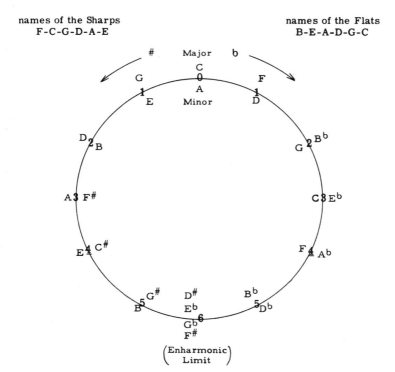

JUST INTONATION

The Harmonic series permits the construction of a series of sounds to be used for the expression of music which are arranged in a sequence from low to high frequency by definite interval spacing. This construction is termed a musical scale. Intonation is the process of adjusting or selecting the tones of a scale accurately according to the frequency required.

A scale which employs the frequency intervals found in the natural harmonic series is termed a scale of Just Intonation. The ear easily distinguishes frequencies in certain discrete quantities which correspond to the basic frequencies of the natural harmonic series. While it is certainly obvious that the ear can distinguish smaller intervals for comparative purposes, as discussed under the section on Hearing, it is also equally true that the smallest interval easily expressed as an auditory sensation and most exactly reproduced at will for musical expressive purposes is that of the semi-tone, or the frequency ratio of $11:15$ as found in the harmonic series.

Using the ratios of the integers of the natural harmonic series, the complete scale of Just Intonation may be constructed. Each semi-tone is divided into 100 parts in order to provide a very accurate measurement. These 100th parts of a semi-tone are called cents, and the cent as a measurement unit is derived from the fact that it is an interval between two tones whose basic ratio is that of the twelve-hundredth root of 2. Therefore, the interval in cents is 1200 times the logarithm on the base 2 of the frequency ratio. This calculation provides us with 1200 cents equalling twelve semi-tones and therefore 1200 cents for the interval of the octave, or 100 cents per semi-tone. The octave limit is established physically by calculation and as an auditory sensation which judges the tones of an octave to be exactly the the same except for the separation in high or low sound. The scale of Just Intonation follows:

SCALE OF JUST INTONATION

Interval	Frequency ratio	number of cents in interval
unison	1:1	000.000
semi-tone	16:15	111.731
minor tone	10:9	182.404
major tone	9:8	203.910
Minor Third	6:5	315.641
Major Third	5:4	386.314
Perfect Fourth	4:3	498.045
Augmented Fourth	45:32	590.224
Diminished Fifth	64:45	609.777
Perfect Fifth	3:2	701.955
Minor Sixth	8:5	813.687
Major Sixth	5:3	884.359
Harmonic Minor Seventh	7:4	968.826
Lowered Minor Seventh	16:9	996.091
Minor Seventh	9:5	1017.597
Major Seventh	15:8	1088.269
Octave	2:1	1200.000

All of these intervals are necessary to account for the several ratios of the natural harmonic series. It is obvious that there are several more very close interval measurements produced by using these ratios than are provided for in the system of notation which uses five lines and four spaces and a system of letter names, even though the alteration of intervals by means of raising or lowering them with the modification of sharp and flat signs is provided. With the use of the complete ratios of the harmonic series, there are tones which fall in between the smallest discrete interval provided for in our system, the semi-note.

PYTHAGOREAN INTONATION

Pythogorean Intonation is a system of musical scale construction which was introduced into Greece about the middle of the sixth century B.C. This scale was provided with a standardization by the early Greek mathematician Pythagoras and has remained the common scale in use for western music until the present as far as its practical design is concerned. Pythagoras

noted that the intervals obtained by the division of a string into
its aliquot parts produced pitchs in accord with their arithmetical ratio. Based on this discovery, he found further that by
commencing with any pitch and progressing from that pitch to
the fifth above it, that a cycle of fifths resulted which finally
returned to the original pitch used as a starting point. One
serious error however, complicated this system. The exact ratio
of the fifth as $3:2$, derived from the base tone and its octave
length of string when used as a progressive measurement
throughout the cycle of fifths by increasing the factor $(1{\bullet}5)^{12}$,
which is exactly the ratio of $3:2$ or $1{\bullet}5$ derived as the second
and third harmonics of the same fundamental yields a value of
129.75, or twelve times $1{\bullet}5$. Since the progression through the
cycle of fifths requires twelve tones to bring us back again to the
starting tone, such a frequency of $129{\bullet}75$ is seen not to be the
same as the tone from which we started which should be exactly
128. The difference is found to be a difference greater than that
of our starting point by a factor of $1{\bullet}0136$. This difference is
known as the 'comma of Pythagoras" and amounts to about one-
quarter of a semi-tone.

The difficulty of Pythagorean intonation is very simply that
by attempting to build a cycle of fifths as a basis for deriving all
of the twelve tones of the scale, that the use of the fifth as found
in the perfect ratio of Just Intonation which is that of $3:2$ or
amounting to $1{\bullet}5000$ as a ratio to the $1{\bullet}000$ of the fundamental
is not the same as the ratios obtained by dividing the octave
into the exactly twelve equal parts which would be necessary
in order to arrive at the same pitch used as a base tone. The
octave divided into twelve equal parts, as we shall see by the
discussion of Equal temperament yields a fifth as the ratio of
$1{\bullet}4983$. Multiplying the difference between these two fifths
twelve times gives the 'comma'.

The Pythagorean system, when used for only one octave, was
quite satisfactory for the limitations of the older musical instruments. The Church modes were all derived from this system
and it continued to be useful until the more complicated forms
of music and instrumental development demanded an intonation
which would permit more uniform construction of musical instruments and a notation for them which could use interchangable
reference symbols.

THE SCALE OF EQUAL TEMPERAMENT

As seen by the scale of Just intonation derived from the natural harmonic series, the number of tones required for the octave is much too great to allow for mechanically convenient musical instrument construction, and is also difficult to notate with an interchangable reference system. The Pythagorean scale, while useful as a solution to the interval problems of the Just intonation does not allow for complications extending beyond the octave.

At a very early date, about 1482, a Spanish musician by the name of Bartolo Rames proposed that the "comma" of Pythagoras be distributed throughout the octave in such a way that the cycle of twelve tones which make up the progression of fifths as discovered by Pythagoras are each flatter in pitch by an interval of about one forty-eighth of a semi-tone. In this way the frequency ratio of $128 \bullet 1$ found as the ratio by the progression of fifths would each then represent a ratio of $^{12}\sqrt{128}$ or 1.4983. In this way, all semi-tones become equal, and each have precisely the same ratio of $1 \bullet 05946$.

These ratios were subsequently calculated and published by the French mathematician Mersenne, in his Harmonie Universelle, in 1636. The first practical use that has been noted however, was in the organ constructed by Schnitger in Hamburg in 1688-92. Johann Sebastian Bach attempted to put the equal temperament into practice and wrote his Well-Tempered Clavichord to prove that compositions in all keys could be played without disagreeable dissonances. After Bach's death, his son, Philipp Emanuel did much to urge the establishment of this intonation. There was much resistance to it however and it was not until as late as 1850 that pianos were tuned to this scale in England.

The Tempered scale is now in universal use, and as it provides a system which permits the uniformity that is required for key-board instruments as well as allowing the flexibility exercised by the melodic line instruments, it appears that the compromise between Just intonation and Tempered intonation has satisfactorily been accomplished as far as the practical performance of music is concerned. There remains an area of discussion and freedom as far as intonation is concerned but this is only another dimension of the art which lends a personal and desirable flexibility to its performance.

SCALE OF EQUAL TEMPERAMENT

Interval	frequency ratio	number of cents
Unison	1:1	000
Semi-tone or Minor Second	1.059463:1	100
Whole-Tone or Major Second	1.122462:1	200
Minor Third	1.189207:1	300
Major Third	1.259921:1	400
Perfect Fourth	1.334840:1	500
Augmented Fourth or Diminished Fifth	1.414214:1	600
Perfect Fifth	1.498307:1	700
Minor Sixth	1.587401:1	800
Major Sixth	1.681793:1	900
Minor Seventh	1.781797:1	1000
Major Seventh	1.887749:1	1100
Octave	2:1	1200

It will be noted that the tempered intonation combines several of the just intonation intervals in such a manner as to eliminate any tone which would be smaller than the number of 100 cents or a multiple of such a number, thus confining any musical tone in pitch or in interval measurement in this system within the limits of a semi-tone or multiples of the semi-tone.

The following Chart gives an opportunity to quickly contrast the three Intonation patterns, of Pythagorean, Just and Tempered Scales.

PYTHAGOREAN SCALE
Requires 22 Separate Tones, to complete the octave C-C²

Note	Decimal Ratio	Cents	Frequency
C	1.000	0	261.62
B#	1.013	23.5	265.20
D♭	1.053	90.2	275.62
C#	1.067	113.7	279.38
D	1.125	203.9	294.33
E♭	1.185	294.1	310.08
D#	1.201	317.6	314.31
F♭	1.248	384.4	326.66
E	1.265	407.8	331.12
F	1.333	498.0	348.83
E#	1.351	521.5	353.59
G♭	1.404	588.3	367.49
F#	1.423	611.7	372.51
G	1.500	702.0	392.42
A♭	1.580	792.2	413.44
G#	1.601	815.6	419.07
A	1.687	905.9	441.49
B♭	1.777	996.1	465.11
A#	1.802	1019.6	471.46
C♭	1.872	1086.3	489.99
B	1.898	1109.8	496.69
C	2.000	1200.0	523.25

JUST SCALE
Requires 22 separate tones, to complete the octave C-C²

Note	Decimal Ratio	Cents	Frequency
C	1.000	0	261.62
C#	1.041	70.7	272.51
D♭	1.066	111.7	279.07
D	1.125	203.9	294.33
D#	1.171	274.6	306.51
E♭	1.200	315.6	313.95
E	1.250	386.3	327.04
F♭	1.280	427.4	334.88
E#	1.302	457.0	340.66
F	1.333	498.0	348.83
F#	1.406	590.2	367.91
G♭	1.440	631.3	376.74
G	1.500	702.0	392.44
G#	1.562	772.6	408.79
A♭	1.600	813.7	418.60
A	1.666	884.4	436.04
A#	1.757	976.5	459.89
B♭	1.800	1017.6	470.93
B	1.875	1088.3	490.55
C♭	1.920	1129.3	502.32
B#	1.953	1159.0	519.99
C	2.000	1200.0	523.25

TEMPERED SCALE
Requires 13 Separate Tones, to complete the octave C-C²

Note	Decimal Ratio	Cents	Frequency
C	1.000	0	261.62
C# ⎫ D♭ ⎬	1.059	100	277.18
D	1.122	200	293.67
D# ⎫ E♭ ⎬	1.189	300	311.13
E ⎫ F♭ ⎬	1.259	400	329.63
E# ⎫ F ⎬	1.334	500	349.23
F# ⎫ G♭ ⎬	1.414	600	369.99
G	1.498	700	392.00
G# ⎫ A♭ ⎬	1.587	800	415.31
A	1.681	900	440.00
A# ⎫ B♭ ⎬	1.781	1000	466.16
B ⎫ C♭ ⎬	1.887	1100	493.88
B# ⎫ C	2.000	1200	523.25

*Note that for comparison to Just and Tempered Scale that increase in Frequency is not the same as Chromatic Notation.
Based on A = 440 cps and C = 261.62 cps for equally Tempered Scale

CHAPTER XI

Part 1: Hearing

The vibrations of an elastic body transmitted through the air as sound pressure changes are sensed by the ear and perceived as the auditory response which is termed hearing.

The human ear is a fantastically developed organ which is able to detect changes in air pressure smaller than a change in the atmospheric pressure of some ten-thousandth-millionth part of the whole pressure. This amounts to a change in altitude, if compared to the barometric pressure, of an ascent of only some 30,000th part of an inch.

These minute changes in air pressure are collected by the external part of the ear and led through a narrow channel called the meatus, at the end of which is found the thin membrane of the eardrum. This thin membrane is deformed by the air-pressure changes and transmits its vibrations as caused by the deformations through a series of little bones, and tenons and thence through the oval window of the inner ear to a liquid in the inner ear. The inner ear consists of three semicircular bony canals lying at right angles to each other, terminating in a shell-like shape. This whole complex structure of canals with its termination is called the cochlea. The cochlea contains an additional thin little membrane only about 1¼ inches in length and one eight-thousandth of an inch in thickness. In this membrane are embedded some 24,000 fibres varying in length from one-fifteenth to one and one-hundred-seventieth inch in length. This membrane, called the basilar membrane, moves as the motion transmitted from the eardrum to the liquid in the cochlea sets it in motion. The tiny fibers transmit this motion to the brain as electric impulses which are finally recognized as sounds.

The complicated transmission of the sound waves through the mechanism of the ear is so designed that the ear is protected

THE MECHANISM OF THE HUMAN EAR

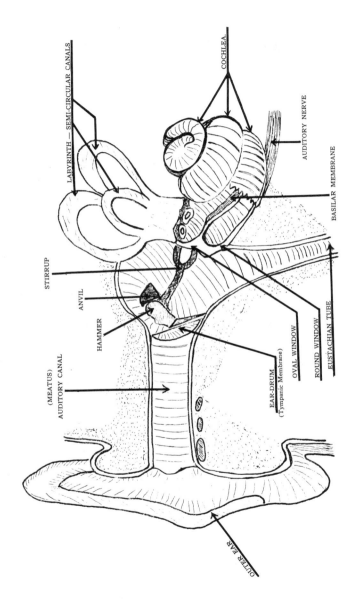

SEMI-CIRCULAR CANALS

LABYRINTH

COCHLEA.

AUDITORY NERVE

BASILAR MEMBRANE

STIRRUP

ANVIL

HAMMER

(MEATUS)
AUDITORY CANAL

EAR-DRUM
(Tympanic Membrane)

OVAL WINDOW

ROUND WINDOW

EUSTACHIAN TUBE

OUTER EAR

in its reaction to the several possible kinds of vibration and the results of this transmission. This mechanical property of protection of its function allows the ear to be extremely sensitive throughout the full range of sound pressure, or frequency changes, with respect to its capacity, which is a range of from about 16 to 20,000 vibrations per second. In addition to the sensitivity of response to this range of possible vibration, the ear is able to respond to all of the several frequencies within its capacity at the same time. This added property of response provides for the hearing of more than one sound at the same time, and accounts for the discrimination possible as to the combination of frequencies which produce the recognition of tonal structure differences, or the difference between the sounds of the several musical instruments

The frequency response of the ear basically determines the pitch of music. The length of time that the sound persists is of course its duration, and the intensity of the sound pressure wave is recognized as the 'volume' of the sound. The combination of the several frequencies is referred to as the color or quality of the tone which is being heard.

In addition, the ear, being actually a sort of musical instrument itself, due to its vibrational potentials, adds certain tones of its own to its resonant response.

VIBRATIONAL PATTERNS ADDED TO SOUND BY THE EAR

The membrane of the ear, or the ear-drum is not symmetrical in its action since on one side it is in contact with the air, and on the other side it is impeded by the action of the small bones which are activated by its movement.

The vibrations which reach the ear-drum from the outer ear, cause it to move in the pattern which they present. As the ear-drum moves outward it is pulled back by its own elasticity, but when it moves inward, these small bones receive its motion for transmission to the inner ear and restrict and absorb its action in this direction.

If the ear-drum were symmetrical, that is, perfectly similar in action both as it vibrates inwardly and outwardly, it would follow the pattern of the sound vibrations in perfect accord with their shape. Since it is not symmetrical, it adds a vibrational pattern of its own to the sound wave shape which is a new motion transmitted to the inner ear, and which is of course formed in this way by the ear itself in the process of response to the stimulation of the sound wave from the outer air. This additional pattern which is created by the ear itself, provides a shape which must be added to the original sound wave from the outer air in order to determine what tone is finally conveyed to the brain.

It is thus obvious, that what we recognize as the tones we hear is something of a more complex nature than the original natural phenomena of external vibration. It can be truly said therefore, that the hearing of a musical tone is in a sense always something of a subjective mattern for the hearer, since part of what he hears is created by his own ears and by no others. This is not so unusual since all of our senses accomplish the same personal treatment of the external world.

The ear-drum due to its asymmetrical action, adds to any pure tone that is presented to it, the octave, and all of the other natural harmonics. This is quite simple to illustrate.

If a sound wave is represented by a simple curve which may be designated as a frequency of 100 cycles per second, the added response of the ear because of its asymmetry may be shown. Since the original sound curve, due to Fourier's theorem may be analyzed into all of the simple harmonic curves which are repeated 100 times per second it is obvious that the new curve added by the asymmetry of the ear will also have all of the simple harmonic curves of its frequency occuring each second. Helmholtz first showed this to be a fact by his investigations, and established by demonstration, that when a single pure tone is presented to the ear that by its own accord, due to its asymmetry, it adds a second simple harmonic vibration of just double the frequency, or the octave.

In addition, Helmholtz demonstrated that when two pure tones are presented to the ear, that not only are octaves of each of the two pure tones added by the ear, but that also the new frequencies represented by their summation and by their difference are also added. Two tones of 100 and of 300 cycles for example, not only cause the ear to add tones of 200 and 600 cycles for their octaves but also tones of 200 cycles or the 'difference', and also of 400 cycles, as the 'summation', of their frequencies. Not only this, but the ear also adds all of the octaves, and all of the difference and summation tones of all the frequencies which are presented to it simultaneously.

The ear therefore acts as a vibrator in its own right in addition to carefully receiving, filtering and recording for us the vibrations which it receives from the outer air. When the import of this vast possibility of complexity of vibrational pattern is appreciated, it will be at once understood that the complexity of the term 'tone-quality' is not an exaggerated matter of concern for the musician in his search for a certain definite medium for his musical expression.

Fortunately, the problem of energy distribution as concerns the sound wave patterns and the natural design of the ear as a self-protecting mechanism which 'damps' or controls vibrational activity, allows the situation to be somewhat simplified in actual practice. The full possibility of the ear's vibrational pattern can be illustrated in order to suggest the tremendous scope of the hearing system. But it must be remembered that we, very selectively, due primarily to the amount of energy expended in both the vibrational patterns initiated in the outer air by our musical instruments, and by our concentration on certain aspects of our psychological response to stimuli, simplify the situation in a manner which permits the practice of music.

The possibilities of the ear are such that if three original frequencies are presented to it, that a table of responses would show in order of importance.

Fundamental tones

Difference tones between the fundamentals

Second Harmonics of the Fundamentals

Summation tones of the Fundamentals

Difference Tones between the second harmonics

Third Harmonics

Summation tones of the Third Harmonics

The fourth, fifth and sixth Harmonics of the Fundamentals

Additional harmonics of all the fundamentals to the eighteenth

It is a fact that when the fourth fifth and six harmonics are sounded without the fundamental tone that the ear adds the fundamental and all of the harmonics up to the eighteenth. Also, the ear responds in such a manner that when any two or more pure tones are presented to it simultaneously, which happen to be harmonics of the same fundamental, that the ear then adds the fundamental and many of the harmonics. If the pure tones are odd-numbered harmonics of the fundamental, the ear adds all of the even numbered harmonics.

As the frequencies of two pure tones approach each other until they differ only slightly, the resulting difference tone becomes a 'beat' to the ear rather than a definite pitch. The summation tone that results from such a situation approaches the second harmonic of either of the two frequencies and also produces the effect of a beat.

Difference tones can be easily heard by sounding, rather loudly, almost any two tones that are a fifth apart. The tone an octave below the lower of the two test tones, will then be heard. Difference tones are also produced easily by sounding consonant intervals of the fifth, fourth and third by treble clef instruments in their higher range. Difference tones resulting from fifths will sound as an octave below the lowest of the test tones; those from the fourths an ocatve below the upper test tones; those from the major third an octave below the lower test tone; and from the minor third an octave and a fifth, or a twelfth below the upper test tone. Difference tones are usually concordant, that is, in tune with the test tone but a very interesting result is demonstrated with respect to the harmonic structure of tone when a major third is produced as a test in the treble range above the staff. If such an interval is played in just intonation, the difference tone will be in perfect tune. If the major third is played with equal temperament, the difference tone will result in almost a semi-tone difference between the desired octave causing a very annoying 'hum'. This difference was referred to by Helmholtz as the 'horrible' bass, and is one of the problems of the equal temperament system of tuning. String players and singers are very much aware of this matter and for this reason are quite prone to 'correct' tempered tuning especially on sustained chords to that of just intonation in order to avoid it.

Summation tones are much more difficult to hear since they lie in the area of the harmonic structure already established by the natural harmonics of the tone structure, which is above the fundamental. Under certain conditions they may be heard, especially in concert halls where the period of resonance is prolonged. Summation tones are not necessarily concordant, since the 'sum' of the frequencies of the fundamental tones does not guarantee a harmonic result.

Usually, summation tones are discordant, and effect the tonal structure as an impurity while difference tones, being concordant under most circumstances, do not disturb the tonal value. The value of the concordance of difference tones has actually been turned to an acoustical advantage, and the telephone as well as our loudspeakers for audio purposes, provide us with a demonstration of the fact that although the frequency range of these instruments is limited due to their size the reconstruction of the difference tones by the ear's action of asymmetry, provides us with the sound as it is originally produced. The transmission of sound by our audio speakers provides us with a source rich in harmonics but totally lacking in the bass. The ear however supplies the bass by means of its action in producing difference tones, and the effect of the music is the same as if these bass tones had actually been transmitted. Organ builders use this phenomenon to provide low bass sounds by tuning two treble pipes in the proper manner, and it has been stated that even the lower notes of the piano are generally heard as a result of the ear providing difference tones, rather than by hearing the fundamental directly as produced. Tones produced by mechanical means at frequencies higher than the ear, can hear produce difference tones which are then found to be in the audio range.

For a long time it was believed that both difference and summation tones were completely subjective and had no existence outside of the human ear itself. However, Helmholtz provided proof that under certain conditions these tones are objective, and can be detected by means of resonators. No one has been able to challenge his proof of this to date. The mathematical condition that these tones should actually have real being in the objective world is very simple to describe. All sound is represented by the figure of a sound curve, and since the effect of the sound wave represented by a smooth curve on the asymmetry of the ear causes the ear to produce the difference and summation tones by adding to the smooth sound wave curve another component, there is no reason to suppose that the same effect of asymmetry is not present to distort the smooth sound wave curve every time it passes from one source to another. In fact, there are to be found no absolutely symmetrical resonators in any of our many musical instrument designs. Therefore, the production of asymmetrical wave patterns from symmetrical waves, is actually more common than not. Since this is true, there is no reason to believe otherwise, than that the objective reality of difference and summation tones is a fact. They are however, attributed for the most part, to the impurity of sound production, and the noise quotient associated with musical tone generation, and for that reason are not given the value of the main body of the sound which we use as a base. The impurities in a musical tone are for the most part due to this phenomenon.

That the human mind can willingly concentrate on certain things and ignore others, allows us the possibility of selectively 'hearing' what we wish to hear, provided the energy output of that which we choose to ignore is not so strong as to be at a level which prevents our selectivity. We do the same thing with our eyes in seeing that which we wish to observe, unless the distraction is so great as to be above the level of our selective ability of observation. The energy out-put of the great majority of the tone pattern vibrations shown in our table is below the level of our selective powers of concentration and therefore negligible to the matter of musical practice. The various noise quotients contained in any of the sound production methods used in the initiation of vibrations by musical instruments fall into this same category. The hiss of the air-stream or 'wind-rush' in pipes, the scrape of the violin bow on the strings, the percussive sounds of the key-board instruments, the clatter of wood-wind instrument keys, and all of the rest of the noise associated with playing musical instruments can be, and is, ignored, unless it reaches a level which is beyond a certain tolerance on the part of our selective concentration.

The ear has definite limits of capacity for hearing discrimination, due to its mechanical processes. These mechanical processes which determine recognition of the auditory sensation, thus limit the understanding of what our ears tell us about sound, by comparison to the information from electronic or mechanical measurements which are transmitted to us by means of our eyes.

The limitations of pitch are those frequencies which fall in the frequency response range of the ear—16 to 20,000 cycles. The limit of discrimination as to pitch difference must therefore be musically limited to this range. In addition, the range of frequency discrimination, changes with age and condition of the ear. Laboratory proof of frequencies much higher than those that the ear can hear are evident. Other organisms and animals, also have a higher aural frequency discrimination than the human ear.

Discrimination with regards to duration is a discrete quantity as far as the human ear is concerned. After a certain point, reiterated pulses become a steady tone for the ear. In fact, the auditory response to any tone is the result of the acceptance of this steady stream of pulses instead of a hearing of each pulse separately, as an individual sound wave.

Discrimination of tone quality is also dependent on a limitation as far as the human ear is concerned. Difference and summation tones which the ear adds to the external signal received account for much of our interpretation of tone quality as such. The vivid impact of the beginning of a tone, or its transient values, causes the ear to evaluate a tone much differently than if this transient is absent. This has been shown very clearly by the recording of a musical tone played by several different instruments and then by removing the beginning of the tone from the recording. The ear has great difficulty in determining exactly what instrument is playing without the information given by the transient.   The complete partial structure of the one at its beginning, with the subsequent very rapid damping of several of the higher partials, or other weaker partials in the tone structure, when not supplied to the ear, by the transient condition, causes it to lose its powers of discrimination in this way.

The self-protective mechanical design of the human ear also causes a difficulty in discrimination of the actual value of the sound as measured by its energy by laboratory instruments. The ear will refuse to react for too loud a sound—in fact after a certain loudness has been reached it has been found that the tone seems to suddenly decrease in volume rather than to become louder, even though additional energy is added. The same is true of different frequency evaluations with relation to the energy actually present. A human ear hears higher frequencies as louder than lower frequencies, even though the actual energy value may be less in the higher tone.

Thus we see that it is necessary to know what the ear does in order to interpret what we mean when we refer to any physical measurement of sound obtained by laboratory means. We must be able to accurately interpret and equate the psychological or psycho-acoustic values of music.

The psychological aspects of hearing must be related to the actual physical properties of the phenomenon of sound in order to properly equate and evaluate sound used for musical purposes. While it is possible to measure sound by means of mechanical or electronic means, and so provide visual displays which are useful in discussion and in calculation, it is also vitally necessary for the musician to be able to refer, and to relate, these calculations accomplished by such laboratory techniques, to the actual process of his hearing as such. A great deal of misinterpretation and difficulty in the study of music and in its development which demands the recognition of both the physical and psychological aspects of sound analysis, which should supplement each other, is caused by a difficulty in terminology and in definition by description. See Chapter III, Some Qualitative and Quantitative Aspects of Sound as Used for Music.

CHAPTER XI

Part 2: The Tuning of the Clarinet

Musical instruments may be roughly divided into two general categories. First, those instruments of fixed intonation, such as the keyboard instruments which cannot be affected by the desire of the player for tuning except by a mechanical adjustment, which is not part of the performance practice; and second, those instruments which, although basically designed, constructed or adjusted for a certain general intonation, may be affected by the physical activities of playing them in such a way as to vary their intonation, at the will of the player, as a general performance practice. These are the instruments of flexible intonation.

The second category of musical instruments may be divided again into two subdivisions of instruments which, first, can be very flexibly adjusted to the desires of the player as in the case of the stringed instruments, the trombone, and the human voice; and secondly, where, although there are limitations by design, the player can and does exercise a control of variation within definite limits. This subdivision includes the case of the woodwind and most brass instruments.

The clarinet is of the second classification of the flexible intonation instrument subdivision. The clarinet is designed and constructed in such a way as to provide a certain basic intonation pattern provided by the placement of the tone holes and the key mechanism of the instrument. The calculation of this matter is a problem of acoustical mechanics.

This calculation consists in first determining the fundamental length of the instrument to be constructed, and second, in then providing the proper placement and spacing of the various tone holes. A key mechanism system is then designed to operate the opening and closing of the tone holes for the facility required in performance.

These constructional necessities will be considered in order as the tuning of the clarinet.

CALCULATION OF FUNDAMENTAL LENGTH

Clarinets are constructed in several different pitches or frequency ranges. These have been previously noted under elaboration of design.

Calculation for the acoustics of the clarinet have been referred to in the chapter *Acoustics of the Clarinet.*

Briefly, the clarinet must be constructed with a fundamental length of pipe, which will then have the tone holes calculated to provide the proper scale desired. The fundamental resonant frequency for a pipe closed at one end and open at the other is:

$$\text{fundamental frequency} = \frac{\text{velocity of sound}}{\text{wave-length}} = \frac{\text{velocity of sound}}{4 \times \text{length of pipe}}$$

and:

$$\frac{\text{velocity of sound}}{\text{fundamental frequency}} = \frac{\text{wave-length of sound}}{4}$$

The resonant overtones of a pipe closed at one end and open at the other are the odd harmonics or $f2 = 3f_1$, $f3 = 5f_1$ etc.

For these formulas no end correction has been applied. As has been noted in the chapter dealing with the acoustics of the clarinet there are two factors of acoustical impedance at the end of a pipe. These are, the resistance due to the radiation of the sound into the open air, and the reactance due to the motion of the air beyond the open end of the pipe which is caused by this radiation of sound. The air beyond the end of a pipe is actually in motion of course, due to the vibrations which have been emitted from the end of the pipe. The end correction for such a pipe depends on whether or not the end is equipped with a flange, or radiator, or in the case of the clarinet a bell. The bell of the clarinet provides a radiation pattern which is calculated as an angle of radiation of 2π steradians. This amounts to a correction of 0.82R where R is the radius of the pipe. This length must be added to the open end of the pipe in order to obtain the effective length necessary for the fundamental frequency desired. This effective length is used to determine the resonant frequencies of pipes from their physical dimensions.

If a pipe is to be used for the production of a single tone, as in the case of the pipe organ, such a pipe may be of a fixed length with the end correction applied. However, when a single pipe is required to produce many frequencies over a wide range, it is necessary to accommodate the change in the effective length of such a pipe and effect a corresponding change in its resonant frequency. The provision of tone holes in the body of such a pipe accomplishes this change in effective length.

Another formula for the calculation of fundamental frequency which has been used for many years by organ builders is as follows:

For a cylindrical pipe, 6 × length + 10 × diameter divided into 20,080 for inches or into 510,000 for millimeters.

For a conical pipe, 3 × length + 5 × diameter divided into the same factors for inches or millimeters as above.

This calculation will hold for a temperature of about 60 degrees Fahrenheit. For each degree of temperature increase add a frequency increase of one-half of a cycle.

Obviously an end correction must also be added to complete the approximate computation. It should also be remembered that organ builders presume a certain constant pressure of air, which for these formulas is a pressure of about three and one-eighth inches or eight centimeters, which means a wind pressure that will support a column of water of that height in a gauge called a "windgauge". This pressure is not too different from that of a wind-instrument blown by a wind instrument player at about the mezzo-forte level.

CALCULATION OF TONE HOLES.

In order to calculate the effect and placement of a tone hole in a pipe as described, it is necessary to use additional formulas, since the acoustical impedance at the end of the pipe will now be changed due to the change of its effective length, and the additional acoustical impedance of the tone hole open to the air from which vibrational effects will radiate.

The fundamental length of the pipe without a hole in its side will be corrected for effective length, by means of a formula which will account for the acoustical impedance at the open end. However, the same pipe with a hole in its side will require a formula which will first of all provide a change of effective length according to the spacing of the hole from the end of the pipe. This is easily obtained by calculating the effective length for various segments of the pipe, as if it were to be cut off at the point where the tone hole is to be drilled. This formula will provide the end correction in terms of the acoustical impedance for any length of the pipe where it is desired to place a tone hole. This calculation will take into consideration the relation of the cross section or bore of the pipe to its length.

$$\frac{\text{velocity of sound}}{\text{fundamental frequency}} = \frac{\text{wave-length of sound}}{4} + 0.82\,R$$

where R is the radius of the bore measurement.

The actual drilling of the tone hole in the pipe will add to the situation a need for calculating the inertance or vibrational radiation leak through this tone hole to the open air. This develops a relationship which requires a formula which will express the length of the pipe necessary for the fundamental frequency to be obtained by the length of the pipe from the end to the tone hole in combination with the effect of the acoustical impedance occasioned by the tone hole with respect to the remainder of the pipe length from the tone hole to the other end of the pipe, since the pipe was not really cut off, but only shortened by drilling the tone hole in its side.

A theoretical expression of this situation is obtained simply by using the tone-hole diameter as an open end of the pipe and adding its end correction requirement to the preceeding formula. In effect this is what has been done practically, by all makers of clarinets by trial and error, or by calculation.

The most accurate calculation as well as measurement will be obtained by a final formula as follows;

$$\frac{\text{velocity of sound}}{\text{fundamental frequency}} = \frac{\text{wave-length of sound}}{4}$$
$$\text{plus } 0.82\,R\,(\text{pipe}) \text{ and plus } 0.82\,R\,(\text{tone-hole})$$

The fact that the pipe has not been cut off, but that a hole has been drilled in it causes the pitch of the tone produced by means of the tone hole to be lower than would be a tone produced by a pipe cut to this length. The size of the tone hole also determines the pitch result as can be readily understood, and this fact makes the tuning of the clarinet an obvious matter as far as the fundamental scale is concerned. It is necessary to take into account these factors: The pipe length and diameter of bore must be basically determined; the tone hole calculation must be determined by the pitch desired, and the size and place-ment of these holes in the side of the pipe must be made with respect to the requirements of a key mchanism to operate them.

The 'scale' of the pipe, or the ratio of its diameter to its length is a necessary factor in tone-hole placement calculation.

In general, the smaller the diameter with respect to the length of the pipe, or the narrower the 'scale' of proportion, the lower the primary vibrational mode will be, and the more resistance, or acoustical impedance will be encountered. How-ever, at the same time, such a scale will yield a greater number of harmonics for the primary vibrational mode, and a richer timbre of sound as well as a more accurate and easily controlled production of the secondary and subsequent vibrational modes.

The wider the 'scale' proportion, or the greater the diameter in ratio to the length of the pipe, the higher the primary vibra-tional mode will be with respect to fundamental length and the easier the response or the less acoustical impedance to vibra-tory initiation will be encountered. However, with such a scale, the fewer harmonics present in the primary mode will yield a less rich and a thinner timbre of sound, and the less controlled and accurate will be the secondary and subsequent vibrational modes.

These acoustical facts are easily proven by the experience of the player in testing the severally designated 'large-bore' and 'small-bore' designed clarinets. Even with the most accurate and careful adjustment of the tone-generating system, the fundamental differences of these two 'scales' assert themselves.

The Boehm clarinet is essentially a design of wider scale than the German style clarinet. This fact precludes the mutation of the two basic designs by any attempts to employ a tone-generat-ing system suited for one design on a clarinet of the other design. The many variations available within the range of tolerance for each 'pure' design allows for compensation, but at the same time causes much difficulty for those who are ignorant of the acoustical facts involved.

The following facts should be remembered:

1. The length of the air-column determines the pitch frequency with respect to the wave-length or the speed of vibration travel along the length of the pipe. The difference in travel has been explained with respect to the 'open' and the 'closed' pipes under the Chapter, "Acoustics of the Clarinet."

2. The 'scale' of the pipe, or its ratio of diameter to length determines the harmonic content of the primary vibrational mode, or the harmonic response.

3. The length and the 'scale' jointly, therefore, determine the actual pitch frequency of the pipe.

4. The shape of the pipe is the principle determinant of the harmonic content of the pipe.

5. The shape and the 'scale' jointly therefore determine the actual complete harmonic content of the sound of the pipe.

The size of the tone-holes decreases the further they are placed from the end of the pipe open to the air, or the end opposite to that of the tone-generating system. The size of the tone-hole is determined jointly by the length of the pipe and by the ratio of the 'scale'. Since the tube of the clarinet is that of a parallel walled or cylindrical shape, the size of the tone-holes must diminish in order to accommodate the 'scale' which cannot be accomplished by a change in the size of the bore.

A method of obtaining a rough approximation of 'scale' by means of tone-hole diminution is provided by a construction formula similar to that of obtaining 'scale' for a rank of organ pipes.

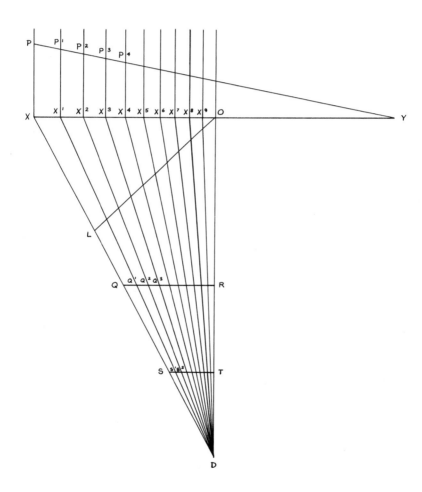

SCALE DETERMINANT

Construction of Scale Determinant

1. Line **XOY** is drawn in proportion to the length of the pipe.

2. Line **OD** is constructed at midpoint of **XOY** and at right angles to it for the same length as **XOY**.

3. A line is drawn connecting **X** and **D**.

4. Right angle **XOD** is bisected and a line extended to meet **XD** at **L**.

5. Line **LO** is divided into aliquot parts equal to one-third the total number of divisions which are desired for the length of the pipe.

6. Lines are then drawn through each point of division so established on **LO** to point **D** and extended to meet **XO**.

7. **OD** is divided at midpoint and **QR** drawn at right angles to it.

8. **ST** is constructed likewise at a midpoint between **R** and **D**.

9. Vertical lines are erected on **X** at each point established by the extension of lines drawn from **D** through **LO**.

10. A line is drawn from point **Y** to a point on the vertical line erected at point **X** which is the proportion of the bore diameter of the pipe as selected. This will establish point **P**.

11. The intersections of line **PY** and the vertical lines erected on **XO** will yield proportional tone-hole dimunitions in terms of bore diameter for the length of the pipe from **X** to **O**, or at mid-point. Points established on **OY** by transposing points provided by the intersection of lines drawn from **D** to **XY** through points on **QR** and points likewise established on **ST** will provide remaining tone-hold diminutions for the length of the pipe.

This is for the reason that the diameter of the pipe at any point would be the diameter with respect to its length if the pipe were cut off at this point. Since the pipe is not cut off, but a tone-hole is drilled in it, the size of the tone-hole is basically that of the diameter at this point.

In practice, the exact 'scale' of diminution of tone-holes according to the formula is not followed, since constructional factors have been simplified in the case of the clarinet to some seven differently sized tone-holes which are then placed either slightly higher or lower on the pipe, or are 'phrased' to accomplish tuning.

The larger a hole, the higher the pitch and the smaller the hole, the lower the pitch, is a general rule. Also the further from the open end the tone hole is placed the higher in pitch the tone produced will be. It is also understood that the greater the diameter of the tone hole (which provides the radius for the end-correction formula) with respect to the bore of the instrument at that point, the higher in pitch the tone will be. The enlargement either of the tone hole or of the bore at this point has the same effect. For this reason, tone-holes are undercut or enlarged at the point where they meet the bore of the instrument. Fine tuning and adjusting of the clarinet is accomplished by this 'phrasing', or undercutting, of the tone-hole chimneys. The thickness of the walls of the instrument therefore have a great deal of effect on the possibility of the 'phrasing' of the tone holes.

Phrasing or Counterboring of the Tone-Holes.

The tone holes of the clarinet which are drilled through the walls of the instrument meet the bore at a sharp angle. This is necessary in order to have the proper acoustical effect of the calculated length for the pitch desired. Tone-holes bored at an angle to the bore have been used in some constructional designs and are still used on the bassoon. The necessity for tone-holes drilled at an angle was a simple practical one of attempting to adjust the placement of the holes for the easiest hand position. Before the mechanical improvement of interlocking keys and rings it was necessary to accommodate the position of the hole with reference to the pitch required, at a point on the inner, or bore end of the hole which was such that if this point were opposite on the outside of the instrument, the fingers would be so stretched that they could not possibly cover the hole easily. In fact, on the larger instruments, this would have been utterly impossible for the human hand to accomplish. The boring of the tone-hole at an angle, repositioned the hole on the outside, for finger placement but retained the point on the inside required for the proper pitch.

However, with the present key mechanism, the clarinet has all of its tone-holes drilled directly through the walls of the tube, at right angles to the length of the bore. This practice leaves a very sharp edge on the interior end of the hole which requires that it be somewhat smoothed in order to avoid the catching of a swab when this is run through the bore, and also to allow the moisture which is condensed from the breath to run past, and not collect on the sharp edge. Most of the so-called counter-boring of the tone-hole chimneys is done for this very simple and practical reason. It is true, however, that the very slight removal of the sharp edge increases the size of the bore, particularly when this is done to a number of the tone-hole chimneys. For this reason, the amount of material removed from the bore by this operation must be carefully calculated and allowed for in the design and measurements required.

Some of the control of intonation is accomplished by a much greater removal of material from the tone-hole at the bore side, and the effect of a larger hole at this point on the tube can be achieved by such 'phrasing', as it is termed. However, this is not done on many of the holes, and is in fact a very delicate way for the expert 'finisher' to tune and adjust the instrument. Many uninformed persons, however, having found that phrasing serves to vary the effect of the tone-hole very quickly, ruin the calculations of the design of the instrument by 'phrasing' unnecessarily. Here again, we find the same situation of balance that is required between the measurements of design. The 'phrasing' of one tone-hole, while it may improve a single note, will have an adverse, and in general the exactly opposite effect on other tones of the instrument which use the same tone-hole in a different register, or for a different tone-hole pattern.

It will also be noted that since the entire length of the pipe has an effect on the frequency of each tone hole, because the instrument is really not cut off at that point, and since this added effect of the entire length lowers the expected pitch calculation for the length of a pipe which would coincide with the tone-hole length, that a tone hole drilled exactly in the center of a pipe will not raise its pitch by one half, or an octave, as would be the case with a string stopped at one half its length. The different vibrational pattern of the air column, since it is longitudinal instead of transverse has a different set of practical problems, but mention of this easy method of thinking of the tone-hole effect is not out of order.

The emission of vibrational patterns to the open air through the tone-hole openings, also has the same problem as the radia-tion of sound from the end of the pipe. The effect of the bell of the clarinet as a radiator and as a device for smoothing the end correction, is also a factor in the 'phrasing' of the tone-hole chimneys. The better venturi or air-channel form achieved by the 'phrasing', allows a better flexibility of control on the part of the player, and heightens the effects which he is able to exer-cise by the performance techniques at his disposal.

In order to demonstrate the supplementation of theory and practice, it will be interesting to calculate the placement of a tone-hole on the clarinet according to our formulas and com-pare this with the actual measurement of the placement of the same tone-hole on a clarinet.

For the example let us select the pitch of A 220 which will be fingered on the clarinet as B natural with the middle finger of the right hand on the middle finger tone-hole of the lower joint. In this case the emission of the sound is accomplished primarily through the first finger tone-hole of the lower joint.

If a centimeter rule is laid along the tube of an ordinary Boehm system clarinet, and the measurement taken from the top of the upper tenon of the upper joint downwards to the center of the first finger tone-hole as described, it will be found to be 24.9 centimeters $+$ or $-$. If the distance of 8.9 centimeters which is the approximate length of the bore of the tuning barrel plus the cone shaped bore chamber of the mouthpiece is added to this, the total measurement for the placement of this tone-hole will be 33.8 centimeters $+$ or $-$.

Now if the position of this tone hole is calculated according to the following formula, we should achieve a theoretical place-ment which is in accord with the actual measurement.

The speed of sound is approximately 1100 feet or about 33528.0 centimeters to the second. Applying our formula as follows:

$$\frac{\text{velocity of sound}}{\text{frequency}} = \frac{\text{wave length of sound}}{4} =$$

we have:

$$\frac{33528}{220} = \frac{152:4}{4} = 38.1 \text{ centimeters}$$

As we see from a comparison of the two figures, 33.8 centimeters by actual measurement, and 38.1 centimeters by use of the formula, there is a distance of 4.3 centimeters to be accounted for between the calculation and the actual practice of making an instrument. Furthermore, if we add to the calculated distance of 38.1 the additional length of the end-correction for a bore of 14.5 millimeters, we will have a total of 38.1 plus 6.0+ millimeters, or an actual distance calculated to be 38.7 centimeters as compared with our measured distance of 33.8 centimeters.

If we will however, remember our rule that the larger the hole the higher the pitch, and the smaller the hole the lower the pitch, as well as the relation of the bore diameter in size to the length of the tube under consideration, and apply the corrections which are required due to 'under-cutting' and phrasing of the several tone-holes, we will find that the distance of a total of 4.9 centimeters difference is accounted for due to these factors.

In addition to this is the design of the Tone-generating Mechanism of the instrument which may require a shorter or longer tuning barrel or mouthpiece chamber measurement as well as a different design of the reed.

The comparison of an actual measurement with a calculation of design may therefore easily be seen to be a supplementation, and not a substitution in the case of musical instruments. See Chapter VIII on The Measurement and Design of Musical Instruments.

One other matter with respect to the placement and effect of tone holes must be described here. It will be noted that the tone-hole system as developed for the clarinet, provides for a number of apertures spaced along almost the entire length of the instrument. When a tone hole adjacent to a closed tone hole is closed, the effect is of course to immediately achieve the total effect of the pipe closed to this point. When an adjacent tone hole is opened the effect is the opposite, and the shorter length of pipe is immediately achieved. However, the further away from any tone hole that other tone holes are opened or closed, the less effect the opening or closing has on the basic pitch produced by the first tone hole in question. This is due to the inter-tone-hole spacing effect of the whole system, and provides the player with another control of his performance which will be described in detail later, namely, the intonation- and resonance-fingering possibilities of the clarinet. See *'Playing in Tune'*.

The positioning and spacing of the tone holes on the clarinet with respect to the axis of the instrument, have no effect on the pitch formula, but obviously have a great effect on the tonal emission. For this reason, the sound of the various tones on the clarinet may be different, depending on the direction of their radiation from the tone-hole pattern. Efforts have been made to design clarinets in such a way that most of the tone holes and the mechanism for operating them are on the top of the clarinet. This is both for fingering ease and tonal emission. However, certain positions for the tone holes are necessary because of the nature of its mechanism. While this has been exceedingly well accomplished by the present design of the Boehm clarinet, it is a decided factor in the judgement necessary for the player for performance requirements, especially since the instrument is so close to him when he is playing it. Across the room, or in the concert hall, the distance involved, smooths out the emission of the tones and quite a different effect is obtained from listening to a clarinet from a concert distance, and from judging its effect when immediately at the side of the player. The same is true of course with the radiation pattern of other instruments. The fine, stringed instruments of the early Italian school, are an excellent illustration of the radiation pattern which causes the greatest effect of tonal focus at a concert distance rather than very close to the tone-generation source.

The basic tuning of the scale for the clarinet is placed at the accepted international standard of 440 cps at 68 degrees Fahrenheit as established in 1939. Most instruments, except on special order, are designed for this standard.

The clarinet, since it is a cylindrical tube, and acts as a stopped pipe, has as its vibrational mode possibilities the odd harmonic series, and this causes a difficult design problem after the basic tone-hole calculation and fundamental length have been established. Since the first vibrational mode above the fundamental for the odd harmonic series pipe will be the octave plus a fifth above this fundamental, or the twelfth, the clarinet will speak a twelfth above its fundamental when the second vibrational mode is accomplished by means of the twelfth or speaker key.

Providing the proper length of tube and the proper tone-hole placement for a correctly tuned scale in the fundamental register of the clarinet is relatively simple in calculation. However, since the second vibrational mode is a twelfth above the fundamental, it will be found that the twelfth which is precisely in tune with the fundamental, will also be that of the octave plus the perfect or 'just' fifth. This can easily be ascertained by playing the fundamental register of the clarinet and listening carefully until the twelfth or third partial is distinctly heard in the sound. This is really not difficult to accomplish, although it may take a little practice to discriminate with the ear, if unaccustomed to listening for this effect. More careful attention to the sound will also provide the keen ear with the fifth and seventh partials as well.

When the third partial is distinguished in the sound while the fundamental is being played, if an acoustical measurement of the third partial is obtained, by adjusting some calibrating sound source in accord with it, it will then be found that when the instrument is thrown into its second vibrational mode by actually opening the speaker key, that the resulting pitch obtained will be flatter than the partial heard when the fundamental is being played. This is due of course to the fact that the just fifth is not the tempered fifth, or interval necessary for the tempered scale, and indicates that the size and placement of the speaker hole have been calculated to provide a better tempered fifth, than could be expected if the tuning were so attempted as to allow the instrument to play its third partials as freely as possible. However, if this were not the case, the design of the clarinet would provide intolerably sharp intervals for the clarion or third partial register, which could not be brought under control by the player in his performance technique.

Actually what is needed is a different size and placement of a speaker hole for each fundamental pitch of the clarinet. This is indeed not at all practical, and since the flexibility of performance practice is what it is, and since players also have at their disposal certain instrumental adjustments in addition to the tone-hole mechanism and pattern, most clarinet makers and manufacturers have simply effected a compromise placement and size of the speaker key. The problem has of course been aggravated by the fact that the speaker key is also used as a tone hole for the production of the middle line Bb (written). A change in size and placement to accommodate the emission of the proper tuning and quality of this particular pitch would negate the effect of it as a speaker key. This is easily proven by an examination of the side trill key which yields a good Bb but cannot be used as a speaker key since it is too large an aperture.

The correction of this difficulty by means of a resonance hole as supplementary to the speaker key, when this Bb middle line is played, and the closing of the resonance hole leaving the properly-sized speaker hole for use in producing the third partial register, was only recently devised and adopted. This correction is the first major step forward in clarinet acoustical correction since the application of the Boehm system to the instrument in 1850. A complete description of this correction is presented elsewhere in this discussion. "The S-K Mechanism," Chapter VII, The Acoustical Evolution of the Clarinet.

However, even with the acoustical correction of the properly-sized Bb hole and resonance key mechanism, and the more properly-sized and placed speaker hole, the basic tuning of the clarinet cannot be accomplished either theoretically or practically with perfection, since the problem of the just and tempered fifths which make up its acoustical nature must always be admitted.

The tuning of stringed instruments is somewhat of the same nature. The string player tunes his open strings in perfect fifths, that is, without beats, but he then finds that he must 'temper' his produced pitches by stopping the strings at a slightly different point than he would for perfect measurement with the length of the string for subsequent perfect intervals. This limit of flexibility for the stringed instruments is a perfect illustration of the difference between the two subdivisions made with respect to flexible intonation instruments at the outset of the discussion.

The end correction length, the correction for the tone-hole size and placement and the bore of the instrument, cannot be calculated to be exact for both the fundamental vibrational mode and at the same time be perfectly calculated for additional vibrational modes when a great frequency range is expected from the same pipe.

Fortunately the differences between the theoretical possibilities and the dilemna of calculation is accomplished by the flexibility inherent in the system, which permits the player to control the instrument in such a manner, that it yields satisfactory results. Failing this, the clarinet as an acoustical device for sound production in music, would either have to be greatly limited in frequency range, or abandoned as inadequate— neither of which is likely to happen.

Tuning adjustments of the instrument may also be made mechanically by means of the tone-generating system of the clarinet, the reed and the mouthpiece. Reference to these adjustments will be found in Chapters V & VI, The Tone-Generating System of the Clarinet and Reed-Making.

CHAPTER XI

Part 3: Playing in Tune

After a certain degree of proficiency has been attained on the instrument and a familiarity with its basic idiocyncrasies is established, the performer will find that other matters which were not so troublesome at the beginning cause him increasing concern. Not the least of these troubles is the problem of the intonation of the clarinet and in the simplest of phrases, 'how to play in tune.'

In dealing with this problem we must provide ourselves with a technique of playing which will make the most of the possibilities of the instrument and in some manner compensate for its physical pecularities.

As concerns the matter of intonation in general, it must be understood that intonation is wholly a relative matter. By relative we mean that all comparison of pitch is *(comparison)*. There is no absolute pitch in the sense that nature provides an absolute standard to which all pitch considerations are directed. All standards of pitch are artificial standards which have been established and accepted as standards, just as are all weights and measures artificial standards. There is no 'A' in nature more than is there a natural inch or pound. Over a period of years in our particular development of a system of music, we have established these standards to suit our taste. Moreover, it should be remembered that our standard of taste is not an arbitrary thing, but the result of a series of experiences, trials, and errors, which have gradually been formulated. No man sat himself down and figured out our system of music completely and to the world's acceptance and satisfaction, than did another crystallize the social government of the world. The development of music has been thematic in the larger sense. It has been rather a series of ideas by many men, building on what has gone before, altering, refining, substituting, here and there adding a bit, until now in this present, we find a certain body of what we enjoy calling factual material at our disposal, and which makes conventional demands on our action. And furthermore, we have only to look a little beyond our own noses to find that our system is not the only way of doing a thing. Other groups of people not so different from ourselves, have developed other systems in some ways even more complicated than our own. The important idea to keep in mind, is that our own or any other system, is a developed and artificial system which is the result of a growth, and not the result of the discovery of an absolute. It may be argued that physical laws such as the relationship of pitch in the harmonic series is an absolute, but we need only remember that the tempered scale is a relative derivation from this supposed absolute, and furthermore that instruments which can produce the so-called absolute pitch relation of the harmonic series do play in relative harmony with the piano, from which no deviation of the tempered scale can be allowed. And further, we know that the ear of the performer, as well as the ear of the piano tuner, can and does reach a basis of comparative stability when the music is finally played. For there is no such thing as absolute pitch. What is known as absolute pitch is a highly developed recognition sense of the relationship of one pitch to another.

The general problem of intonation is then, a problem of relationship and of comparison of pitch to pitch. It is this possibility of such relationship which permits us to play in ensemble, and to achieve a harmony between two instruments or more, which will please our taste according to the system of music which we have developed and accepted.

Fortunately, although our ears are rude and coarse as far as fine discriminations are concerned, we are able within a certain limited vibrational range to meet with other ears, and consequently agree on a relatively constant pitch when we are playing our instruments. When this is accomplished we are 'playing in tune,' as we say, and our musical activities can be exercised in any further manner in which we take pleasure, be it in the full expanse of a large ensemble such as the band or orchestra or a smaller group.

But in addition to meeting the ears of others and in causing our instruments to thereby reach a concordance, we have another and more basic difficulty, which is that of making our own ears reach a concordance with themselves. In short, to achieve a relationship between pitches within our own ears, and thus play in tune on our own instrument without the helpful guide of another ear or instrument for a comparison. In many ways it is easier to play in tune in an ensemble where the comparison is definite, than it is to play in tune alone, where the only comparison can be our own ear. This is a matter which is not very well understood. If there is any approach to an absolute pitch, it is that individual comparison on pitch relationship which every one makes by himself. For each individual that comparison is unique, and cannot be duplicated by anyone else, anymore than can what each of us sees from his own eyes be duplicated exactly by anyone else.

The necessity for some artificial standard is therefore easily proven, and it is not difficult to understand why we have developed such standards. For the individual must therefore accept a standard, and endeavor to develop his recognition of pitch relationship in such a way, that it will be consistent with the pitch relationship of others; if there is to be anything other than a number of isolated individuals each playing according to his own pitch recognition standard. It is possible, but not probable that any two individuals might arrive at the same pitch recognition individually, for the same difference as individuals will hold true in this case as holds true of their individuality as individuals in all other senses. In other words, no two people can be alike because there are not two people who are identical— each of us occupies some space and time of his own—we are in short—individuals. By the adoption of a certain relative standard of pitch recognition, we can all give a little as individuals, and meet somewhere in the limited vibrational scale to the extent that we can call, as far as the very coarse measurement of our ears is concerned, our pitch recognition standard constant, and can therefore 'play in tune.'

This much then we have discovered to be a common problem of intonation for all instruments which have the possibility of choice in pitch production. What we must remember, from this discussion to apply to our specific problem of intonation on the clarinet, is that all intonation is relative, certain accepted standards of pitch recognition must be met, that we as individuals must train ourselves to produce a pitch recognition comparable to this standard, both as individuals playing on our own instrument alone, and as members of an ensemble group where we must meet the common concordance of the group.

Whatever we desire to do as far as meeting the standard of pitch recognition which we have set for ourselves, must be accomplished with regard to the specific instrument on which we are to perform, and in the case of the clarinet, we are immediately met with numerous physical and mechanical difficulties which we must master.

The clarinet is an instrument which embodies the acoustical problem of the cylindrical pipe. This phenomenon of nature is such that any fundamental pitch produced on a pope of cylin- *pipe* drical bore will contain as harmonic overtones the third, fifth, seventh, ninth, eleventh, etc., partials which give it is characteristic quality. These overtones may easily be produced in the case of the clarinet, and would be as follows for the pitch of low F on the clarinet.

In order to produce these harmonics on the clarinet experimentally, finger low F, and simply vary the breath pressure and pressure on the reed, slightly closing the throat and exerting more pressure on the reed as the higher harmonics are reached. With very little practice anyone can cause these tones to speak quite easily. The A above the staff is a sharp fifth harmonic; the high G is a flat ninth harmonic and the high Bb is a flat eleventh harmonic. This variation is due to the construction of the instrument, and is necessary in order to balance the scale. For purposes of illustration as to the harmonic series involved, this experiment will suffice to show that a cylindrical pipe produces a pitch which contains every other harmonic overtone in the harmonic series. An open pipe or conical bored pipe on the other hand, contains a different set of harmonic overtones. The most notable difference between the open or conical bore and the stopped or cylindrical bored pipe, and the difference with which we are most concerned, as it relates to the problem of intonation, is the fact that on the clarinet as compared with the oboe for example, the clarinet, which is a cylindrically-bored instrument, will produce as its first overtone in the harmonic series a twelfth above the fundamental or the third partial; and the oboe will produce the octave or second partial above the fundamental as its first overtone in the harmonic series. See Chapter IV, The Acoustics of the Clarinet.

Now any instrument which will produce the second partial or the octave above its fundamental as the first overtone, permits the placement of a speaker or octave key at a mode or air-column vibratory point, which requires no particular compensation between the lower or fundamental register, and the higher or harmonic register of the instrument. In other words, the fundamental register of the conically-bored pipe will be transferred in pitch to an octave higher by the addition of the speaker key, and no difference of fingering will be required to produce this harmonic octave except the addition of this speaker key. Such is the case of the oboe and saxophone. The bassoon, being a combination bore, has its peculiar problems, but is fundamentally a conical bore and reacts in the same manner as a conical pipe except that the register is broken by means of the embouchure and breath instead of by means of a speaker key. The flute will be found to react as a conical pipe in its register change although here again the change is made without benefit of a speaker key.

In the case of the clarinet, the addition of a speaker key produces a twelfth above the fundamental register, and requires a different fingering combination to produce the octave above any given fundamental. Such a fundamental physical difficulty causes a basic problem in intonation, inasmuch as either the natural or the tempered scale octave remains in a constant ratio of 2:1, that is, any fundamental note doubles its number of vibrations for the octave above, as A 880 is one octave above a 440. The other notes of the scale such as the third, fifth, etc., must be slightly lowered or raised to compensate for the temperment, and due to the fact that the octave fingering must be altered in the case of the clarinet, more than two notes, (the fundamental and the first overtone), must be altered in order to achieve a balanced scale. For example let us take the case of the fundamental pitch of low F on the clarinet

when the speaker key is opened C on the third space is the resultant register change

Since it is the second overtone or third partial in the natural harmonic series based on this pitch. In order to meet the artificial standard set by our taste as concerns the relationship of pitch, this C must be exactly twice the number of vibrations per second of the C one octave lower. But the C one octave lower is not fingered the same as this C without the speaker key, and is in fact fingered the same as the G above the staff without the speaker key. To further complicate matters, the C on the third space produced as the third partial in the series based on the fundamental pitch of F, is supposed to be a perfect fifth above the F one octave higher than the fundamental pitch, of which this C is the third partial. In order to make this C a perfect fifth above the middle F, it is necessary to slightly alter its pitch; but when this is done, it may not then be perfect twelfth above the fundamental **F**, and such alteration may change the fundamental **F**, due to the fact that this fundamental **F** is produced by the basic fingering under consideration, to such an extent that it will not be a perfect octave below the middle **F** which required the **C** as a perfect fifth above. See Part 2, Chapter **XI**, The Tuning of the Clarinet.

If an instrument can be correctly tuned in octaves, that is, if the fundamental pitch can be adjusted within a one octave scale so that the octave scale is correct, either in the natural or the tempered scale as is desired, then the octaves above or below this scale can be made to conform to the fundamental octave scale which has been so adjusted, and the instrument will be in tune. This is of course the basic method of tuning a piano. But if the basic scale requires a slight alteration each time an octave above or below it is reached, due to the fact that a different harmonic must be accounted for, as is the case of the clarinet, then that instrument cannot be constructed in perfect tune, either to a natural or to a tempered scale, and the closest approximation will be the best that can be accomplished.

In addition, it must be remembered that we are not dealing with any instrument which plays merely within one octave. In order to satisfy our demands for variety, we must have an adequate range in pitch. In the case of the clarinet this range encompasses some three octaves and a sixth. Even beyond the possibility of balancing the fundamental register with the resultant primary harmonic register, we find that in order to increase the range of the instrument it is possible, and necessary, to use a further harmonic series which is produced by a combination of opening and closing tone holes in a series of cross-fingerings. Such opening and closing of tone holes provides us with another speaker node as is the case with the notes above **C** above the staff on the clarinet. In this case the opening of the first tone hole with the left forefinger provides us with the requisite node for breaking the air column. In this case further complication is the result. For example, we find that by using a fingering combination which would produce the pitch of Bb in the fundamental register, and by opening the first tone hole with the left forefinger and adding the speaker key which we have previously used for the harmonic change, the resultant pitch is that of D above the staff. This resultant, if a regular harmonic series is followed, would be either a sharp fourth or a flat fifth harmonic, and is too far from the fundamental to be adjusted directly with it. It is necessary to approach is through the fundamental register by deriving it from F fifth line of the staff, which is dependent on the fundamental Bb. This addition of range to the instrument demands therefore a whole new series of adjustments to make it approximately in tune.

Added to the constructional difficulties of the instrument are of course the delicate measurements of the mouthpiece and the reed, and the physical problems of the embouchure and the breath, all of which may destroy the most careful adjustment of the mechanical balance of the best instrument.

There must be therefore, a means of providing oneself with a basic knowledge of the instrumental technique involved in playing the clarinet. A basic study must be made of the problems of the Tone, Technique and Tongue, for which suggestions the writer refers to the chapter on The Essentials of Clarinet Playing.

In general, beginning students must be taught to maintain a tone of even quality and consistent pitch. With good embouchure and normal breath-control this should not be difficult. Matters such as the selection of a good instrument and mouthpiece, and the use of a good reed, are obvious.

However, after adequate technique, tone and general playing ability has been developed, the problem of intonation will begin to be more and more troublesome. The student will find that intonation is rapidly becoming his greatest problem, his most severely criticized weakness and his saddest of musical experiences.

Intonation for melodic instrumental performance consists of measuring and adjusting the distance or musical interval, between the successive musical pitches required. In order to accomplish this measurement, it is necessary to have two points to work with, the reference point from which to measure and the point to which it is desired to make a measurement. Good intonation, which is a process of good measurement, is achieved only by continuous and accurate aural measurement of pitch discrimination. The musician's ear is the gauge which is to be used for this purpose.

It is a common error to think of tuning a melodic instrument as a process of simply adjusting one or more basic reference pitches to a standard musical pitch source with the assumption that subsequent pitch relationships will follow with accuracy as a matter of course. By very little consideration of the problems involved with the factors concerned, it is evident that particularly in the case of the wind instruments, and most certainly in the construction of the clarinet, that considerable variation is inherent in the design and acoustical action of the instruments themselves. Added to this matter is the physical action of the player which is of course subject to an infinite variation, under a great number of conditions of performance.

Given the best possible instrument, and the best instruction in performance techniques, the basic problem of intonation as a matter of aural judgment, remains a continuous and constant challenge to the performer, and is as much a part of performance as any other basic technic such as tone-production or fingering dexterity or articulation.

The melodic instrumentalist is limited by the nature of his instrument to the extent of producing but one pitch at a time on his instrument successively. Double-stopping of stringed instruments is excluded as being a possibility, since it is not the usual method of melodic line performance, and in any case, stringed instruments are melodic by definition.

Since the melodic instrument produces but one pitch at a time, it is necessary to leave the first pitch in order to progress to the next subsequent pitch required. If the first pitch is a reference for the point of measurement, the second pitch is measured aurally on the basis of a pitch memory of the first. If an outside source of reference is used for the adjustment of a reference pitch, subsequent pitches on the instrument must still be produced by aural measurement. No guarantee of what is termed 'internal tuning' of the instrument is thus accomplished.

The equal tempered scale, which is the basis of our system of musical intonation has been adopted during the last two hundred years as the standard system of arranging the thirteen sounds of the octave in such a manner as to provide an equal distance between each of them when measured consecutively. Other arrangements of these tones are possible, and are occasionally used for special purposes. The major difference between the tempered scale arrangement and the others is a very simple one. The tempered scale provides the only possible solution to the problem of a division of the octave in such a manner as to allow a universal enharmonicity of pitch reference. By means of the tempered scale the sharps and flats of any scale step, or the raised or lowered contiguous intervals of any scale step exactly equal each other. It is possible by means of the tempered scale to use the lowered or flat interval of G, for example, which would be G flat, as the same pitch as F# or the raised or sharp interval of F. In no other arrangement of the intervals of the octave is this possible. The tempered scale is definitely an artificial device which has been developed for the facility of the performance of music and instrument construction is based o nits principles.

Since construction of key-board instruments would be almost impossible in complication of construction with other than the tempered scale as a basis and since other instruments would suffer in the same way, artificial and limited as it may seem in some respects, the tempered scale has permitted the development of western music to attain its high degree of sophistication. The rather subtle differences of pitch which string players often refer and attain by employing 'just' intervals, and the effects of choral groups singing 'a cappella' are interesting and beautifully represent certain dimensions of the art of sound usage which are possible. But the practical demands of our system of music demands a stable system such as the tempered intonation and all calculation of instrumental construction, performance, composition and concept of our present musical notation must be based on its use. Tempered intonation is to music what formal mathematical technique is to science. It is a means by which man has learned to control his environment. No pure mathematical concept can be found in nature. There are no 'perfect' circles in the physical world. Likewise, there are no 'perfect' musical intervals in the physical world. But there are principles of these 'perfections', which, when applied, provide us with a control of our world impossible without them. We must think of 'things' 'as they ought to be' and not as they are, in order to even think of them.

Tempered intonation has been adopted as the basic scale pattern of our musical system. It consists of the division of the octave into twelve equal semi-tones, each of which is further divided for finer calculations into 100 cents. A semi-tone of 100 cents is 1/12 of an octave, and an octave contains 1200 cents or twelve semi-tones of 100 cents each.

For practical intonation purposes, a musician does not concern himself with the measurement of so many cents, but rather with the rougher division of the octave into the twelve semi-tones. However, a difference of a few cents causes the phenomenon of being 'out-of-tune' since approximately four cents equals one sound vibration. This difference is heard by the musician and is corrected by his control of his instrument.

Some knowledge of the action of sound is necessary to all musicians since it is the raw material from which their art is made. It is particularly important for the melodic line instrumentalist since he can hear and adjust for extremely fine differences in the pitch that he produces. If he can develop a system for easily hearing the differences of pitch he can control the situation better. This is possible by means of utilizing the natural phenomenon of 'beats".

The propogation of sound in the air is produced by the oscillation of some elastic body as it (the body) moves back and forth periodically, or vibrates. See Phenomenon of Sound as Basis for Music.

Any oscillating body has the effect of producing a condensation, or compression of air in front of it, and a vacuum or rarefaction in back of it as it moves in one direction and a subsequent condensation and rarefaction in the same manner as it returns in the opposite direction. This is illustrated by the movement of a pendulum as shown in the following:

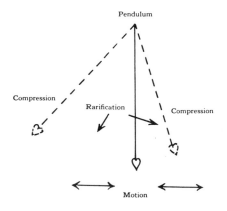

These alternate condensations and rarefactions may be measured as to the distance between them, which distance is determined by the size and the speed of the vibrating body. The distance so measured is termed the wave-length of the sound. The more wave-lengths that there are in any given unit of time, the shorter they will be. Sound travels in the air at about 1100 feet per second. Therefore, the wave-length of a sound which has the measurement of 100 cycles, or vibrations per second is 1100 divided by 100 or approximately 11 feet long.

The wave-length of a sound is illustrated in Figure 1:

It is thus seen that a sound-wave propogated in the air consists of an alternate condensation and rarefaction. Repeated propogations of similar sound waves constitute a steady-state of the sound. The musical use of sound is based on these steady-state sound waves, no matter how short in duration they may be.

WAVE LENGTH OF SOUND

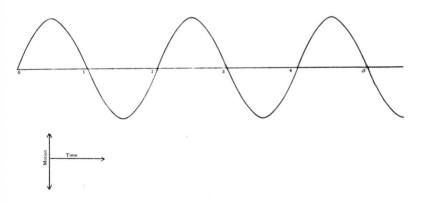

Figure 1

PHASE RELATION OF SOUND WAVES

If two similar sound-waves from two exactly similar vibrating bodies begin at exactly the same time, it is obvious that these two sound-waves will follow an identical pattern in the air.

When a situation such as this occurs, the two waves are said to be 'in phase' with each other.

However, on the other hand, let us assume that the same two sound-waves from the same identical vibrating bodies are started at a different time. In order to make this easily seen, let us have sound-wave number 2 start exactly one-half second later than sound-wave number one. (Figure 2) In this case we can see that the two waves will pass a different point at a different time, as shown in the following illustration:

OUT OF PHASE

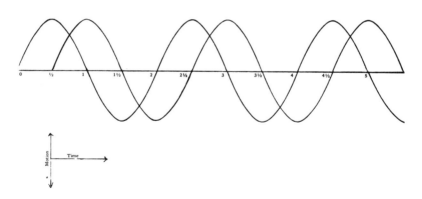

Figure 2

In this case the sound-waves are termed 'out of phase' with each other.

Now, if sound-wave number two, as in the previous drawing, is started exactly one second later later than sound-wave number one, as in Figure 3 it follows that at the end of one second that sound-wave number two will be exactly one cycle behind sound-wave number one, or 'in phase' with it, but at the time of one second later. Also, at the end of one-half second, sound-wave number two will be exactly one-half cycle behind sound-wave number one, or at exactly the opposite point of sound-waves number one's vibrational pattern. Therefore, in such a case, it is termed that at this point, the two sound-waves are in 'opposite phase'. Also, at the end of one whole second they will again be 'in phase'.

OPPOSITE PHASE

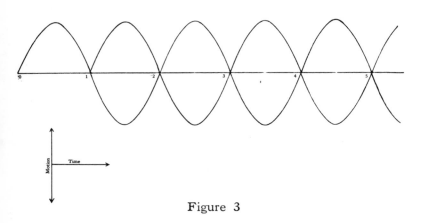

Figure 3

Now, by drawing the curves of two sound-waves of different lengths, or frequencies, but which begin at the same time, Figure 4 that when the two waves are moving in the same direction that the sum of their combined motion together is greater than the motion of each wave alone, and also that when they are moving in opposite directions that the effect of one of them is cancelled by the other to the extent of their difference in motion. When the effect of the sum of their combined motion is noted, it is termed 'resonance', and when the cancellation effect is noted, it is termed 'interference'.

RESONANCE AND INTERFERENCE

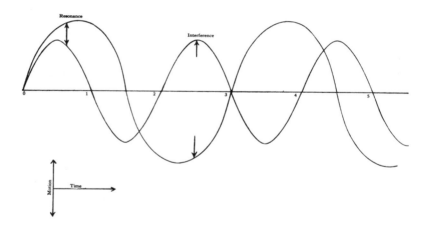

Figure 4

This change in the effect of combined motion and cancellation which results in a periodic fluctuation of the relationship of one sound-wave to another creates a swelling and a diminishing effect on the 'loudness' of the sound heard by the ear. During the time required for a cycle of vibration of the two waves to be completed, the ear notes this difference in timing or "in phase" and the result as heard is termed a 'beat'.

The number of such 'beats' so produced will always be the simple arithmetical difference between the respective sound-wave lengths, or frequencies. Thus, if the two sound-waves illustrated in Figure 4 were vibrating at the frequency of 440 cycles per second for sound-wave number one and 445 cycles per second for sound-wave number two, the arithmetical difference would be 445-440 or 5 beats per second difference which the ear would hear.

Since an accurate counting of the beat-rate between two musical pitches gives an accurate measurement of the musical interval, it is possible to test the intonation of a melodic line instrument by playing a sustained tone on it against a known test tone reference source.

Several excellent instruments have been developed for the purpose of such practice for the study of intonation. Perhaps the most satisfactory of these is the Tempo-Tuner* which has been devised as a convenient and reliable test-tone source. The use of this instrument is as advantageous to the player of a melodic line instrument for intonation study as is the use of the metronome for indicating tempo and the divisions of time. The Tempo-Tuner combines both the metronome and the intonation test-tone reference, making it complete and versatile as to use.

If we can appreciate the "measuring" of pitch by our ears as an acoustical phenomenon, and can develop skill in this area, we have the first requisite to 'playing in tune'. It will then be necessary for us to use the inherent flexibility of the instrument and of our physical equipment, to achieve what our ears hear, and demand. To accomplish this we must remember first of all, that pitch is wholly relative, and we must proceed to make a comparison of any pitch produced with any pitch desired.

We must so listen as to be able to distinguish the smallest possible variation between what we play and what we desire to play. By close listening we can develop our sensitivity of pitch to a degree which can be characterized by the word 'feeling.' One

---

*Full information concerning the Tempo-Tuner may be obtained from Electronic Research Products, box 705, Los Altos, California.

can 'feel' that he is in or out of concordance even when he cannot 'hear' it, as for example a forte chord in a large ensemble
may destroy the individual hearing of an instrument but maintain a pitch recognition factor.

We must also be able to alter the breath pressure by either
increasing or diminishing it under all possible circumstances.
And we must be able to increase or diminish the pressure of the
embouchure by infinitesimal degrees. Lest the uninitiated
remark that it is all very well to say what we must do but give
no answer as to how, we remark again that such fineness of control both for breath and for embouchure is again the product of
practice, and until the first development of playing technique
has been made, these words will mean little. The two variables
involved, breath and embouchure are compensatory and must
be understood fully. An increase of breath pressure will cause a
slight flattening of the pitch. A decrease of breath pressure will
cause a sharpening. An increase of embouchure pressure will
cause a sharpening of pitch and a decrease of pressure will cause
a flattening. It may readily be seen from this that a combination
of these factors will cause a compensating action which must
always be guided by the desire to maintain a constant tone
quality.

The use of the breath-embouchure method of intonation control is the first method which is used by all players and although
it is instinctively used from the very beginning, its development
goes hand-in-hand with the other developments in performance
technique.

Fortunately there is another method of intonation control in
addition to the breath-embouchure control, which may be used
to advantage by most players beyond the beginning stages, and
this method constitutes the crux of our information. This method
is the use of the various intonation and resonance fingerings of
which there are literally dozens, varying of course with every
instrument, and with every player, but constant enough in practice to be allowed as generalizations.

Every player must know his own instrument thoroughly and
completely. We have shown how the mechanical and physical
problems of the clarinet account for its great variability, and it
is only by the most careful attention to all of the possibilities of
the resonance and intonation fingerings that the best can be

brought out of even the finest instrument.

Basically the fingering for any given woodwind instrument is the same for all instruments of the same kind, and any good fingering chart will supply these basic fingerings. But even within these charts themselves it will be noted that several fingerings are occasionally possible for the same pitch. It will also be noted that these so-called alternate fingerings are of two types. The first type are those alternate fingerings which affect only the mechanism of the instrument and do not change the tone-hole combination, such as the two alternate fingerings for B natural third line for the clarinet. The second type of alternate fingerings employs a different tone-hole combination for the instrument and may also affect the mechanism, such as the alternate fingerings for Bb above the staff on the clarinet. Alternate fingerings of the first type will render identical intonation and resonance results; those of the second type will render in every case a slightly different pitch and a slightly different resonance. A careful study of every alternate fingering should be made for the instrument under consideration, and the consequent change both in pitch and resonance should be noted. It will then be possible to play certain intervals with different intonation control based on the results obtained. It should always be remembered that the easiest fingering combination is not always to be desired when the intonation is in question. For this reason it is again stressed that such study should be reserved until the student has an adequate grasp of all basic problems of playing.

In addition to this simple alternate fingering control of intonation by alternate basic fingerings, it will be found that the following rules hold true in general on all woodwind instruments. First, when any key or tone hole can be closed which does not affect the basic fingering combination to the extent of changing its basic pitch, the pitch will become slightly flatter and/or additional resonance of quality will result. Secondly, when any key or tone hole can be opened which does not affect the basic fingering combination to the extent of changing the basic pitch, the pitch will become slightly sharper and/or additional resonance will result.

In order to prove our rules we will take for example several of the most generally known of these intonation and resonance fingerings.

As may readily be seen, the improvement of these fingerings is of great value in the production of a more even scale and the achievement of a better intonation and resonance. It is suggested that an individual fingering chart for each instrument be constructed by each player for his own instrument. This will take thought, time and study, but it is well worth the effort. A convenient model chart follows:

It must be remembered that clarinets become out of tune over a period of time and must be brought back to adjustment by an expert. No amount of intonation or resonance fingerings can overcome a basic mechanical difficulty. For this reason such a chart must be occasionally rechecked.

CHAPTER XII

Musicianship, Phrasing of Music

Provided with an understanding of the musical instrument and with information concerning its use as a sound producer for musical purposes and also with command and control of the musical instrument as provided by a developed skill in the techniques of its practical use, still does not assure that the performance of music will be 'musical'.

The interpretation of a musical composition requires more than a perfect rendition of the score no matter how admirable the skill involved. The musical 'idea' as we have noted, is not an intellectual nor a reasoned evaluation of philosophical thought, but rather an appeal to the feelings of the listener, and a motivation of a mood and an emotional response created by the sound patterns and designs presented to his aural sense. That these psychological responses are are real as intellectual activity there is no question. Perhaps they are even more closely defined as natural responses of the living organism to external phenomena than are the functionings of the organism within itself as concerned with the subjective attitudes of the 'thinking man'. We are a dichotomy of being, 'feeling' and 'thinking' representing our usual assigned categories of self-description. And, since the boundaries between the two are even more vague than any definition which we might care to make of either, we shift from one to another of the two sides of our being with unpredictable flexibility.

However, just as it is possible to evoke 'thought' by the initiation of the process by means of an intellectual 'idea', it is also possible to initiate 'feeling' by means of an initiation of sense appeal in the form of a musical 'idea' or sound design and pattern.

The form of this musical idea must be accomplished in presentation by the use of the technical data concerning its manufacture and its transmission which is vital to any initiation of 'feeling' for the listener. But beyond this technical presentation, and due to the nature of the art, the subtleties of such presentation, based on the technical aspects as they may be, are nevertheless subject to an infinite variety of practices of performance.

When we listen to music, do we listen to the player of the music, or to the music exclusive of the player, treating him simply as an impersonal agent of transmission, or do we shift from one phase of contemplation to another concerning the situation as it develops? If one will but pause and examine the response which he 'feels', with respect to a musical experience, it is unquestionable that it is the combination of the two which is experienced as a whole, and that the very alternation between the two phases is the factor that provides the living aspect to the art of music.

Now for the player himself, does he consider the music as exclusive of his performance of it, or is he so involved in it as a performance, that the considerations of transmitting it as an art are lost entirely simply because he is so busy accomplishing his task as a musician that he has no time or place for concentration other than on the 'doing' of what he is doing?

Of the several areas concerned with the activity of musical performance, certainly the one most vague, and personal, is that which is variously referred to by the terms, 'phrasing', 'musicality', 'musical feeling', 'musical artistry', or some such strictly indefinable but nonetheless constant and real performance practice problem for the player.

This matter is indefinable since it is not a technical dimension for which quantitative measurements can be provided. It is rather the cumulative result of many techniques, tempered by the behavioristic characteristics of human psychology. In short, it is the subjective matter of judgment brought to bear on the objective frame-work and structure of an art-form.

It is expected that the player will be aware of and in control of his instrument. And it is further expected that the instrument will be properly prepared for its use as an acoustical sound producing tool. It is further expected that the notation for the instrument will be understood by the player and that such notation will be within the realm of possibilities according to the laws of acoustics and of physical dexterity. But—if the study of music performance is to end at this point, then we will have produced by all of our efforts only another controlled automaton, a musical sound computer, and a repetitive marvel.

It is very true that the student and the aspiring performer on a musical instrument is so concerned, and must be so concerned with his efforts at the mechanical aspects of performance such as playing the right note at the right time, with the right intonation and the right dynamic level, with the right kind of sound, that he has very little if any time or attention left for more than accomplishing this basic chore. Indeed, it is such a very difficult art in terms of skill quotient, that few players enjoy, but seldom, the true feeling of freedom for the art of communicating sound which is the whole achievement of musical art.

Given the power to play every note perfectly as desired, in any possible way at any time on a musical instrument, would seem for every instrumental aspirant a true nirvana of sensuous delight. But alas, if this sudden power were provided, it would be found to be an empty heaven after all, with no meaning other than that of a skilled perfection in itself. The attempt to discover perfection in musical art by all of this practice, and all of this careful attention to the minute detail of the structure of the art, as in all of the other arts, is a truly lost effort, and is an illusion of the very first order, which represents a logical prognosis of such effort for even the most generally trained aesthete.

Let it be said once and for all that the greatest exponents of the art, be they performers, composers or conductors, make mistakes, and make them constantly, throughout all of their career and under all circumstances, even during their most gratifying and brilliant performances. He who is searching for a time and a place, and a person or an instrument, or an undiluted experience of sheer absolutism of exactness and accuracy, had better for himself, and for the good of those with whom he may associate, isolate himself at once in the ultimate security of a psychopathic institution, for this is where he will at last find his answer—in the realm of wondered fantasy and the dreamland of the twilight mind. This is not the real world of music—nor of music performance—nor of musical art.

There is no more sure proof of a person's own mediocrity and lack of capacity for greatness, than the assumption on his part that there are those who make no mistakes. It is true as well, that preachers of the false gospel of perfection, will be the first to seize upon and ridicule the mistakes of others. Psychologically, this attitude is developed from an inherent feeling of inferiority, and the attack on inferiority in others, is to them the answer to their own inadequacy.

The art of music is not so fortunate to have so many devotees. Rather the good fortune rests in the fact that so many men tread the path to Parnassus with the firm conviction that it will never lead them there, but that the journey is not done as a penance but as a pilgrimage!

Mistakes, errors, or what one may choose to call them, are as much a part of art as are the very varieties of possibility that the molecules of a Stradivarius violin, in their particular arrangement, at any particular time, might be the real reason for the instrument producing a good sound when bowed by an artist-performer. How closely would one look at a Rembrant—through a microscope? And what would he see but the tiny flecks of pigment. How closely do we examine the rose—and do we find its beauty in the arrangement of its cellular structure? Is the genius of an Einstein or a Mozart in the follicles of his hair, or even in a bit of brain cell that might be analyzed in a laboratory?

We do not find beauty in perfection, really; nor do we find perfection in beauty. There is a certain cumulative measurement of desire, aim, goal, result, techniques, preparation, effort, humidity, temperature, chronology of time and place, eggs or not for breakfast, sophistication of culture, morality, God and Devil; yes, and cosmic significance, in every true work of art, but, alas not in even the smallest atom of it, when viewed as an isolated entity.

The search for a method, or a means to accomplish the matter of musicality in musical performance therefore, lies in a direction other than that of a search for perfection in detail. It lies rather in the concept and understanding of a 'doing' rather than a 'thinking' and in a 'feeling' rather than in dissection. That we should take at least this brief time to note the situation and to give the problem a shape and form, is enough to insure the perspective necessary.

Now the practical performer, or he who engages in the practice of musical performance must at once find a means to achieve the security of purpose necessary for him to engage in his business. He must of necessity take stock of the mechanics of his art, and he must further recognize, even though without complete understanding, the purpose of his art. And, he must recognize that the purpose of his art, while served by the mechanics, requires more from him at the level of performance than is accomplished by any effort on his part to attain what has been shown to be an impossible 'perfection'.

Music must live, and move, since it is not a static art. We make it come alive by making the mechanics of it serve a further purpose of communication. Phrasing, musicality, etc., is the communicative device. What may be communicated by sounds is largely 'mood', or the creation of an emotional trauma for the listener. How the performer does this is by means of the 'why' and not the 'how' of his playing.

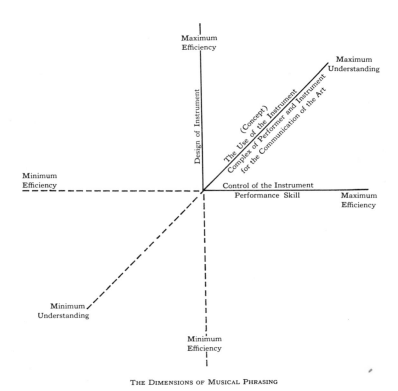

THE DIMENSIONS OF MUSICAL PHRASING

Now as we have seen, this matter of phrasing is a cumulative one. It is not based on one concern but on several, and of the several which the musician has at his disposal, are those same various techniques of dimension which can be technically modified and controlled. The musician uses these techniques *for* playing—he does not simply use them as an excuse for playing. This is the difference between a 'musician' and a 'player' and it is the same difference as we should see between a stonemason and a sculptor. There are stonemasons more skilled at carving stone than some sculptors—and then there is Michelangelo! There are players of musical instruments more skilled at playing them than some of our greatest concert artists, and to name a name here would in any case not be a parallel to Michelangelo. Skill is not an end—it is a means.

As an example of a skill often used as a determinant of musical excellence, the matter of memorization and its relation to musical performance bears a brief discussion.

The memorization of music, as such, affecting the performance of music *per se* is a pedantic question. If one does not *see* the performer, one cannot determine whether or not he is reading music. Memorization is, therefore, a visual, rather than an aural, matter of judgement. Music is, however, an aural and not a visual art; and, therefore, the memorization of it has no meaning with respect to its aural aspects of performance unless there can be found factors which can contribute to the success or failure of the "action" of performance. The factors in this respect are two: convenience, and demonstration of a *tour de force* as a skill in itself.

As a convenience, memorization eliminates the need for music reading, music stand, glasses, page turning, and all other little physical necessities required by attention to the printed page. Such action as is required by these physical necessities is thus eliminated. However, this action is not in parallel with the actor and his lines, as is so often observed fallaciously; since the musician, in order to play an instrument, is necessarily limited in his action. "Action," as concerns the physical requirements of music, does not affect the effect of music in the same way as reading of lines would *affect* the *action* of a play.

Furthermore, the effect of music without seeing the musician is fully appreciated, since it is a completely communicative art aurally. In fact, the impact of the musical experience is, more often than not, affected adversely by the idiosyncrasies of the musician's actions. Listening to music with the eyes closed, or to recordings, is ample proof of the positive value of this observation.

As a *tour de force*, memorization shows, but does not sound, the effect of a mental effort. However, this effort cannot be communicated aurally. It is a simple matter to challenge the musical appreciation of anyone to determine infallibly from a recording whether or not the artist was playing from memory. And, would anyone be so rabid on the subject as to insist that no good performance of any symphony had ever been presented simply because the orchestra had always used music?

The hazards of performance are enough alone. It is better to put up with the physical requirements of playing with music, and all of the little irritations involved, than to draw a blank of memory, with nothing to save the performance as a reference. It is as ridiculous to assume that memory serves as a base of performance as it would be to assume that no one needs a reference library if he memorizes all facts in his field. The physicist need not memorize all the logarithmic tables or formulas of stress. A technique of method and intellectual aptitude is not measured in terms of memory. Fantastic feats of memory have been performed by near-idiots throughout history.

If, therefore, the performance of music is not served by memorization other than as a convenience for physical necessity or as a *tour de force* to show mental prowess, the value of memorization is wholly pedantic in nature. For purposes of study and concentration of the attention of the student, it is a valuable technique of learning and teaching, but, to insist that memorization is a determinant of excellence of musical performance is fallacious.

It is possible to play beautifully, and it is possible not to play beautifully. It is possible to play from memory, and it is possible not to play from memory. It is also possible to play beautifully either with music or without it, but it is not possible to determine whether music is played beautifully more or less, simply because it is memorized or not.

If we are to achieve phrasing on a practical performance basis, and we will accept it as a cumulative skill result premised on a purposeful artistic intent as being the communication of a 'mood' by means of sound, we can return to our technical areas for a look at the possibilities of their dimensions for such use. Thus, and only thus, can we study and learn the art of musical phrasing.

Consider our dimensions of music; pitch, ryhthm and dynamics, plus timbre. Add to this the performance techniques of the clarinet in terms of breath, embouchure, articulation and finger dexterity. Provide adequate information concerning the acoustical nature and possibilities of our instrument and specifications for its design and modification. Provide in addition the understanding of music as an art medium, and the nature of its emotional derivation and exploitation. Devise a system of notation for preservation and communication of at least its barest outlines across the gap of time from man to future man, and we have the elements which we need for the task at hand.

One final and brief word must be provided at this point on a matter which is constantly discussed with respect to all of the arts. This matter is that vague and never satisfactorily defined, but universally used term, 'talent'.

I shall try my own personal definition as a parting observation. Talent is not a quantitative measure of 'how much' of it any one person may have, but is rather a qualitative measure with respect to how well anyone uses the mental and physical attributes with which he is born. Talent is a gauge and not an absolute in the same way that any of the many measurement ideas behind the physical measurement standards are qualitative gauges. Of what use is a measurement of a quantity if the quantity of what it measures is of no importance? If a measurement measures 'nothing', it is nothing but a measurement of 'nothing'. If a measurement measures 'something', the 'something' that it is, is what we are measuring 'how much' of, and consequently it is important to know the size of our 'something'. Nothing is always 'nothing', no matter how much of it may be measured or how often. It is first of all the 'quality' and then the 'quantity' that is of prime importance to all that we may think or do.

So, for example, with respect to all that has been said in this book regarding our subject and knowledge of it. There will be those who ask with a certain smugness, "do I have to know all that is in this book in order to play the clarinet—and—do all of the best clarinetists know all of the things that are in this book—and use them?"

In answer to this we can only say very simply, "no!" But, we must qualify our answer by one other statement which is of equal importance, and that is, that if they did, no matter what their accomplishments may be—how much better they could do—and how much more easily they could have done what they have already done—and with how much greater satisfaction.

The Art of Clarinetistry is 'playing the clarinet', to be sure, but it is much more than that alone. Clarinetistry is to the clarinetist what the Art of Music is to all musicians. It is as we have said before, not something which depends upon us as individuals except for the passing of the moment of time in which we live. We partake of it to the extent of our capacity and it gives us our full reward. But it does not depend on us, for we are most fortunate to be of it, not it of us. The food of Art is spread before all of us as a banquet. That we may prefer pickled pig's-feet to filet mignon is all a matter of taste.

No one is ready for the cumulative use of the dimensions of music without preparation, but no one can achieve such cumulative usage simply by preparation alone. Fortunately, the truth of the whole situation lies in the fact, that the normal course of study and practice, by devoted and intelligent effort will yield of its own self the personal answers for each of us. Our measure will be our own, and it will be weak if we are weak, and strong if we are strong. We will find that the communication of our musical art is communicated to us as well, by our attempt to communicate it. No one is taught by 'teaching', but communication is learned by each of us as is our mother-tongue, by our own efforts to communicate with our fellowmen. The elements of communication in music, or musical phrasing may be provided, and learned as elements, and that is all. This indeed, is the greatest service that a teacher may render to his students.

Finis

Bibliography

Acoustical Society of America Journal, many articles of interest to this area will be found listed in the indices of the Journal.

American Institute of Physics Handbook, McGraw-Hill Book Co., Inc., New York, 1957.

Analysis of Sensations, Ernest Mach, Dover

Altman, Phillip L., Handbook of Respiration, Publ. Sanders, Philadelphia, 1958.

Baines, Anthony, Woodwind Instruments and Their History, W. W. Norton and Co., New York, 1957.

Basic Corellates of the Auditory Stimulus, J. C. Lecklider, Handbook of Experimental Psychology, Wiley and Sons, New York, 1951.

Barnes, W. H. The Contemporary American Organ, 3rd ed., New York; J. Fischer and Brothe, 1937.

Bartholomew, W. T., Acoustics of Music, New York, Prentice Hall, Inc., 1942.

Benade, Arthur, Horns, Strings and Harmony, Doubleday and Co., Garden City, N.Y., 1960.

Beatty, R. T., Hearing in Men and Animals. London: Geo. Bell and Sons, 1932.

Bohm, T., The Flute and Flute Playing in Acoustical, Technical and Artistic Aspects. 2nd ed. revised by Dayton C. Miller, Cleveland, Dayton C. Miller, 1922.

Bragg, W. H., The World of Sound, New York: E. P. Dutton and Co., 1920.

Broadhouse, J., Musical Acoustics, New York, Charles Scribner's Sons, 1926.

Buck, P. C., Acoustics for Musicians, New York, Oxford University Press, 1918.

Bosanquet, Bernard, History of Aesthetics, London, 1904.

Buck, Percy Carter, Psychology for Musicians, London, Oxford Press. 1944.

Campbell, Edward and Moran, James, The Respiratory Muscles and the Mechanism of Breathing, London, Lloyd-Luke, 1958.

Colby, M. Y., Sound Waves and Acoustics, New York: Henry Holt and Co., 1938.

Culver, Charles A., Musical Acoustics, Philadelphia, The Blakiston Co., 1947.

Davis, A. H., Modern Acoustics, New York: The Macmillan Co., 1934.

Ducasse, C. J., The Philosophy of Art, New York, 1929.

Douglas, Alan, The Electronic Music Instrument Manual, London, I. Pitman Co., 1954.

Farnsworth, Paul R., Musical Taste, Its Measurement and Cultural Nature, Standford, Standford Univ. Press, 1950.

Fletcher, H., Speech and Hearing, New York: D. Van Nostrand Co., 1929.

Giltay, J. W., Bow Instruments, Their Form and Construction, New York: Charles Scribner's Sons, 1923.

Graf, Max, From Beethoven to Shostakovich, New York, Philosophical Library, 1947.

309

Haldane, John Scott, Respiration, New Haven, Yale Univer. Press, 1935.

Hamilton, C. G., Sound and its Relation to Music, Philadelphia: Oliver Ditson Co., 1912.

Hogben, Lancelot, Mathematics for the Million, Norton and Co., New York, 1951.

Helmholtz, H. L. F. von, "On the Sensations of Tone as a Physiological Basis for the Theory of Music. Translated and revised by A. J. Ellis, 3rd. ed., Longmans, Green and Co., 1895.

Jeans, J., Science and Music, New York: The Macmillan Co., 1937.

Journal of Research of Music Education, Washington, D.C.

Lamb, H., The Dynamical Theory of Sound, Dover Publ. Co.

Lundin, Robt. W., An Objective Psychology of Music, New York, Ronald Press Co., 1953.

Mach, Ernest, Analysis of Sensations, Dover Publishing Co.

Mathematics, Measurement and Psychophysics, S. S. Stevens, Handbook of Experimental Psychology, Wiley and Sons, New York, 1951.

McMahon, Philip, The Meaning of Art, New York, 1930.

The Mechanical Properties of the Ear, G. Von Bekesy, Handbook of Experimental Psychology, Wiley and Sons, New York, 1951.

Mechanics via the Calculus, P. W. Norris, W. S. Legge, Dover.

Miller, D. C., The Science of Musical Sounds, New York: The Macmillan Co., 1916.

Morse, P. McC., Vibration and Sound, New York: McGraw-Hill Book Company, 1936.

Meyer, Max, How We Hear, Boston, C. T. Bradford Co., 1950.

Munroe, M. Evans, The Language of Mathematics, The University of Michigan Press, Ann Arbor, Michigan, 1963.

Mursell, James L., The Psychology of Music, New York, W. W. Norton Co., 1937.

Ogden, R. M., Hearing, New York: Harcourt, Brace and Co., 1924.

Ogden, C. K., Richards, I. A. and Wood, James, The Foundations of Aesthetics, New York, 1922.

Olson, H. F., Elements of Acoustical Engineering, New York: D. Van Nostrand Co., 1940.

Opperman, Kalmen, The Art of Making and Adjusting the Single Reed, Chappell and Co., New York, 1960.

Peirce, B., An Elementary Treatise on Sound, Boston: James Munroe Co., 1836. (An especially valuable historical bibliography).

Psychophysiology of Hearing and Deafness, H. Davis, Handbook of Experimental Psychology, Wiley and Sons, 1965.

Rader, Melvin, A Modern Book of Aesthetics, New York, Henry Holt and Co., 1935.

Redfield, J., Music, a Science and an Art, New York, Alfred Knopf, 1928.

Reik, Theodor, The Haunting Melody, New York, Farrar, Straus and Young, 1953.

Geoffry Rendall, The Clarinet, Philosophical Library, New York, 1954.

Reuesz, G., Introduction to the Psychology of Music, Norman, University of Oklahoma, 1954.

Richardson, E. G., The Acoustics of Orchestral Instruments and of the Organ, London, Edward Arnold and Co., 1933.

Richardson, E. G., Wind Instruments from Musical and Scientific Aspects, Cantor Lectures, Royal Society of Arts, London, 1929.

Sabine, P. E., Acoustics and Architecture, New York, McGraw-Hill Book Company, Inc., 1932.

Sabine, P. E., Collected Papers on Acoustics, Cambridge, Harvard University Press, 1922.

Saunders, F. A., The Mechanical Action of Violins, J. Acoustical Society IX, (1937) pp. 81-98.

Schlesinger, Kathleen, The Greek Aulos, Methuen and Co., London, 1939.

Schoen, Max, The Psychology of Music, New York, The Ronald Press Co., 1940.

Seashore, C. E., In Search of Beauty in Music, New York, The Ronald Press Co., 1947.

Seashore, C. E., Psychology of Music, New York, McGraw-Hill Book Co., 1938.

Spain, H., Equal Temperament in Theory and Practice, New York, H. W. Gray and Co.

Stevens, S. S., and H. Davis, Hearing, Its Psychology and Physiology, New York, John Wiley and Sons, 1938.

Stubbins, W. H., The Study of the Clarinet, Geo. Wahr, Ann Arbor, Michigan, 10th edition, 1964.

Stubbins, W. H., Essentials of Technical Dexterity for the Clarinetist, Geo. Wahr Co., Ann Arbor, Michigan, 1959.

Tyndall, J., Sound, London, Longmans Green and Co., 1867.

Wallaschek, R. Primitive Music, London, Longmans, Green and Co., 1893.

Watt, H. J., The Foundations of Music, New York, The Macmillan Co., 1919.

Watt, H. J., The Psychology of Sound, New York, The Macmillan Co., 1917.

West, W. Acoustical Engineering, New York, Pitman Publishing Co., 1932.

White, W. B., Piano Tuning and the Allied Arts, Boston, Tuner's Supply Co., 1938.

Wood, A. B., A Textbook of Sound, New York, London, G. Bell and Sons, 1960 third revised edition.

Wood, Alexander, The Physical Basis of Music, New York, The Macmillan Co., 1913.

Wood, Alexander, Sound Waves and Their Uses, London, Blackie and Son, Ltd., 1930.

Willaman, Robert, The Clarinet and Clarinet Playing, New York, 1949.

Yasser, J. A Theory of Evolving Tonality, New York, American Library of Musicology, 1932.

Zahm, J. A., Sound and Music, Chicago, A. C. McClurg and Co., 1892.

Index